The Collected Works of Billy the Kid

Running in the Family

In the Skin of a Lion

The Cinnamon Peeler

BOOKS BY Michael Ondaatje

PROSE

The English Patient
1992

In the Skin of a Lion
1987

Running in the Family (memoir)
1982

Coming Through Slaughter
1976

The Collected Works of Billy the Kid
1970

POETRY

The Cinnamon Peeler: Selected Poems
1991

Secular Love
1984

There's a Trick with a Knife
I'm Learning to Do: Poems 1963–1978
1979

The Collected Works of Billy the Kid

Running in the Family

In the Skin of a Lion

The Cinnamon Peeler

———□———

MICHAEL
ONDAATJE

Quality Paperback Book Club
New York

CONTENTS

The Collected Works of Billy the Kid

This book is for many but especially for
Kim, Stuart and Sally Mackinnon,
Ken Livingstone, Victor Coleman and Barrie Nichol.

I send you a picture of Billy made with the Perry shutter as quick as it can be worked — Pyro and soda developer. I am making daily experiments now and find I am able to take passing horses at a lively trot square across the line of fire — bits of snow in the air — spokes well defined — some blur on top of wheel but sharp in the main — men walking are no trick — I will send you proofs sometime. I shall show you what can be done from the saddle without ground glass or tripod — please notice when you get the specimens that they were made with the lens wide open and many of the best exposed when my horse was in motion.

These are the killed.

(By me) —
Morton, Baker, early friends of mine.
Joe Bernstein. 3 Indians.
A blacksmith when I was twelve, with a knife.
5 Indians in self defence (behind a very safe rock).
One man who bit me during a robbery.
Brady, Hindman, Beckwith, Joe Clark,
Deputy Jim Carlyle, Deputy Sheriff J. W. Bell.
And Bob Ollinger. A rabid cat
birds during practice,

These are the killed.

(By them) —
Charlie, Tom O'Folliard
Angela D's split arm,

                    and Pat Garrett

sliced off my head.
Blood a necklace on me all my life.

Christmas at Fort Sumner, 1880. There were five of us together then. Wilson, Dave Rudabaugh, Charlie Bowdre, Tom O'Folliard, and me. In November we celebrated my 21st birthday, mixing red dirt and alcohol — a public breathing throughout the night. The next day we were told that Pat Garrett had been made sheriff and had accepted it. We were bad for progress in New Mexico and cattle politicians like Chisum wanted the bad name out. They made Garrett sheriff and he sent me a letter saying move out or I will get you Billy. The government sent a Mr. Azariah F. Wild to help him out. Between November and December I killed Jim Carlyle over some mixup, he being a friend.

Tom O'Folliard decided to go east then, said he would meet up with us in Sumner for Christmas. Goodbye goodbye. A few days before Christmas we were told that Garrett was in Sumner waiting for us all. Christmas night. Garrett, Mason, Wild, with four or five others. Tom O'Folliard rides into town, leaning his rifle between the horse's ears. He would shoot from the waist now which, with a rifle, was pretty good, and he was always accurate.

Garrett had been waiting for us, playing poker with the others, guns on the floor beside them. Told that Tom was riding in alone, he went straight to the window and shot O'Folliard's horse dead. Tom collapsed with the horse still holding the gun and blew out Garrett's window. Garrett already halfway downstairs. Mr. Wild shot at Tom from the other side of the street, rather unnecessarily shooting the horse again. If Tom had used stirrups and didnt swing his legs so much he would probably have been locked under the animal. O'Folliard moved soon. When Garrett had got to ground level, only the horse was there in the open street, good and dead. He couldnt shout to ask Wild where O'Folliard was or he would've got busted. Wild started to yell to tell Garrett though and Tom killed him at once. Garrett fired at O'Folliard's flash and took his shoulder off. Tom O'Folliard screaming out onto the quiet Fort Sumner street, Christmas night, walking over to Garrett, no shoulder left, his jaws tilting up and down like mad bladders going. Too mad to even aim at Garrett. Son of a bitch son of a bitch, as Garrett took clear aim and blew him out.

Garrett picked him up, the head broken in two, took him back upstairs into the hotel room. Mason stretched out a blanket neat in the corner. Garrett placed Tom O'Folliard down, broke open Tom's rifle, took the remaining shells and placed them by him. They had to wait till morning now. They continued their poker game till six a.m. Then remembered they hadnt done anything about Wild. So the four of them went out, brought Wild into the room. At eight in the morning Garrett buried Tom O'Folliard. He had known him quite well. Then he went to the train station, put Azariah F. Wild on ice and sent him back to Washington.

In Boot Hill there are over 400 graves. It takes
the space of 7 acres. There is an elaborate gate
but the path keeps to no main route for it tangles
like branches of a tree among the gravestones.

300 of the dead in Boot Hill died violently
200 by guns, over 50 by knives
some were pushed under trains — a popular
and overlooked form of murder in the west.
Some from brain haemorrhages resulting from bar fights
at least 10 killed in barbed wire.

In Boot Hill there are only two graves that belong to women
and they are the only known suicides in that graveyard

The others, I know, did not see the wounds appearing in the sky, in the air. Sometimes a normal forehead in front of me leaked brain gasses. Once a nose clogged right before me, a lock of skin formed over the nostrils, and the shocked face had to start breathing through mouth, but then the mustache bound itself in the lower teeth and he began to gasp loud the hah! hah! going strong — churned onto the floor, collapsed out, seeming in the end to be breathing out of his eye — tiny needle jets of air reaching into the throat. I told no one. If Angela D. had been with me then, not even her; not Sallie, John, Charlie, or Pat. In the end the only thing that never changed, never became deformed, were animals.

MMMMMMMM mm thinking
moving across the world on horses
body split at the edge of their necks
neck sweat eating at my jeans
moving across the world on horses
so if I had a newsman's brain I'd say
well some morals are physical
must be clear and open
like diagram of watch or star
one must eliminate much
that is one turns when the bullet leaves you
walk off see none of the thrashing
the very eyes welling up like bad drains
believing then the moral of newspapers or gun
where bodies are mindless as paper flowers you dont feed
or give to drink
that is why I can watch the stomach of clocks
shift their wheels and pins into each other
and emerge living, for hours

When I caught Charlie Bowdre dying
tossed 3 feet by bang bullets giggling
at me face tossed in a gaggle
he pissing into his trouser legs in pain
face changing like fast sunshine o my god
o my god billy I'm pissing watch
your hands
                    while the eyes grew all over his body

                    Jesus I never knew that did you
                    the nerves shot out
                    the liver running around there
                    like a headless hen jerking
                    brown all over the yard
                    seen that too at my aunt's
                    never eaten hen since then

Blurred a waist high river
foam against the horse
riding naked clothes and boots
and pistol in the air

Crossed a crooked river
loving in my head
ambled dry on stubble
shot a crooked bird

Held it in my fingers
the eyes were small and far
it yelled out like a trumpet
destroyed it of its fear

After shooting Gregory
this is what happened

I'd shot him well and careful
made it explode under his heart
so it wouldnt last long and
was about to walk away
when this chicken paddles out to him
and as he was falling hops on his neck
digs the beak into his throat
straightens legs and heaves
a red and blue vein out

Meanwhile he fell
and the chicken walked away

still tugging at the vein
till it was 12 yards long
as if it held that body like a kite
Gregory's last words being

get away from me yer stupid chicken

Tilts back to fall
black hair swivelling off her
shattering the pillow
Billy she says
the tall gawky body spitting electric
off the sheets to my arm
leans her whole body out
so breasts are thinner
stomach is a hollow
where the bright bush jumps
this is the first time
bite into her side leave
a string of teeth marks
she hooks in two and covers me
my hand locked
her body nearly breaking off my fingers
pivoting like machines in final speed

later my hands cracked in love juice
fingers paralysed by it arthritic
these beautiful fingers I couldnt move
faster than a crippled witch now

The barn I stayed in for a week then was at the edge of a farm and had been deserted it seemed for several years, though built of stone and good wood. The cold dark grey of the place made my eyes become used to soft light and I burned out my fever there. It was twenty yards long, about ten yards wide. Above me was another similar sized room but the floors were unsafe for me to walk on. However I heard birds and the odd animal scrape their feet, the rotten wood magnifying the sound so they entered my dreams and nightmares.

But it was the colour and light of the place that made me stay there, not my fever. It became a calm week. It was the colour and the light. The colour a grey with remnants of brown — for instance those rust brown pipes and metal objects that before had held bridles or pails, that slid to machine uses; the thirty or so grey cans in one corner of the room, their ellipses, from where I sat, setting up patterns in the dark.

When I had arrived I opened two windows and a door and the sun poured blocks and angles in, lighting up the floor's skin of feathers and dust and old grain. The windows looked out onto fields and plants grew at the door, me killing them gradually with my urine. Wind came in wet and brought in birds who flew to the other end of the room to get their aim to fly out again. An old tap hung from the roof, the same colour as the walls, so once I knocked myself out on it.

For that week then I made a bed of the table there and lay out my fever, whatever it was. I began to block my mind of all thought. Just sensed the room and learnt what my body could do, what it could survive, what colours it liked best, what songs I sang best. There were animals who did not move out and accepted me as a larger breed. I ate the old grain with them, drank from a constant puddle about twenty yards away from the barn. I saw no human and heard no human voice, learned to squat the best way when shitting, used leaves for wiping, never ate flesh or touched another animal's flesh, never entered his boundary. We were all aware and allowed each other. The fly who sat on my arm, after his inquiry, just went away, ate his disease and kept it in him. When I walked I avoided the cobwebs who had places to grow to, who had stories to finish. The flies caught in those acrobat nets were the only murder I saw.

And in the barn next to us there was another granary, separated
by just a thick wood door. In it a hundred or so rats, thick rats,
eating and eating the foot deep pile of grain abandoned now and
fermenting so that at the end of my week, after a heavy rain
storm burst the power in those seeds and brought drunkenness
into the minds of those rats, they abandoned the sanity of eating
the food before them and turned on each other and grotesque
and awkwardly because of their size they went for each other's
eyes and ribs so the yellow stomachs slid out and they came
through that door and killed a chipmunk — about ten of them
onto that one striped thing and the ten eating each other before
they realised the chipmunk was long gone so that I, sitting on
the open window with its thick sill where they couldnt reach me,
filled my gun and fired again and again into their slow wheel
across the room at each boommm, and reloaded and fired again
and again till I went through the whole bag of bullet supplies —
the noise breaking out the seal of silence in my ears, the smoke
sucked out of the window as it emerged from my fist and the
long twenty yard space between me and them empty but for the
floating bullet lonely as an emissary across and between the
wooden posts that never returned, so the rats continued to wheel
and stop in the silences and eat each other, some even the bullet.
Till my hand was black and the gun was hot and no other
animal of any kind remained in that room but for the boy in the
blue shirt sitting there coughing at the dust, rubbing the sweat
of his upper lip with his left forearm.

PAULITA MAXWELL: THE PHOTOGRAPH

In 1880 a travelling photographer came through Fort Sumner.
Billy posed standing in the street near old Beaver Smith's saloon.
The picture makes him rough and uncouth.

The expression of his face was really boyish and pleasant.
He may have worn such clothes as appear in the picture out on
the range, but in Sumner he was careful of his personal appear-
ance and dressed neatly and in good taste. I never liked the
picture. I don't think it does Billy justice.

Not a story about me through their eyes then. Find the beginning, the slight silver key to unlock it, to dig it out. Here then is a maze to begin, be in.

Two years ago Charlie Bowdre and I criss-crossed the Canadian border. Ten miles north of it ten miles south. Our horses stepped from country to country, across low rivers, through different colours of tree green. The two of us, our criss-cross like a whip in slow motion, the ridge of action rising and falling, getting narrower in radius till it ended and we drifted down to Mexico and old heat. That there is nothing of depth, of significant accuracy, of wealth in the image, I know. It is there for a beginning.

She leans against the door, holds
her left hand at the elbow
with her right, looks at the bed

on my sheets — oranges
peeled half peeled
bright as hidden coins against the pillow

she walks slow to the window
lifts the sackcloth
and jams it horizontal on a nail
so the bent oblong of sun
hoists itself across the room
framing the bed the white flesh
of my arm

she is crossing the sun
sits on her leg here
sweeping off the peels

traces the thin bones on me
turns toppling slow back to the pillow
Bonney Bonney

I am very still
I take in all the angles of the room

January at Tivan Arroyo, called Stinking Springs more often. With me, Charlie, Wilson, Dave Rudabaugh. Snow. Charlie took my hat and went out to get wood and feed the horses. The shot burnt the clothes on his stomach off and lifted him right back into the room. Snow on Charlie's left boot. He had taken one step out. In one hand had been an axe, in the other a pail. No guns.

Get up Charlie, get up, go and get one. No Billy. I'm tired, please. Jesus watch your hands Billy. Get up Charlie. I prop him to the door, put his gun in his hand. Take off, good luck Charlie.

He stood there weaving, not moving. Then began to walk in a perfect, incredible straight line out of the door towards Pat and the others at the ridge of the arroyo about twenty yards away. He couldnt even lift his gun. Moving sideways at times but always always in a straight line. Dead on Garrett. Shoot him Charlie. They were watching him only, not moving. Over his shoulder I aimed at Pat, fired, and hit his shoulder braid. Hadnt touched him. Charlie hunched. Get up Charlie kill him kill him. Charlie got up poking the gun barrel in snow. Went straight towards Garrett. The others had ducked down, but not Garrett who just stood there and I didnt shoot again. Charlie he knew was already dead now, had to go somewhere, do something, to get his mind off the pain. Charlie went straight, now closer to them his hands covered the mess in his trousers. Shoot him Charlie shoot him. The blood trail he left straight as a knife cut. Getting there getting there. Charlie getting to the arroyo, pitching into Garrett's arms, slobbering his stomach on Garrett's gun belt. Hello Charlie, said Pat quietly.

Snow outside. Wilson, Dave Rudabaugh and me. No windows, the door open so we could see. Four horses outside.

Jim Payne's grandfather told him that he met Frank James of the James Brothers once.

It was in a Los Angeles movie theatre. After the amnesty he was given, Frank had many jobs. When Jim's grandfather met him, he was the doorman at the Fresco Theatre.

GET YOUR TICKET TORN UP BY FRANK JAMES the poster said, and people came for that rather than the film. Frank would say, 'Thanks for coming, go on in'.

Jim's grandfather asked him if he would like to come over and have a beer after the film, but Frank James said 'No, but thank you' and tore up the next ticket. He was by then an alcoholic.

Miss Angela Dickinson of Tucson
  tall legs like a dancer
  set the 80's style
  by shaving them hairless
  keeps saying
  I'm too tall for you Billy
  but we walk around a bit
  buy a bottle and she stands
  showing me her thighs
  look Billy look at this
  she folded on the sheet
  tapping away at her knees
  leans back waving feet at me
  catching me like a butterfly
  in the shaved legs in her Tucson room

A river you could get lost in
and the sun a flashy hawk
on the edge of it

a mile away you see the white path
of an animal moving through water

you can turn a hundred yard circle
and the horse bends dribbles his face
you step off and lie in it propping your head

till dusk and cold and the horse shift you
and you look up and moon a frozen bird's eye

His stomach was warm
remembered this when I put my hand into
a pot of luke warm tea to wash it out
dragging out the stomach to get the bullet
he wanted to see when taking tea
with Sallie Chisum in Paris Texas

With Sallie Chisum in Paris Texas
he wanted to see when taking tea
dragging out the stomach to get the bullet
a pot of luke warm tea to wash it out
remembered this when I put my hand into
his stomach was warm

Pat Garrett, ideal assassin. Public figure, the mind of a doctor, his hands hairy, scarred, burned by rope, on his wrist there was a purple stain there all his life. Ideal assassin for his mind was unwarped. Had the ability to kill someone on the street walk back and finish a joke. One who had decided what was right and forgot all morals. He was genial to everyone even his enemies. He genuinely enjoyed people, some who were odd, the dopes, the thieves. Most dangerous for them, he understood them, what motivated their laughter and anger, what they liked to think about, how he had to act for them to like him. An academic murderer — only his vivacious humour and diverse interests made him the best kind of company. He would listen to people like Rudabaugh and giggle at their escapades. His language was atrocious in public, yet when alone he never swore.

At the age of 15 he taught himself French and never told anyone about it and never spoke to anyone in French for the next 40 years. He didnt even read French books.

Between the ages of 15 and 18 little was heard of Garrett. In Juan Para he bought himself a hotel room for two years with money he had saved and organised a schedule to learn how to drink. In the first three months he forced himself to disintegrate his mind. He would vomit everywhere. In a year he could drink two bottles a day and not vomit. He began to dream for the first time in his life. He would wake up in the mornings, his sheets soaked in urine 40% alcohol. He became frightened of flowers because they grew so slowly that he couldnt tell what they planned to do. His mind learned to be superior because of the excessive mistakes of those around him. Flowers watched him.

After two years he could drink anything, mix anything together and stay awake and react just as effectively as when sober. But he was now addicted, locked in his own game. His money was running out. He had planned the drunk to last only two years, now it continued into new months over which he had no control. He stole and sold himself to survive. One day he was robbing the house of Juanita Martinez, was discovered by her, and collapsed in her living room. In about six months she had un-iced his addiction. They married and two weeks later she died of a consumption she had hidden from him.

What happened in Garrett's mind no one knows. He did not drink, was never seen. A month after Juanita Garrett's death he arrived in Sumner.

PAULITA MAXWELL:

> I remember the first day Pat Garrett ever
> set foot in Fort Sumner. I was a small girl
> with dresses at my shoe-tops and when he
> came to our house and asked for a job, I
> stood behind my brother Pete and stared
> at him in open eyed wonder; he had the
> longest legs I'd ever seen and he looked so
> comical and had such a droll way of talking
> that after he was gone, Pete and I had a
> good laugh about him.

His mind was clear, his body able to drink, his feelings, unlike those who usually work their own way out of hell, not cynical about another's incapacity to get out of problems and difficulties. He did ten years of ranching, cow punching, being a buffalo hunter. He married Apolinaria Guitterrez and had five sons. He had come to Sumner then, mind full of French he never used, everything equipped to be that rare thing — a sane assassin sane assassin sane assassin sane assassin sane assassin sane

(Miss Sallie Chisum, later Mrs. Roberts, was living in Roswell in 1924, a sweet faced, kindly old lady of a thousand memories of frontier days.)

ON HER HOUSE

> *The house was full of people all the time*
> *the ranch was a little world in itself*
> *I couldn't have been lonesome if I had tried*

> *Every man worth knowing in the Southwest,*
> *and many not worth knowing, were guests*
> *one time or another.*
> *What they were made no difference in their welcome.*
> *Sometimes a man would ride up in a hurry*
> *eat a meal in a hurry and depart in a hurry*

> *Billy the Kid would come in often*
> *and sometimes stayed for a week or two.*
> *I remember how frightened I was the first time he came.*

Forty miles ahead of us, in almost a straight line, is the house. Angela D and I on horses moving towards it, me bringing her there. Even now, this far away, I can imagine them moving among the rooms. It is nine in the morning. They are leaning back in their chairs after their slow late Saturday breakfast. John with the heels of his brown boots on the edge of the table in the space he cleared of his plate and cup and cutlery, the cup in his hands in his lap. The table with four plates — two large two small. The remnants of bacon fat and eggs on the larger ones, the black crumbs of toast butter and marmalade (Californian) on the others. One cup in a saucer, one saucer that belonged to the cup that is in John Chisum's hands now. Across the table on the other side is Sallie, in probably her long brown and yellow dress, the ribbon down her front to the waist with pale blue buttons, a frill on either side of her neck along her shoulders. By now she would have moved the spare chair so she too could put her feet up, barefoot as always, her toes crinkling at the wind that comes from the verandah door. Her right arm would be leaning against the table and now and then she'll scrape the bottom of her cup against the saucer and drink some of the coffee, put it down and return the fingers of her right hand to bury them in the warm of her hair. They do not talk much, Sallie and John Chisum, but from here I can imagine the dialogue of noise — the scraping cup, the tilting chair, the cough, the suction as an arm lifts off a table breaking the lock that was formed by air and the wet of the surface.

On other days they would go their own ways. Chisum would be up earlier than dawn and gone before Sallie even woke and rolled over in bed, her face blind as a bird in the dark. It was only later, when the sun eventually reached the bed and slid over her eyes, that she slowly leaned up to find her body, clothesless, had got cold and pulling the sheet from the strong tuck fold at the foot of the bed brings it to her, wraps it around her while she sits in bed, the fists of her feet against her thighs trying to discover which was colder — the flesh at her feet or the flesh at her thighs, hugging the sheet to her tight until it would be a skin. Pretending to lock her arms over it as if a tight dress, warming her breasts with her hands through the material.

Once last year seeing her wrapped I said, Sallie, know what a mad man's skin is? And I showed her, filling the automatic indoor bath with warm water and lifting her and dropping her slow into the bath with the sheet around her and then heaving her out and saying that's what it is, that white thing round you. Try now to dig yourself out of it. Placed her in the bed and watched her try to escape it then.

On weekdays anyway, she'd sit like that on the bed, the sheet tight around her top and brought down to her belly, her legs having to keep themselves warm. Listening for noises around the house, the silence really, knowing John had gone, just leaving a list of things he wanted her to do. She would get up and after a breakfast that she would eat wandering around the house slowly, she would begin the work. Keeping the books, dusting his reading books, filling the lamps in the afternoon — they being emptied in the early morning by John to avoid fire danger when the sun took over the house and scorched it at noon, or dropping sideways in the early afternoon sent rays horizontal through the doors and windows. No I forgot, she had stopped that now. She left the paraffin in the lamps; instead had had John build shutters for every door and window, every hole in the wall. So that at eleven in the morning all she did was close and lock them all until the house was silent and dark blue with sunless quiet. For four hours. Eleven till three. A time when, if inside, as I was often, your footsteps sounded like clangs over the floors, echoes shuddering across the rooms. And Sallie like a ghost across the room moving in white dresses, her hair knotted as always at the neck and continuing down until it splayed and withered like eternal smoke half way between the shoulder blades and the base of cobble spine.

Yes. In white long dresses in the dark house, the large bones somehow taking on the quietness of the house. Yes I remember. After burning my legs in the fire and I came to their house, it must have been my second visit and Sallie had begun using the shutters at eleven. And they brought the bed out of the extra bedroom and propped me up at one end of the vast living room of their bungalow. And I sat there for three days not moving an inch, like some dead tree witnessing the tides or the sun and the moon taking over from each other as the house in front of me changed colour — the night, the early morning yellow, the gradual move to dark blue at 11 o clock, the new white 4 o clock sun let in, later the gradual growing dark again.

For three days, my head delirious so much I thought I was going blind twice a day, recognizing no one, certainly not the Chisums, for I had been brought out cold and dropped on their porch by someone who had gone on without waiting even for water for himself. And Sallie I suppose taking the tent sheet off my legs each morning once the shutters closed. No. Again. Sallie approaching from the far end of the room like some ghost. I didn't know who it was, a tray of things in her right hand, a lamp in the other carrying them. Me screaming stop stop STOP THERE you're going to *fall* on me! My picture now sliding so she with her tray and her lamp jerked up to the ceiling and floated down calm again and jerked to the ceiling and floated down calm again and continued forward crushing me against the wall only I didnt feel anything yet. And Sallie I suppose taking the sheet off my legs and putting on the fan so they became cold and I started to feel them again. Then starting to rub and pour calamine like ice only it felt like the tongue of a very large animal my god I remember each swab felt like the skin and flesh had been moved off completely leaving only raw bone riddled with loose nerves being blown about and banging against each other from just her slow breath.

In the long 20 yard living-dining room I remember the closing of shutters, with each one the sudden blacking out of clarity in a section of the room, leaving fewer arcs of sun each time digging into the floor. Sallie starting from one end and dis-appearing down to the far end leaving black behind her as she walked into the remaining light, making it all a cold darkness. Then in other rooms not seen by me. Then appearing vast in the thick blue in her long white dress, her hands in the pockets strolling in the quiet, because of her tallness the hips moving first, me at the far end all in black.

Her shoes off, so silent, she moves a hand straying over the covers off John's books, till she comes and sits near me and puts her feet up shoeless and I reach to touch them and the base of them is hard like some semi-shelled animal but only at the base, the rest of her foot being soft, oiled almost so smooth, the thin blue veins wrapping themselves around the inside ankle bone and moving like paths into the toes, the brown tanned feet of Sallie Chisum resting on my chest, my hands rubbing them, pushing my hands against them like a carpenter shaving wood to find new clear pulp smelling wood beneath. My own legs black with scars. And down the room, the parrot begins to talk to itself in the dark, thinking it is night.

She had lived in that house fourteen years, and every year she demanded of John that she be given a pet of some strange exotic breed. Not that she did not have enough animals. She had collected several wild and broken animals that, in a way, had become exotic by their breaking. Their roof would have collapsed from the number of birds who might have lived there if the desert hadnt killed three quarters of those that tried to cross it. Still every animal that came within a certain radius of that house was given a welcome, the tame, the half born, the wild, the wounded.

I remember the first night there. John took me to see the animals. About 20 yards away from the house, he had built vast cages, all in a row. They had a tough net roof over them for the day time when they were let out but tended to stay within the shade of their cages anyway. That night John took me along and we stepped off the porch, left the last pool of light, down the steps into the dark. We walked together smoking his long narrow cigars, with each suck the nose and his mustache lighting up. We came to the low brooding whirr of noise, night sleep of animals. They were stunning things in the dark. Just shapes that shifted. You could peer into a cage and see nothing till a rattle of claws hit the grid an inch from your face and their churning feathers seemed to hiss, and a yellow pearl of an eye cracked with veins glowed through the criss crossed fence.

One of the cages had a huge owl. It was vast. All I could see were its eyes — at least 8″ apart. The next morning however, it turned out to be two owls, both blind in one eye. In those dark cages the birds, there must have been 20 of them, made a steady hum all through the night — a noise you heard only if you were within five yards of them. Walking back to the house it was again sheer silence from where we had come, only now we knew they were moving and sensing the air and our departure. We knew they continued like that all night while we slept.

Half way back to the house, the building we moved towards seemed to be stuffed with something yellow and wet. The night, the dark air, made it all mad. That fifteen yards away there were bright birds in cages and here John Chisum and me walked, strange bodies. Around us total blackness, nothing out there but a desert for seventy miles or more, and to the left, a few yards away, a house stuffed with yellow wet light where within the frame of a window we saw a woman move carrying fire in a glass funnel and container towards the window, towards the edge of the dark where we stood.

(To come) to where eyes will
move in head like a rat
mad since locked in a biscuit tin all day
stampeding mad as a mad rats legs
bang it went was hot
under my eye
was hot small bang did it
almost a pop
I didnt hear till I was red
had a rat fyt in my head
sad billys body glancing out
body going as sweating white horses go
reeling off me wet
scuffing down my arms
wet horse white
screaming wet sweat round the house
sad billys out
floating barracuda in the brain

With the Bowdres

She is boiling us black coffee
leaning her side against the warm stove
taps her nails against the mug
Charlie talking on about things
and with a bit the edge of my eye
I sense the thin white body of my friend's wife

Strange that how I feel people
not close to me
as if their dress were against my shoulder
and as they bend down
the strange smell of their breath
moving across my face
or my eyes
magnifying the bones across a room
shifting in a wrist

Getting more difficult
things all over crawling
in the way
gotta think through
the wave of ants on him
millions a moving vest up his neck
over his head down his back
leaving a bright skull white smirking
to drop to ankles
ribs blossoming out like springs
the meat from his eyes

Last night was dreamed into a bartender
with an axe I drove into glasses of gin lifted up to be tasted

I have seen pictures of great stars,
drawings which show them straining to the centre
that would explode their white
if temperature and the speed they moved at
shifted one degree.

Or in the East have seen
the dark grey yards where trains are fitted
and the clean speed of machines
that make machines, their
red golden pouring which when cooled
mists out to rust or grey.

The beautiful machines pivoting on themselves
sealing and fusing to others
and men throwing levers like coins at them.
And there is there the same stress as with stars,
the one altered move that will make them maniac.

MISTUH. . .PATRICK. . .GARRETT ! ! !

Mescalaro territory is a flat region, no rivers, no trees, no grass.
In August the winds begin and at that time everybody who can
moves away. If you stayed, you couldnt see the sun for weeks
because, if opened, your eyes would be speckled and frosted
with sand. Dust and sand stick to anything wet as your eyeball,
or a small dribble from your nostril, a flesh wound, even sweat
on your shirt. A beard or mustache weighs three times as much
after you are caught in the storms. Your ears are so blocked that
you cannot hear for a good while afterwards, which is just as
well for all there is is the long constant screech and scream of
wind carrying anything it can lift.

I had been caught in the Mescalero that August for two days.
Blindfolding the horse I veered it east when the storm let down,
came to stony land and tumbleweed. Tumbleweed wont survive
in the Mescalero for it is blasted to pieces in minutes. But here,
tumbleweed moved like tires out of nowhere; you could be
knocked off your horse by them. In another half day I got to the
Chisum ranch. Had been there once a few years earlier and
had liked them very much. It was, anyway, the only place you
could have superb meals which became even better by your
realisation that there was nothing near them for almost a 100
miles. I arrived at their house mind blasted, and spent those
strange three hours while the Chisums rushed around me,
giving me drinks, gesturing towards the bath they had poured —
all in total silence for I heard nothing, only the wind I
remembered from 24 hours back — before my ears had been
gradually sprayed and locked. I put my head under water and
weaved about, the hot water stinging even more my red face.
Drunk on water, I staggered from the tub and passed out
on the bed.

Sallie came in when I was waking and threw me a towel. Can
you hear now? I nodded. Her voice like piercing explosions.
Yes, but softly, I said. She nodded. We got visitors, she said.
Do you know him? William Bonney? He's brought his girl-
friend that he plans to marry. My mind awake then. I'd of course

heard of him. But leaning back to think of it, I fell asleep. Sallie must have covered me up properly with a sheet because I woke up a long while later and was warm. I could hear the boy Bonney arguing with John.

I joined them just as they were finishing dinner. Bonney seemed relaxed and dressed very well, his left heel resting on his right knee. He ate corn, drank coffee, used a fork and knife alternately — always with his right hand. The three days we were together and at other times in our lives when we saw each other, he never used his left hand for anything except of course to shoot. He wouldn't even pick up a mug of coffee. I saw the hand, it was virgin white. Later when we talked about it, I explained about how a hand or muscle unused for much work would atrophy, grow small. He said he did fingers exercises subconsciously, on the average 12 hours a day. And it was true. From then on I noticed his left hand churning within itself, each finger circling alternately like a train wheel. Curling into balls, pouring like waves across a tablecloth. It was the most hypnotising beautiful thing I ever saw.

He jumped up, and introduced himself informally to me, not waiting for Chisum to, and pointed out Angie. She was a good 6″ taller than him, a very big woman, not fat, but big bones. She moved like some fluid competent animal.

Bonney was that weekend, and always was, charming. He must, I thought, have seduced Angie by his imagination which was usually pointless and never in control. I had expected him to be the taciturn pale wretch — the image of the sallow punk that was usually attached to him by others. The rather cruel smile, when seen close, turned out to be intricate and witty. You could never tell how he meant a phrase, whether he was serious or joking. From his eyes you could tell nothing at all. In general he had a quick, quiet humour. His only affectation was his outfit of black clothes speckled with silver buttons and silver belt lock. Also his long black hair was pulled back and tied in a knot of leather.

It was impossible to study the relationship he had with the large tall Angie. After dinner they sat in their chairs. He would usually be hooked in ridiculous positions, feet locked in the chair's arms, or lying on the floor with his feet up. He could never remain in one position more than five minutes. Angie alternately never moved violently like Billy. Only now and then she shifted that thick body, tucked her legs under those vast thighs that spread like bags of wheat, perfectly proportioned.

After an evening of considerable drinking we all retreated to our rooms. And the next morning, Billy and Angie who had been planning to leave, decided to stay. I was glad as I didnt understand either of them and wanted to see how they understood each other. At breakfast a strange thing happened that explained some things.

Sallie had had a cat named Ferns who was very old and had somehow got pains in its shoulders during the last two days. I looked at it after breakfast and saw it had been bitten by a snake. It was in fact poisoned and could not live. It already had gone half blind. John decided then to kill it and lifted the half paralysed body to take it outside. However, once out, the cat made a frantic leap, knowing what was going to happen, fell, and pulled itself by two feet under the floor boards of the house. The whole of the Chisum house was built in such a way that the house stood on a base which was 9″ off the ground. The cat was heard shifting underneath those floors and then there was silence. We all looked under the boards from the side of the house, seeing into the dark, but we couldnt see Ferns and couldnt crawl under to get him. After a good hour, from the odd thrashing, we knew the cat was still alive and in pain. It would I theorized probably live for a day and then die. We sat around on the verandah for a while and then Billy said, do you want me to kill it. Sallie without asking how said yes.

He stood up and took off his boots and socks, went to his room, returned, he had washed his hands. He asked us to go into the living room and sit still. Then he changed his mind and asked us to go out of the house and onto the verandah and keep still and quiet, not to talk. He began to walk over the kitchen floor, the living room area, almost bent in two, his face about a foot from the pine floorboards. He had the gun out now. And for about half an hour he walked around like this, sniffing away it seemed to me. Twice he stopped in the same place but continued on. He went all over the house. Finally he came back to a spot near the sofa in the living room. We could see him through the window, all of us. Billy bent quietly onto his knees and sniffed carefully at the two square feet of floor. He listened for a while, then sniffed again. Then he fired twice into the floorboards. Jumped up and walked out to us. He's dead now Sallie, dont worry.

Our faces must have been interesting to see then. John and Sallie were thankful, almost proud of him. I had a look I suppose of incredible admiration for him too. But when I looked at Angie, leaning against the rail of the verandah, her face was terrified. Simply terrified.

Down the street was a dog. Some mut spaniel, black and white. One dog, Garrett and two friends, stud looking, came down the street to the house, to me.

Again.

Down the street was a dog. Some mut spaniel, black and white. One dog, Garrett and two friends came down the street to the house, to me.

Garrett takes off his hat and leaves it outside the door. The others laugh. Garrett smiles, pokes his gun towards the door. The others melt and surround.
All this I would have seen if I was on the roof looking.

You know hunters
are the gentlest
anywhere in the world

they halt caterpillars
from path dangers
lift a drowning moth from a bowl
remarkable in peace

in the same way assassins
come to chaos neutral

Snow outside. Wilson, Dave Rudabaugh and me. No windows, the door open so we could see. Four horses outside. Garrett aimed and shot to sever the horse reigns. He did that for 3 of them so they got away and 3 of us couldnt escape. He tried for 5 minutes to get the reigns on the last horse but kept missing. So he shot the horse. We came out. No guns.

One morning woke up
Charlie was cooking
and we ate not talking
but sniffing wind
wind so fine
it was like drinking ether

we sat hands round knees
heads leaned back taking lover wind
in us sniffing and sniffing
getting high on the way
it crashed into our nostrils

This is Tom O'Folliard's story, the time I met him, eating red dirt to keep the pain away, off his body, out there like a melting shape in the sun. Sitting, his legs dangling like tails off the wall. Out of his skull.

What made me notice him was his neck. Whenever he breathed the neck and cheek filled out vast as if holding a bag of trapped air. I introduced myself. Later he gave me red dirt. Said want to hear a story and he told me. I was thinking of a photograph someone had taken of me, the only one I had then. I was standing on a wall, at my feet there was this bucket and in the bucket was a pump and I was pumping water out over the wall. Only now, with the red dirt, water started dripping out of the photo. This is his story.

At fifteen he took a job with an outfit shooting wild horses. They were given a quarter a head for each one dead. These horses grazed wild, ate up good grass. The desert then had no towns every 50 miles. He sucked the clear milk out of a chopped cactus, drank piss at times. Once, blind thirsty, O'Folliard who was then 17 killed the horse he sat on and covered himself in the only liquid he could find. Blood caked on his hair, arms, shoulders, everywhere. Two days later he stumbled into a camp.

Then half a year ago he had his big accident. He was alone on the Carrizoza, north of here; the gun blew up on him. He didnt remember anything after he saw horses moving in single file and he put the gun to his shoulder. Pulling the trigger the gun blew to pieces. He was out about two days. When he woke up, he did because he was vomiting. His face was out to here. From that moment, his horse gone, he lived for four days in the desert without food or water. Because he had passed out and eaten nothing he survived, at least a doctor told him that. Finding water finally, he drank and it poured out of his ear. He felt sleepy all the time. Every two hours he stopped walking and fell asleep placing his boots into an arrow in the direction he was going. Then he would get up, put boots on and move on. He said he would have cut off his left hand with a knife to have something to eat, but he realised he had lost too much blood already.

He killed lizards when he got onto rock desert. Then a couple of days later the shrubs started appearing with him following them, still sleeping every two hours. First village he came to was Mexican. José Chavez y Chavez, blacksmith. The last thing O'Folliard noticed was Chavez sandbagging him in the stomach. O'Folliard going out cold. When he woke José had him in a bed, his arms trapped down.

Chavez had knocked out Tom as he had gone to throw himself in water which would have got rid of his thirst but killed him too. Chavez gave it to him drop by drop. A week later he let Tom have his first complete glass of water. Tom would have killed Chavez for water during that week. When he finally got to a doctor he found all the muscles on the left side of his face had collapsed. When he breathed, he couldnt control where the air went and it took new channels according to its fancy and formed thin balloons down the side of his cheek and neck. These fresh passages of air ricocheted pain across his face every time he breathed. The left side of his face looked as though it had melted by getting close to fire. So he chewed red dirt constantly, his pockets were full of it. But his mind was still sharp, the pain took all the drug. The rest of him was flawless, perfect. He was better than me with rifles. His feet danced with energy. On a horse he did tricks all the time, somersaulting, lying back. He was riddled with energy. He walked, both arms crooked over a rifle at the elbows. Legs always swinging extra.

MISS SALLIE CHISUM : ON BILLY

> *I was sitting in the living room*
> *when word was brought he had arrived.*
> *I felt in a panic. I pictured him*
> *in all the evil ugliness*
> *of a bloodthirsty ogre.*
> *I half expected he would slit my throat*
> *if he didnt like my looks.*
>
> *I heard John saying with a wave of his hand,*
> *Sallie, this is my friend, Billy the Kid.*
> *A good looking, clear-eyed boy stood there*
> *with his hat in his hand, smiling at me.*
>
> *I stretched out my hand automatically to him,*
> *and he grasped it in a hand as small as my own*

Crouching in the 5 minute dark
can smell him smell that mule sweat
that stink need a shotgun
for a searchlight to his corner

Garrett? I aint love-worn
torn aint blue I'm waiting
smelling you across the room
to kill you Garrett going
to take you from the knee up
leave me   my dark   AMATEUR!

A motive? some reasoning we can give to explain all this violence. Was there a source for all this? yup —

"Hill leaped from his horse and, sticking a rifle to the back of Tunstall's head blew out his brains. Half drunk with whisky and mad with the taste of blood, the savages turned the murder of the defenceless man into an orgy. Pantillon Gallegos, a Bonito Cañon Mexican, hammered in his head with a jagged rock. They killed Tunstall's horse, stretched Tunstall's body beside the dead animal, face to the sky, arms folded across his breast, feet together. Under the man's head they placed his hat and under the horse's head his coat carefully folded by way of pillows. So murdered man and dead horse suggested they had crawled into bed and gone to sleep together. This was their devil's mockery, their joke — ghastly, meaningless. Then they rode back to Lincoln, roaring drunken songs along the way.

"Lucky for Billy the Kid and Brewer that they had gone hunting wild turkeys, else they would have shared Tunstall's fate. From a distant hillside they witnessed the murder."

To be near flowers in the rain
all that pollen stink buds
bloated split
leaves their juices
bursting the white drop of spend
out into the air at you
the smell of things dying flamboyant
smell stuffing up your nose
and up like wet cotton in the brain
can hardly breathe nothing
nothing thick sugar death

In Mexico the flowers
like brain the blood drained out
packed with all the liquor perfume
sweat like lilac urine smell
getting to me from across a room

if you cut the stalk
your face near it
you feel the puff of air escape
the flower gets small smells sane
deteriorates in a hand

When Charlie Bowdre married Manuela, we carried them
on our shoulders, us on horses. Took them to the Shea
Hotel, 8 rooms. Jack Shea at the desk said
Charlie — everythings on the house, we'll give you the
Bridal.
No no, says Charlie, dont bother, I'll hang onto her ears
until I get used to it.
                    HAWHAWHAW

White walls neon on the eye
1880   November 23   my birthday

catching flies with my left hand
bringing the fist to my ear
hearing the scream grey buzz
as their legs cramp their
heads with no air
so eyes split and release

open fingers
the air and sun hit them like pollen
sun flood drying them red
catching flies
angry weather in my head, too

I remember this midnight at John Chisum's. Sallie was telling me about Henry. They had had it imported from England by ship, then train, then Sallie had met the train and brought it the last seventy miles in a coach. Strangest looking thing she said. It could hardly walk up a stair at first because it was so heavy and long. Its tail, which was dark brown with an amber ridge all down the middle of its length, stood up like a plant, so when he moved up and down hills the first thing you saw was this tail. In the house, John's clock banged away in the kitchen, the noise and whir reeling out onto us on the porch. John and Sallie, the mut Henry, and me. I had come in that morning.

They call it a bassett says Sallie, and they used to breed them in France for all those fat noblemen whose hounds were too fast for them when they went hunting. So they got the worst and slowest of every batch and bred them with the worst and slowest of every other batch and kept doing this until they got the slowest kind of hound they could think of. Looks pretty messy to me, I said. John scratched his groin awkwardly but politely — I mean not many would have noticed if they hadnt been on the lookout, expecting it as it were. John began a story.

When I was in New Orleans during the war I met this character who had dogs. I met him because I was a singer then, and he liked to sing, so we used to sing together quite a lot. He seemed a pretty sane guy to me. I mean, he didnt twitch or nothing like that. Well, a month or two after I left New Orleans, I got a note from another friend who sang with us once in a while, and he said Livingstone, who was the first singer, had been eaten by his dogs. It was a postcard and it didnt say anymore. When I was in New Orleans again, 2 or 3 years later I found out.

Livingstone had been mad apparently. Had been for a couple of years, and, while he couldnt fight in the war — he had a limp from a carriage accident — he hung around the soldiers like me. There was a rumour though that the reason he was not accepted was because no one that knew him would trust him with a gun. He had almost killed his mother with a twelve bore, fortunately only shooting an ugly vase to pieces and also her foot. (Her surgeon's bills were over $40 for he took nearly three hours getting all the buckshot out of her thighs because she wouldnt let anyone go any further than her knees, not even a professional doctor.) After that, Livingstone stayed away from guns, was embarrassed by it all I suppose, and besides the episode was a joke all over town.

Some time later he bought a spaniel, one of the American kind. A month later he bought another. He said he was going to start breeding dogs, and his mother, pleased at even a quirk of an ambition, encouraged him. But she didnt realize what he had been really doing until after his death and even then the vet had to explain it to her once more. Livingstone, and this was at the same time as he sang with me in the evenings, had decided to breed a race of mad dogs. He did this by inbreeding. His mother gave him money to start the business and he bought this wooden walled farm, put a vast fence around an area of 50 square feet, and keeping only the two original dogs he had bought, literally copulated them into madness. At least not them but their pups, who were bred and re-bred with their brothers and sisters and mothers and uncles and nephews. Every combination until their bones grew arched and tangled, ears longer than their feet, their tempers became either slothful or venomous and their jaws were black rather than red. You realize no one knew about this. It went on for two or three years before the accident. When people asked him how the dogs were coming along, he said fine; it was all a secret system and he didnt want anyone looking in. He said he liked to get a piece of work finished before he showed it to people. Then it was a surprise and they would get the total effect. It was like breeding roses.

You are supposed to be able to tell how inbred a dog is by the width of their pupils and Livingstone knew this, for again he picked the two most far gone dogs and bred them one step further into madness. In three years he had over 40 dogs. The earlier ones he just let loose, they were too sane. The rest, when the vet found them, were grotesque things — who hardly moved except to eat or fornicate. They lay, the dogs, when they found his body, listless as sandbags propped against the 14 foot fence Livingstone had built. Their eyes bulged like marbles; some were blind, their eyes had split. Livingstone had found that the less he fed them the more they fornicated, if only to keep their mind off the hunger. These originally beautiful dogs were gawky and terrifying to that New Orleans vet when he found them. He couldnt even recognize that they had been spaniels or were intended to be. They didnt snarl, just hissed through the teeth — gaps left in them for they were falling out. Livingstone had often given them just alcohol to drink.

His mother continued to give him money for his business, which still of course hadnt turned a penny. He had never sold a dog and lived alone. He came into town on Thursdays for food and on Thursday evenings when I was stationed in New Orleans he sang with me. We usually drank a lot after the bouts of singing. And again, even when drunk he never showed any sign of madness or quirkiness. As if he left all his madness, all his perverse logic, behind that fence on his farm and was washed pure by the time he came to town every Thursday. Many he had known when younger said how much more stable he had become, and that now they probably would accept him in the army. He told me he had a small farm he ran, never mentioning dogs. Then usually about three in the morning or around then he went back home to the house next to those 40 mad dogs, clinically and scientifically breeding the worst with the worst, those heaps of bone and hair and sexual organs and bulging eyes and minds which were chaotic half out of hunger out of liquor out of their minds being pressed out of shape by new freakish bones that grew into their skulls. These spaniels, if you could call them that now, were mostly brown.

When they found Livingstone there was almost nothing left of him. Even his watch had been eaten by one of the dogs who coughed it up in the presence of the vet. There were the bones of course, and his left wrist — the hand that held the whip when he was in the pen — was left untouched in the middle of the area. But there was not much else. The dust all over the yard was reddish and his clothes, not much left of those, scattered round.

The dogs too were blood hungry. Though this scene was discovered, they reckoned, two days after the event occurred, some of the dogs had been similarly eaten. The vet went into the house, got Livingstone's shot gun, the same one that had spread bullets into his mother's leg, couldnt find any bullets, went into town, bought bullets, didnt say a word in town except got the sheriff with him and rode back. And they shot all the dogs left, refusing to go into the pen, but poking the gun through the planks in the fence and blowing off the thirty heads that remained alive whenever they came into range or into the arc that the gun could turn to reach them. Then they went in, dug a pit with a couple of Livingstone's shovels, and buried everything. 40 dogs and their disintegrated owner.

The clock inside whirred for a half second and then clunked 1 o clock. Sallie got up and walked down the steps of the porch. Henry could deal with the steps now, went down with her and they walked into the edge of the dark empty desert. John rocked on in his chair. I was watching Sallie. She bent down, put her hands under Henry's ears and scratched his neck where she knew he liked it. She bent down further to his ear, the left one, the one away from us, and said, very quietly, I dont think John heard it it was so quiet, Aint that a nasty story Henry, aint it? Aint it nasty.

Up with the curtain
down with your pants
William Bonney
is going to dance

Hlo folks —'d liketa sing my song about the lady Miss A D
you all know her — her mind the only one in town high on
the pox

Miss Angela D has a mouth like a bee
she eats and off all your honey
her teeth leave a sting on your very best thing
and its best when she gets the best money

Miss Angela Dickinson
blurred in the dark
her teeth are a tunnel
her eyes need a boat

Her mouth is an outlaw
she swallow your breath
a thigh it can drown you
or break off your neck

Her throat is a kitchen
red food and old heat
her ears are a harp
you tongue till it hurt

Her toes take your ribs
her fingers your mind
her turns a gorilla
to swallow you blind

(thankin yew

Angela — hand shot open
water blood on my shoulder
crying quiet
O Bonney you bastard Bonney
kill him Bonney kill him

this from Angela
she saying this when their bullet for me
split her wrist so flesh burst out

Watching me do it.
Took knife and opened the skin
more, tugged it back
on the other side of her arm
to pick the bullets out
3 of them
like those rolled pellet tongues of pigeons

look at it, I'm looking into your arm
nothing confused in there
look how clear
Yes Billy, clear

So we are sitting slowly going drunk here on the porch. Usually it was three of us. Now five, our bodies on the chairs out here blocking out sections of the dark night. And the burn from the kerosene lamp throwing ochre across our clothes and faces. John in the silent rocking chair bending forward and back, one leg tucked under him, with each tilt his shirt smothering the light and spiralling shadows along the floor. The rest of us are quieter. Garrett sits on the sofa with Sallie the quietest of us all. He doesnt talk much I've noticed and mostly listens. Sallie her legs out resting on the chair at the ankles, the long skirt falling like a curtain off her legs and touching the floor. The cat shifts in her lap. And just to my left, her leg dangling off the rail she sits on, Angela D, the long leg about a foot to my left swaying, the heel tapping the wooden rail.

The thing here is to explain the difference of this evening. That in fact the Chisum verandah is crowded. It could of course hold a hundred more, but that John and Sallie and I have been used to other distances, that we have talked slowly through nights expecting the long silences and we have taken our time thinking the replies. That one was used to the space of black that hung like cotton just off the porch lights' spill. At 1 or 2 then Sallie would get up and bring me the cat and leave to make coffee and get ready for bed. And come back with the three cups and changed into her nightgown, always yellow or white with fabulous bows at her shoulders and the front of her neck. And then hunch up the gown over her folded legs so we joked at her looking like a pelican or some fat bird with vast stomach and short legs. But she didnt move from that, said her legs against herself kept herself warm for the wind had begun now, a slight flapping against the house. And it is now one and Sallie gets up and the cat stays on the sofa in the warm pool of material where she was. And Angela stretches and says bed I guess and I say no we are having coffee now and she leans back and later Sallie brings mugs in on a tray this time. And we all laugh a little cos Garrett has fallen asleep. Nobody noticed it in the semi dark. He hasnt moved an inch. Just the eyes closed. But the coffee tonight doesnt do much for the drink. That is, we are all pretty loaded here and in fact we go back to the whisky. And my throat now feels nothing as the drinks go down. I wonder how Angie can balance on the rail; as I do, she slips down near me and tho I cant see Sallie's eyes I think she must be watching us.

We sit here drinking on, after the coffee. Garrett here but asleep, Sallie, John, and the two of us. My eyes are burning from the pain of change and the whisky and I cant see very well, John's rocker is going slow but his checkered shirt leaves just a red arc daze like some blurred picture. I remember, when they took the picture of me there was a white block down the fountain road where somebody had come out of a building and got off the porch onto his horse and ridden away while I was waiting standing still for the acid in the camera to dry firm.

So, bed, says John and we say yes and sit for a bit longer, then Sallie wakes Garrett and we all get up and go to our rooms. And Angie I find is high as hell and stumbling hanging onto my shoulder. In the room we have been given the same bed I was given when alone. Angie says she'll have to sleep on top of me or me on top of her. And I say I'm too drunk for a balancing act Angie. O fooo she says and buttons open my shirt and her hands are like warm gloves on my back, soft till she uses her nails to scratch me towards her and I come and start giggling, wait the bathroom hold it. Yes, she says laughing. Quiet Sallie's in the next room, got ears like anything.

On the can I have to sit cos I know I cant pee straight. Before I finish she comes in and straddles me and drops her long hair into my open shirt as we slip our tongues into each others mouths. Her skirt over both of us and the can. Billy come on. mmm I say yes, get up first. No. Shit Angie. No. And slowly and carefully she lifts her legs higher and hangs them on tight to my shoulders like clothespins. Come on Angie I'm drunk 'm not a trapeze artist. Yes you are. No. And slowly I lift her up pressing her to me. The smell of her sex strong now daubing my chest and shirt where she rubs it. Youre too heavy for this I think, and we move careful to the floor, she leaning back like timber, lifts her legs to take clothes off and I grab the skirt and pull it over her head. Let me out Billy. Out Billy. Quiet she's next door. No! I know you Billy! Youre fucking her. No Angie, no, I say, honest Angie you got too much, and enter her like a whale with a hat on, my drowning woman my lady who drowns, and take my hat off.

Waking in the white rooms of Texas after a bad night must be like heaven I think now. About 9 o clock and the room looks huge like the sun came in and pushed out the walls, now the sun — as if reflected off the bushes outside — hitting and swirling on the white walls and the white sheets on the bed as I can see when I put my head up.

I'm sure everyone in the house threw up last night. All except Garrett anyway. The whisky and coffee and whisky again did in our communal stomach and the bathroom last night was like a confession box. At one point Angela was in the can and Sallie and I stood in the hall, leaning against the wall, eyes half closed, she in a nightgown of white with silver flowers on it and a bow of grey trailing down to her stomach. The hall also grey as nobody wants the light on for our eyes are shifting like old half dried blood under their lids and Sallie's even put her hair over her face for more shade. And in my blur she looks lovely there, her body against the cold stone wall, leaning there, her arms folded, the wrists snuggled into her elbows and her gown down to her white feet scratching at each other. Me in a towel, having now to sit cos I keep slipping down the wall.

Hurry up Angela, Sallie hits the door. More noises in there like an engine starting up. I cant wait, I said, I'll go outside. No reply. And I move through the dark house hitting stools with my feet and hanging onto chairs on my way, cant see a goddam. Realize walls are there just before I hit them and the dog comes out of a corner and along with me licking my bare feet.

Outside with only a towel on and the wind is lifting the sand and lashing me around. I select a spot and start throwing up, the wind carrying it like a yellow ribbon a good foot to my right. The acid burning my gums and tongue on the way out. Stop. Put my fingers into the mushrooms of my throat and up it comes again and flies out like a pack of miniature canaries. A flock. A covey of them, like I'm some magician or something. This is doing nothing for my image is it. Here I am ¾s naked in a towel vomiting 10 yards from the house, to my left a fucking big desert where nothing is except wind picking up sand and dust and the smell off dead animals a hundred miles away and aiming it at me and my body.

And this bloody dog goes over and sniffs it and then methodically begins to eat, preparing no doubt his appetite for tomorrow morning, while now, it puts the machinery in me that organizes my throwing up to sleep, as if I hadnt drunk a thing in a year. I kick the dog away but it comes back to the meal. I cant yell cos my mouth is dry. I try and then the muscles heave deep down and up it comes like a daisy chain whipping out as it gets free into the slip stream of the wind and collapses on the ground right in front of the dog who is having the time of his life. The end. I leave the dog and move back into the now warm of the house, sand on my feet and collapse into my bed. And Angela's there and Sallie wasnt in the hall so I guess she's in there or back in bed. And just as I drop off I hear John getting up and staggering in the dark.

So it was a bad night. But this morning the room is white and silvery shadows roll across the ceiling. All is clean except our mouths and I move to the basin and rinse out last night's throat and pee down the drain and struggle back to bed, and Angela D is golden and cool beside me the sheet over her stomach like a skirt and her arm out straight over the edge of the bed like a peninsula rich with veins and cooler than the rest of her for it has been in the path of the window's wind all night.

She is so brown and lovely, the sun rim blending into lighter colours at her neck and wrists. The edge of the pillow in her mouth, her hip a mountain further down the bed. Beautiful ladies in white rooms in the morning. How do I wake her? All the awkwardness of last night with the Chisums gone, like my head is empty, scoured open by acid. My head and body open to every new wind direction, every nerve new move and smell. I look up. On the nail above the bed the black holster and gun is coiled like a snake, glinting also in the early morning white.

The street of the slow moving animals
while the sun drops in perfect verticals
no wider than boots
The dogs sleep their dreams off
they are everywhere
so that horses on the crowded weekend
will step back and snap a leg

/ while I've been going on
the blood from my wrist
has travelled to my heart
and my fingers touch
this soft blue paper notebook
control a pencil that shifts up and sideways
mapping my thinking going its own way
like light wet glasses drifting on polished wood.

The acute nerves spark
on the periphery of our bodies
while the block trunk of us
blunders as if we were
those sun drugged horses

I am here with the range for everything
corpuscle muscle hair
hands that need the rub of metal
those senses that
that want to crash things with an axe
that listen to deep buried veins in our palms
those who move in dreams over your women night
near you, every paw, the invisible hooves
the mind's invisible blackout   the intricate never
the body's waiting rut.

The eyes bright scales
(watch)   bullet claws coming
at me like women fingers
part my hair slow
go in slow in slow,
leaving skin in a puff
behind and the slow
as if fire pours out
red grey brain the hair slow
startled by it all pour
Miss Angela D her eyes like a boat
on fire her throat is a kitchen
warm on my face heaving
my head mouth out
she swallows your breath
like warm tar pour
the man in the bright tin armour star
blurred in the dark
saying stop jeesus jesus jesus JESUS

73

This nightmare by this 7 foot high doorway
waiting for friends to come
mine or theirs
I am 4 feet inside the room
in the brown cold dark
the doorway's slide of sun
three inches from my shoes
I am on the edge of the cold dark
watching the white landscape in its frame
a world that's so precise
every nail and cobweb
has magnified itself to my presence

Waiting
nothing breaks my vision
but flies in their black path
like inverted stars,
or the shock sweep of a bird
that's grown too hot
and moves into the cool for an hour

If I hold up my finger
I blot out the horizon
if I hold up my thumb
I'd ignore a man who comes
on a three mile trip to here
The dog near me breathes out
his lungs make a pattern of sound
when he shakes
his ears go off like whips
he is outside the door
mind clean, the heat
floating his brain in fantasy

I am here on the edge of sun
that would ignite me
looking out into pitch white
sky and grass overdeveloped to meaninglessness
waiting for enemies' friends or mine

There is nothing in my hands
though every move I would make
getting up slowly walking
on the periphery of black
to where weapons are
is planned by my eye

A boy blocks out the light
in blue shirt and jeans
his long hair over his ears
face young like some pharoah

I am unable to move
with nothing in my hands

We moved in a batch now. Not just Dave Rudabaugh, Wilson and me, but also Garrett, deputies Emory and East, seven others I'd never seen and Charlie lying dead on the horse's back, his arms and legs dangling over the side, tied, so he wouldnt fall off. A sheet covered him to stop him drying too much in the sun. That was a bad week after that. Charlie having taken my hat had got it busted to pieces, so no hat for me as we moved back and forward, side to side over the county, avoiding people and law. Lynchers were out now and, bless him, Garrett didnt want that. So we moved along the Carrizozo plains to the slopes of Oscuros, stayed one night by Chupadero mesa, back to the Carrizozo, passed the Evan tribe, followed now the telegraph to Punta de la Glorietta but over 40 lynchers there. So we moved, no hat for me, uncomfortable times for all of us.

Horses and trains horses and trains. Dave, Wilson and me, our legs handcuffed with long 24" chains under the horse, our hands bound to the bridle. Five days like that. We had to pee as we sat, into our trousers and down the horse's side. We slept lying forward on the horse's neck. All they did to stop us going mad from saddle pain was alternate saddles, or let us ride bareback one day and a saddle the next. All going grey in the eyes. My horse hating me, the chain under his belly, as much as I hated him.

On the fifth day the sun turned into a pair of hands and began to pull out the hairs in my head. Twist pluck twist pluck. In two hours I was bald, my head like a lemon. It used a fingernail and scratched a knife line from front to back on the skin. A hairline of blood bubbled up and dried. Eleven in the morning then. The sun took a towel and wiped the dried dribble off, like red powder on the towel now. Then with very thin careful fingers it began to unfold my head drawing back each layer of skin and letting it flap over my ears.

The brain juice began to swell up. You could see the bones and grey now. The sun sat back and watched while the juice evaporated. By now the bone was dull white, all dry. When he touched the bone with his fingers it was like brushing raw nerves. He took a thin cold hand and sank it into my head down past the roof of my mouth and washed his fingers in my tongue. Down the long cool hand went scratching the freckles and warts in my throat breaking through veins like pieces of long glass tubing, touched my heart with his wrist, down he went the liquid yellow from my busted brain finally vanishing as it passed through soft warm stomach like a luscious blood wet oasis, weaving in and out of the red yellow blue green nerves moving uncertainly through wrong fissures ending pausing at cul de sacs of bone then retreating slow leaving the pain of suction then down the proper path through pyramids of bone that were there when I was born, through grooves the fingers spanning the merging paths of medians of blue matter, the long cool hand going down brushing cobwebs of nerves the horizontal pain pits, lobules gyres notches arcs tracts fissures roots' white insulation of dead seven year cells clinging things rubbing them off on the tracts of spine down the cool precise fingers went into the cistern of bladder down the last hundred miles in a jerk breaking through my sacs of sperm got my cock in the cool fingers pulled it back up and carried it pulling pulling flabby as smoke up the path his arm had rested in and widened. He brought it up fast half tearing the roots off up the coloured bridges of fibres again, charting the slimy arm back through the pyramids up locked in his fingers up the now bleeding throat up squeezed it through the skull bones, so there I was, my cock standing out of my head. Then he brought his other hand into play I could feel the cool shadow now as he bent over me both his hands tapering into beautiful cool fingers, one hand white as new smelling paper the other 40 colours ochres blues silver from my lung gold and tangerine from the burst ear canals all that clung to him as he went in and came out.

The hands were cold as porcelain, one was silver old bone stripped oak white eastern cigarettes white sky the eye core of sun. Two hands, one dead, one born from me, one like crystal, one like shell of snake found in spring. Burning me like dry ice.

They picked up the fold of foreskin one hand on each side and began the slow pull back back back back *down* like a cap with ear winter muffs like a pair of trousers down boots and then he let go. The wind picked up, I was drowned, locked inside my skin sensitive as an hour old animal, could feel everything, I could hear everything on my skin, as I sat, like a great opaque ostrich egg on the barebacked horse. In my skin hearing

Garrett's voice near me on the skin whats wrong billy whats
wrong, couldnt see him but I turned to where I knew he was. I
yelled so he could hear me through the skin. Ive been fucked.
Ive been fuckd Ive been fucked by Christ almighty god Ive been
good and fucked by Christ. And I rolled off the horse's back like
a soft shell-less egg wrapped in thin white silk and I splashed
onto the dust blind and white but the chain held my legs to the
horse and I was dragged picking up dust on my wet skin as I
travelled in between his four trotting legs at last thank the
fucking christ, in the shade of his stomach.

Garrett moved us straight to the nearest railroad depot. We had to wait one night for the train that would take us to Messilla where they would hold the trial. The Polk Hotel there was a bright white place with a wide courtyard and well. The deputies went down in the bucket and washed themselves. They removed Charlie off his horse. Garrett took over and washed the dried blood off the animal. Garrett ordered a box for Charlie Bowdre. Then he made me drink liquids and paste. They had to carry the three of us from the horses to the beds — we couldn't walk after the week on horses. I was to share a room with Garrett and Emory.

Your last good bed Billy, he said, pick your position. I did, face and stomach down. He chained me to the bed. He taped my fingers so thick I couldnt get them through a trigger guard even if they gave me a gun. Then he went out and looked after Wilson who had broken both ankles when the horse stumbled collapsing on his chained legs.

It is afternoon still, the room white with light. My last white room, the sun coming through the shutters making the white walls whiter. I lie on my left cheek looking to that light. I cannot even see the door or if Emory has stayed behind. The bed vast. Went to sleep, my body melting into it. I remember once after Charlie and I stopped talking we could hear flies buzzing in their black across a room, and I remember once, one night in the open I turned to say goodnight to Charlie who was about ten yards away and there was the moon balanced perfect on his nose.

It is the order of the court that you be taken to Lincoln and confined to jail until May 13th and that on that day between the hours of sunrise and noon you be hanged on the gallows until you are dead dead dead
And may God have mercy on your soul

said Judge Warren H. Bristol

THE KID TELLS ALL

'EXCLUSIVE JAIL INTERVIEW'

INTERVIEWER: Billy. . .

BONNEY: Mr. Bonney please.

I: Mr. Bonney, I am from the *Texas Star*. You are now how old?

B: 21.

I: When is your birthday?

B: November 23rd. On that lap I'll be 22.

I: You were reported as saying, as adding, to that phrase — 'If I make it' when asked that question before.

B: Well, sometimes I feel more confident than at others.

I: And you feel alright now. . .

B: Yes, I'm ok now.

I: Mr. Bonney, when you rejected Governor Wallace's offer of an amnesty, were you aware of the possibility that your life would continue the way it has?

B: Well, I don't know; Charlie, Charlie Bowdre that is, said then that I was a fool not to grab what I could out of old Wallace. But what the hell. It didn't mean too much then anyway. All Wallace was offering me was protection from the law, and at that time the law had no quarrels with me, so it seemed rather silly.

I: But you were wanted for cattle rustling weren't you?

B: Yes, but, well let me put it this way. I could only be arrested if they had proof, definite proof, not just stories. They had to practically catch me with stolen cattle in my bed. And when you rustle, you can see law coming a good two miles away. All I had to do was ride off in the opposite direction and that would have been that.

I: But couldn't they catch you with them when you sold them?

B: Well I don't do, I didn't do the selling — I sold them off before they reached the market.

I: How were, or with whom were you able to do that?

B: I'd rather not mention names if you don't mind.

(Here Mr. Bonney withdrew a black cigarette, lit it, and grinned charmingly, then retreated behind his enigmatic half smile, a smile which was on the verge of one. These smiles of 'Billy the Kid' are well known and have become legendary among his friends in this area. Sheriff Garrett has an explanation for this:

"Billy has a denture system which is prominent, buck teeth you at the paper would call it. So that even when he has no intention of smiling his teeth force his mouth into a half grin. Because of this, people are always amazed at his high spirits in a time of stress." Mrs. Celsa Guitterrez adds to this:

"When Billy was 18, a man named John Rapsey ('. . . . head' as he was affectionately called afterwards) broke his (Billy's) nose with a bottle. Billy was knocked unconscious and Rapsey escaped. Bowdre who was with him, to ease the pain when he came to, fed him some tequila, made him drunk. Billy didn't get his nose fixed for three days as Bowdre accompanying him on the tequila also got drunk and forgot all about the broken nose. As a result, when Billy finally got to Sumner to get it fixed his breathing channels, or whatever, were clogged. After that he rarely breathed through his nose again, and breathed by sucking the air in through his mouth, or through his teeth as it seemed. If you were near him when he was breathing heavily — when excited or running, you could hear this hissing noise which was quite loud.")

B: Anyway, Wallace offered me protection from the law, and the only law I knew in Fort Sumner was the Murphy faction which would certainly not uphold Wallace if they found me in a dark street without guns. (Laugh)

I: Did you get on well with Wallace?

B: He was ok.

I: What do you mean by that?

B: Just that he was straight about it all. I mean he was disappointed of course that I couldn't agree, but I think he saw my point. I don't think he thought much of Murphy's men, or trusted them either.

I: But right now you've threatened to kill him if you escape this hanging?

B: WHEN I escape, yes.

I: Why?

B: Well, I've been through all this before. I've already made a statement. But anyway, again. In my trial three weeks ago, the charge that was brought against me was for shooting Sheriff Clark, etc. Now Wallace offered me parole, or amnesty or whatever *after* this shooting. As you know there were no real witnesses of any murder on my part after that incident. But the fact is that the Clark shooting took place during the Lincoln County war — when EVERYBODY was shooting. I mean no one brought charges against those who shot McSween or Tunstall. Now Wallace when he spoke to me admitted that, while he couldn't condone what was done during those three days, he understood that both sides were guilty, and like a state of war there was no criminal punishment that could be genuinely brought against me without bringing it against everyone connected with that war. Two wrongs make a right, right? Now they find that because they cannot charge me with anything else that'll stick they charge me for something that happened during a war . A fact that your Governor Wallace realises and I'm sure privately admits and still won't do anything about.

I: Why do you suppose he doesn't do anything to pardon you now?

B: (Giggling) Well I suppose he's been wished into thinking that I've been pretty nasty since. But the point is that there is no legal proof to all this later stuff. The evidence used was unconstitutional.

I: Do you have a lawyer, I mean working on an appeal now?

B: Slip me a gun and I will have — don't print that.

I: Mr. Bonney, or may I call you Billy. . .

B: No.

I: Mr. Bonney, do you believe in God?

B: No.

I: Why not, and for how long haven't you?

B: Well I did for a long time, I mean in a superstitious way, same way I believe in luck for instance. I couldn't take the risk you see. Like never wearing anything yellow. So before big fights, or even the most minor as well as the really easy ones, I used to cross myself and say, "God please don't let me die today." I did this fast though so no one would see me, see what I was doing. I did this pretty well every day from the age of 12 till I was 18. When I was 18, I had a shooting match with Tom O'Folliard, the prize was a horse. Now it was with rifles and Tom is excellent with them and I wanted that horse very much. I prayed every day. Then I lost the bet with Tom.

I: Do you worry about what will happen after death now you don't believe in God?

B: Well I try to avoid it. Though I suppose not. I guess they'll just put you in a box and you will stay there forever. There'll be nothing else. The only thing I wish is that I could hear what people say afterwards. I'd really like that. You know, I'd like to be invisible watching what happens to people when I am not around. I suppose you thing that's simple minded.

I: Are you happy, or at least were you happy? Did you have any reason for going on living, or were you just experimenting?

B: I don't know whether I'm happy or not. But in the end that is all that's important — that you keep testing yourself, as you say — experimenting on how good you are, and you can't do that when you want to lose.

I: Is that all you looked forward to?

B: Yes I suppose so. And my friends. I enjoy people and being with friends.

I: Is it true that you were going to get married and move east when you were arrested?

B: As I say I don't want to cause trouble, and though I'm not saying about the first part of the question, I *had* intended to leave the area cos people kept coming up to me and saying I was going to get it for what I had done to their friends. Bob Ollinger who's worked his way into being my jailer. He had a close friend who was killed in the Lincoln County war.

I: Who do you consider your friends now, now that Bowdre and O'Folliard are dead?

B: Well I have some. Dave Rudabaugh wherever he is. I guess he's locked up too somewhere. They won't tell me. A couple of guys here and there. A couple of ladies.

I: Garrett?

B: Well Pat's right now a . . . . head. We used to be friends as you probably know. He's got senile. He's getting a lot of money for cleaning the area up — of us supposedly. No I don't think much of him now.

I: He's said that he gave you all plenty of opportunity to get out of New Mexico before he began hunting you.

B: Yeahhhh but one) you don't go around using mutual friends to trap an old friend and two) I love the country around here and Fort Sumner. . .all my friends are here. I'd go now, cos some I thought were friends were really pretty hypocritical.

I: What about pastimes? Did you have many when you were free? Did you like books, music, dancing?

B: Dancing I like, I'm a pretty good dancer. Fond of music too. There's a Canadian group, a sort of orchestra, that is the best. Great. Heard them often when I was up there trying to get hold of a man who went by the name of Captain P————.* Never found him. But that group will be remembered a long time.

I: How about you, do you think you will last in people's memories?

B: I'll be with the world till she dies.

I: But what do you think you'll be remembered as? I mean don't you think that already several feel you are morally vulgar? I mean all these editorials about you. . . .

B: Well. . .editorials. A friend of Garrett's, Mr. Cassavates or something, said something bout editorials. He said editorials don't do anything they just make people feel guilty.

I: That's rather good.

B: Yes. It is.

Am the dartboard
for your midnight blood
the bones' moment
of perfect movement
that waits to be thrown
magnetic into combat

a pencil
harnessing my face
goes stumbling into dots

No the escape was no surprise to me. I expected it. I really did, we all did I suppose. And it is now in retrospect difficult to describe. You've probably read the picture books anyway, seen the films, of how he did it. What he did was to seduce young Bell into a cardgame, shot him, then shot Ollinger returning from lunch. Nobody cared about Ollinger, but Bell was liked. You know how Ollinger used to kill people? He'd go up to them about to shake hands, then grab their right hand with his left, lift out his pistol and fire into the chest. He had hated Billy ever since the Lincoln County War. So Bell and Ollinger died and Billy escaped. Also on the way out of town he hit a man named Ellery Fleck in the face, with his rifle, for no reason at all. He was probably elated.

One funny thing happened apparently (I was out of town). Billy's hands were still chained, and jumping onto a horse to escape he lost his balance and fell off — right in front of the crowd who refused to do anything but watch. In that crowd nobody cracked a smile. Three or four kids helped him catch the horse and held it while he got on carefully. Then with the rifle cradled in his arms he made the horse walk slowly over Ollinger's body and went.

MISS SALLIE CHISUM :

GOOD FRIENDS :

As far as dress was concerned
he always looked as if
he had just stepped out of a bandbox.

In broadbrimmed white hat
dark coat and vest
grey trousers worn over his boots
a grey flannel shirt
and black four-in-hand tie
and sometimes — would you believe it ? —
a flower in his lapel.

A COURTEOUS LITTLE GENTLEMAN:

I suppose it sounds absurd to speak
of such a character as a gentleman,
but from beginning to end
of our long relationship,
in all his personal relations with me,
he was the pink of politeness
and as courteous a little gentleman
as I ever met.

There was a brook full of fish
that ran under the house
across a corner of the kitchen
and I often sat on the back porch
in a rocking chair, with Billy
to bait my hook for me,
and caught a string of perch for dinner.

(Garrett had stuffed birds. Not just the stringy Mexican vultures but huge exotic things. We would sometimes be with him when they arrived. He would have them sent to him frozen in boxes. The box was wooden, a crate really, and with great care after bringing it back from the station, he would remove the nails. He first took out the 8″ of small crushed ice and said look. And it would be a white seagull. It was beautifully spread in the ice, not a feather out of place, its claws extended and brittle from the freezing. Garrett melted it and split it with a narrow knife, parting the feathers first, and with a rubber glove in his right hand removed the body. He then washed the rotted blood from the wings, the outside, and then took it out onto the verandah to dry.)

MISS SALLIE CHISUM : PAT GARRETT

A tremendously tall man.

Despite his crooked mouth
and crooked smile which
made his whole face seem crooked

he was a remarkably handsome man.

BILLY THE KID & PAT GARRETT ; SOME FINAL THOUGHTS :

I knew both these men intimately.
There was good mixed in with the bad
in Billy the Kid
and bad mixed in with the good
in Pat Garrett.

No matter what they did in the world
or what the world thought of them
they were my friends.
Both were worth knowing.

Sound up. Loud and vibrating in the room. My ears picking up all the burning hum of flies letting go across the room. The mattress under Pete Maxwell shifting its straw, each blade loud in its clear flick against another. Even the now and then crack at the glass as the day's heat evaporates from the window against the dark of the desert.

And then that breathing, not Maxwell's but *the other's*. The breathing precise but forced into quiet but regular streams. Think of the dark air going up through the nose, down to the stomach rolling around on itself, and then up and out like a fountain spilling through his teeth hissssssssssssssssssssssssssss

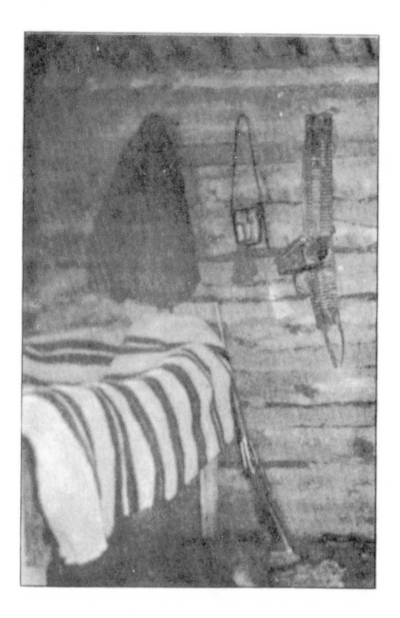

MMMmmmmmm. In the final minutes. It is Texas midnight. A large large square, well and buckets centre. The houses and sheds in rows making up the square. The long narrow porch running all around. Up to the well rides Pat Garrett and deputies Poe and Mackinnon. Scuffling slow, smoking as they dismount gentle and leave the horses and walk to the large hut which is Maxwell's room. They pass the dog.

This is a diagram then of Maxwell's, Pete Maxwell's, room. Bed here against the wall, here's the window where he put his hand through. And here, along here, is the porch. While this, about 20 yards away, is the Guitterrez home. Garrett, Poe, and Mackinnon stop near Maxwell's door. On some vague tip Garrett has come to ask Maxwell where he thinks Billy is hiding out — where in the territory is he — he's been escaped 3 months and nobody's seen him. Garrett leaves the deputies sitting smoking on the porch, flicks away his own cigar and goes into the dark room where Maxwell is asleep *Meanwhile*

Billy is just yards away drinking with Celsa Guitterrez. He came in about an hour ago, he wears only his trousers and guns, hot night. They decide she will cook him something and he offers to go cut some meat. Carrying a knife in his left hand, and barefoot, he is up and begins walking towards the ice house. Passing the Maxwell room he sees the two men outside. Quien es? They do not answer. Again the question. No answer. Billy backs off the porch into Maxwell's room and heads towards his friend's sleeping.

In the dark room Garrett has wakened and is questioning the dazed Maxwell. In fact as Billy enters he is crouching by Maxwell's bed. Quienes son esos hombres afuera, Pete? Garrett recognises the voice. He does the one thing that will save him. Quietly, with his long legs, he climbs over Maxwell's body and gets into bed between Maxwell and the wall. With his rifle in his hands he watches the darkness, trying to make out the shape that is moving towards him. Billy moves over barefoot and asks Pete again. Quienes son esos hombres afuera?

Maxwell doesn't say a word. He can feel Garrett's oiled rifle barrel leaning against his cheek. Billy shakes Maxwell's shoulder and then he hears the other person's breathing. As the only other woman on the ranch, apart from Celsa Guitterrez is Paulita Maxwell — Pete's sister — he doesn't know what to think. Paulita? Pete Maxwell gives a nervous giggle full of fear which Billy mistakes for embarrassment. Paulita! Jesus Christ. He leans forward again and moves his hands down the bed and then feels a man's boots. O my god Pete quien es?

He is beginning to move back a couple of yards in amazement. Garrett is about to burst out laughing so he fires, leaving a powder scar on Maxwell's face that stayed with him all his life.

OUTSIDE
the outline of houses
Garrett running from a door
— all seen sliding round
the screen of a horse's eye

NOW dead centre in the square is Garrett with Poe
— hands in back pockets — argues, nodding his head
and then ALL TURNING as the naked arm, the arm from
the body, breaks through the window. The window —
what remains between the splits — reflecting all the
moving too.

Guitterrez goes to hold the arm but it is manic, breaks
her second finger. His veins that controlled triggers —
now tearing all they touch.

The end of it, lying at the wall
the bullet itch frozen in my head

my right arm is through the window pane
and the cut veins awake me
so I can watch inside and through the window

Garrett's voice going Billy Billy
and the other two dancing circles
saying we got him we got him the little shrunk bugger

the pain at my armpit I'm glad for
keeping me alive at the bone
and suns coming up everywhere out of the walls and floors
Garrett's jaw and stomach   thousands

of lovely perfect sun balls
breaking at each other click
click click click like Saturday morning pistol cleaning
when the bullets hop across the bed sheet and bounce and click

click and you toss them across the floor like . . . up in the air
and see how many you can catch in one hand the left

oranges reeling across the room AND I KNOW I KNOW
it is my brain coming out like red grass
this breaking where red things wade

PAULITA MAXWELL

An old story that identifies me as Billy the Kid's sweetheart has been going the rounds for many years. Perhaps it honours me; perhaps not; it depends on how you feel about it. But I was not Billy the Kid's sweetheart I liked him very much — oh, yes — but I did not love him. He was a nice boy, at least to me, courteous, gallant, always respectful. I used to meet him at dances; he was of course often at our home. But he and I had not thought of marriage.

There was a story that Billy and I had laid our plans to elope to old Mexico and had fixed the date for the night just after that on which he was killed. There was another tale that we proposed to elope riding double on one horse. Neither story was true and the one about eloping on one horse was a joke. Pete Maxwell, my brother, had more horses than he knew what to do with, and if Billy and I had wanted to set off for the Rio Grande by the light of the moon, you may depend upon it we would at least have had separate mounts. I did not need to put my arms around any man's waist to keep from falling off a horse. Not I. I was, if you please, brought up in the saddle, and plumed myself on my horsemanship.

Imagine if you dug him up and brought him out. You'd see very little. There'd be the buck teeth. Perhaps Garrett's bullet no longer in thick wet flesh would roll in the skull like a marble. From the head there'd be a trail of vertebrae like a row of pearl buttons off a rich coat down to the pelvis. The arms would be cramped on the edge of what was the box. And a pair of handcuffs holding ridiculously the fine ankle bones. (Even though dead they buried him in leg irons). There would be the silver from the toe of each boot.

His legend a jungle sleep

THE FIVE CENT
WIDE AWAKE
LIBRARY

No. 40.   Vol. I

BILLY THE KID

Billy the Kid and the Princess

The Castle of the Spanish girl called 'La Princesa' towered above the broad fertile valley . . . in the looming hills there were gold and silver mines . . . Truly, the man chosen to rule beside the loveliest woman in Mexico would be a king. The girl had chosen William H. Bonney to reign with her . . . but a massive brute named Toro Cuneo craved that honor. . .

There'd been a cattle war in Jackson County . . . He'd settled a beef with three gunquick brothers near Tucson. . . and he was weary of gunthunder and sudden death! Billy the Kid turned his cayuse south . . . splashed across the drought dried Rio Grande . . . and let the sun bake the tension out of his mind and body.

"See them sawtooth peaks, Caballo? There's a little town yonder with a real cold cerveza and a fat lady who can cook Mexican food better'n anybody in the world! This lady also got a daughter . . . una muchacho . . . who's got shinin' black hair and a gleam in her brown eyes I want to see again."

And on a distant hill . . .
"He comes, be ready Soto."

"Gunshots . . . a 45 pistol! Runaway! It's a girl! She's goin' to take a spill! Faster Chico!"
"AAAAAHH!"
"Hang on . . . I got yuh! . . . You're okay now Señorita."
"Gracias, Señor. You are so strong and brave . . . and very gallant!"

"Thanks, I heard shots . . . Did they scare your cayuse into runnin' away?"

"I think I can stand now, Señor . . . if you will put me down."

"Huh? Oh sorry, Señorita. I'm Billy Bonney, Señorita. I'm from up around Tucson."

"I am Marguerita Juliana de Guelva y Solanza, la Princesa de Guelva."

"La Princesa? A *real* princess?"

"I am direct descendent of King Phillip of Spain. By virtue of Royal land grants, I own this land west for 200 leagues, south for 180 leagues. It is as large as some European kingdoms . . . larger than two of your American states . . . I am still a little weak. Ride with me to the castle, Señor Bonney."

"*There* Señor Bonney . . . my ancestral home. The castle and the valley farther than you can see . . . I have 20,000 cattle, almost as many horses and herds of goats, pigs, chickens. Everything my people need to live."

"WHOOOEEE! The Governor's mansion up at Phoenix would fit in one end o' that wickiup."

"Come on, Yanqui! It is late . . . you must have dinner with me."

"ATTENTION! HER EXCELLENCY RETURNS!"

Thinks: "She's got a regular army!"

The man called Billy the Kid is not impressed by the magnificent richness of his surroundings. The golden cutlery means nothing . . . The priceless china and crystal matter not, and the food cooked by a French chef? — PFAAGGH!

Thinks: "I'd sooner be in Mama Rosa's kitchen eatin' tortillas an' chile with Rosita battin' them dark eyes at me!"

"This table needs a man like you, Señor Bonney. Others have occupied that chair but none so well as you."

"Gracias, Princesa . . . but I'd never feel right in it . . . if you know what I mean."

"I propose a toast, my gringo friend . . . to our meeting . . . to your gallant rescue of me!"

"I reckon I can't let a lady drink alone, Princesa."

CRASH! ! !

"He could have sunk it in my neck just as easy . . . Start talkin' hombre 'fore I say *my* piece about that knife throwing act!"

"I am a man of action, not words, gringo! I weel crack your ribs . . . break your wrists . . . then send you back where you belong!"

"Come on, animal, I want to finish dinner!"

SOCK! !

Thinks: "If I can nail him quick I'll take the fight out of him . . . PERFECT!"

That was his Sunday punch . . . and Toro laughed at it! Now, Billy the Kid knows he's in for a struggle!

"He's got a granite jaw which means . . . I'll have to weaken him with powerful hooks to the stomach! OOOOWWW!" THUD!

"Now it's my turn!"

"If he lays a hand on me . . ."

SWISSS!

SOCK!

"I keel you gringo!"

Thinks: "My head . . . he busted my jaw!"

TOCK!

Thinks: "He's a stomper . . ."

"I keel your pet gringo Excellencia!"

"Yuh'll take me tuh death maybe, hombre!"

"You no escape Toro now!"

"I didn't figure on escapin' Toro!"

CRACK!

"Over you go, Toro!" "Olé! Olé!"

CRASH!

"Sorry I busted the place up some, Princesa."

"You are mucho hombre, Yanqui, very much man! A man like you could help me rule this wild kingdom! Will you remain as my guest for a time?"

"I come down here to rest up some. I reckon I can do that here as well as in Mama Rosa's cantina."

(Kiss)

"That was to thank you for protecting me from Toro Cueno. I must not go on being formal with you . . ."

In the next few days, Billy the Kid was with La Princesa often. Long rides through wild country . . .

"Wait princess . . . don't get ahead of me!"

"EEEEEeeii! !"

"Duck, princess!"

BANG! BANG!

"Once more Chivoto, you have saved my life, this time from that cougar. You have won my love!"

"Hold on, ma'am . . ."

Before Billy the Kid can defend himself, La Princesa Marguerita has taken him in her arms and . . . .

"It was the Kid who came in there on to me," Garrett told Poe, "and I think I got him."

"Pat," replied Poe, "I believe you have killed the wrong man."

"I'm sure it was the Kid," responded Garrett, "for I knew his voice and could not have been mistaken."

Poor young William's dead
with a fish stare, with a giggle
with blood planets in his head.

The blood came down like river ride
long as Texas down his side.
We cleaned him up when blood was drier
his eyes looked up like turf on fire.

We got the eight foot garden hose
turned it on, leaned him down flat.
What fell away we threw away
his head was smaller than a rat.

I got the bullets, cleaned him up
sold them to the Texas Star.
They weighed them, put them in a pile
took pictures with a camera.

Poor young William's dead
with blood planets in his head
with a fish stare, with a giggle
like he said.

It is now early morning, was a bad night. The hotel room seems large. The morning sun has concentrated all the cigarette smoke so one can see it hanging in pillars or sliding along the roof like amoeba. In the bathroom, I wash the loose nicotene out of my mouth. I smell the smoke still in my shirt.

Running in the Family

For Griffin and Quintin.
For Gillian, Janet, and Christopher.

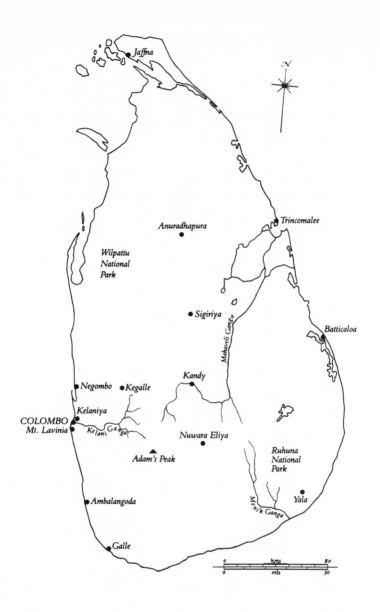

"I saw in this island fowls as big as our country geese having two heads . . . and other miraculous things which I will not here write of."

Oderic (Franciscan Friar, 14th century)

"The Americans were able to put a man on the moon because they knew English. The Sinhalese and Tamils whose knowledge of English was poor, thought that the earth was flat."

Douglas Amarasekera, *Ceylon Sunday Times* 29.I.78

CONTENTS

Drought since December.

All across the city men roll carts with ice clothed in sawdust. Later on, during a fever, the drought still continuing, his nightmare is that thorn trees in the garden send their hard roots underground towards the house climbing through windows so they can drink sweat off his body, steal the last of the saliva off his tongue.

He snaps on the electricity just before daybreak. For twenty five years he has not lived in this country, though up to the age of eleven he slept in rooms like this—with no curtains, just delicate bars across the windows so no one could break in. And the floors of red cement polished smooth, cool against bare feet.

Dawn through a garden. Clarity to leaves, fruit, the dark yellow of the King Coconut. This delicate light is allowed only a brief moment of the day. In ten minutes the garden will lie in a blaze of heat, frantic with noise and butterflies.

Half a page—and the morning is already ancient.

ASIAN
RUMOURS

ASIA

What began it all was the bright bone of a dream I could hardly hold onto. I was sleeping at a friend's house. I saw my father, chaotic, surrounded by dogs, and all of them were screaming and barking into the tropical landscape. The noises woke me. I sat up on the uncomfortable sofa and I was in a jungle, hot, sweating. Street lights bounced off the snow and into the room through the hanging vines and ferns at my friend's window. A fish tank glowed in the corner. I had been weeping and my shoulders and face were exhausted. I wound the quilt around myself, leaned back against the head of the sofa, and sat there for most of the night. Tense, not wanting to move as the heat gradually left me, as the sweat evaporated and I became conscious again of brittle air outside the windows searing and howling through the streets and over the frozen cars hunched like sheep all the way down towards Lake Ontario. It was a new winter and I was already dreaming of Asia.

Once a friend had told me that it was only when I was drunk that I seemed to know exactly what I wanted. And so, two months later, in the midst of the farewell party in my growing wildness—dancing, balancing a wine glass on my forehead and falling to the floor twisting round and getting up without letting the glass tip, a trick which seemed only possible when drunk and relaxed—I knew I was already running. Outside the continuing snow had made the streets narrow, almost impassable. Guests had arrived on foot, scarved, faces pink and frozen. They leaned against the fire-place and drank.

I had already planned the journey back. During quiet afternoons I spread maps onto the floor and searched out possible routes to Ceylon. But it was only in the midst of this party, among my closest friends, that I realised I would be travelling back to the family I had grown from—those relations from my parents' generation who stood in my memory like frozen opera. I wanted to touch them into words. A perverse and solitary desire. In Jane Austen's *Persuasion* I had come across the lines, "she had been forced into prudence in her youth—she learned romance as she grew older—the natural sequence of an unnatural beginning." In my mid-thirties I realised I had slipped past a childhood I had ignored and not understood.

Asia. The name was a gasp from a dying mouth. An ancient word that had to be whispered, would never be used as a battle cry. The word sprawled. It had none of the clipped sound of Europe, America, Canada. The vowels took over, slept on the map with the S. I was running to Asia and everything would change. It began with that moment when I was dancing and laughing wildly within the comfort and order of my life. Beside the fridge I tried to communicate some of the fragments I knew about my father, my grandmother. "So how *did* your grandmother die?" "Natural causes." "What?" "Floods." And then another wave of the party swirled me away.

JAFFNA AFTERNOONS

2:15 in the afternoon. I sit in the huge living room of the old governor's home in Jaffna. The walls, painted in recent years a warm rose-red, stretch awesome distances away to my left to my right and up towards a white ceiling. When the Dutch first built this house egg white was used to paint the walls. The doors are twenty feet high, as if awaiting the day when a family of acrobats will walk from room to room, sideways, without dismantling themselves from each other's shoulders.

The fan hangs on a long stem, revolves lethargic, its arms in a tilt to catch the air which it folds across the room. No matter how mechanical the fan is in its movement the textures of air have no sense of the metronome. The air reaches me unevenly with its gusts against my arms, face, and this paper.

The house was built around 1700 and is the prize building in this northern region of Ceylon. In spite of its internal vastness it appears modest from the outside, tucked in one corner of the fort. To approach the building by foot or car or bicycle one has to cross a bridge over the moat, be accepted by two sentries who unfortunately have to stand exactly where marsh gases collect, and enter the fort's yard. Here, in this spacious centre of the labyrinth of 18th-century Dutch defense I sit on one of the giant sofas, in the noisy solitude of the afternoon while the rest of the house is asleep.

The morning has been spent with my sister and my Aunt Phyllis trying to trace the maze of relationships in our ancestry. For a while we sat in one of the bedrooms sprawled on two beds and a chair. The twin to this bedroom, in another part of the house, is dark and supposedly haunted. Walking into that room's dampness, I saw the mosquito nets stranded in the air like the dresses of hanged brides, the skeletons of beds without their mattresses, and retreated from the room without ever turning my back on it.

Later the three of us moved to the dining room while my Aunt plucked notorious incidents from her brain. She is the minotaur of this long journey back—all those preparations for travel, the journey through Africa, the recent 7-hour train ride from Colombo to Jaffna, the sentries, the high walls of stone, and now this lazy courtesy of meals, tea, her best brandy in the evenings for my bad stomach—the minotaur who inhabits the place one had been years ago, who surprises one with conversations about the original circle of love. I am especially fond of her because she was always close to my father. When someone else speaks, her eyes glance up to the ceilings of the room, as if noticing the architecture there for the first time, as if looking for the cue cards for stories. We are still recovering from her gleeful résumé of the life and death of one foul Ondaatje who was "savaged to pieces by his own horse."

Eventually we move out onto the wicker chairs of the porch which runs 50 yards along the front of the house. From ten until noon we sit talking and drinking ice-cold palmyrah toddy from a bottle we have filled in the village. This is a drink which smells of raw rubber and is the juice drained from the flower of a coconut. We sip it slowly, feeling it continue to ferment in the stomach.

At noon I doze for an hour, then wake for a lunch of crab curry. There is no point in using a fork and spoon for this meal. I eat with my hands, shovelling in the rice with my thumb, crunching the shell in my teeth. Then fresh pineapple.

But I love the afternoon hours most. It is now almost a quarter to three. In half an hour the others will waken from their sleep and intricate conversations will begin again. In the heart of this 250-year-old fort we will trade anecdotes and faint memories, trying to swell them with the order of dates and asides, interlocking them all as if assembling the hull of a ship. No story is ever told just once. Whether a memory or funny hideous scandal, we will return to it an hour later and retell the story with additions and this time a few judgements thrown in. In this way history is organized. All day my Uncle Ned, who is heading a commission on race-riots (and so has been given this building to live in while in Jaffna), is at work, and all day my Aunt Phyllis presides over the history of good and bad Ondaatjes and the people they came in contact with. Her eye, which by now knows well the ceilings of this house, will suddenly sparkle and she will turn to us with delight and begin "and there is another terrible story. . . ."

There are so many ghosts here. In the dark mildewed wing, where the rotting mosquito nets hang, lives the apparition of the Dutch governor's daughter. In 1734 she threw herself down a well after being told she could not marry her lover, and has startled generations since, making them avoid the room where she silently exhibits herself in a red dress. And just as the haunted sections are avoided for sleeping, the living room is avoided for conversation, being so huge that all talk evaporates into the air before it reaches the listener.

The dogs from the town, who have sneaked past the guards, are asleep on the porch—one of the coolest spots in Jaffna. As I get up to adjust the speed of the fan, they roll onto their feet and move a few yards down the porch. The tree outside is full of crows and white cranes who gurgle and screech. A noisy solitude—all the new stories in my mind and the birds totally compatible but screaming at each other, sweeping now and then over the heads of drowsy mongrels.

*   *   *

That night, I will have not so much a dream as an image that repeats itself. I see my own straining body which stands shaped like a star and realise gradually I am part of a human pyramid. Below me are other bodies that I am standing on and above me are several more, though I am quite near the top. With cumbersome slowness we are walking from one end of the huge living room to the other. We are all chattering away like the crows and cranes so that it is often difficult to hear. I do catch one piece of dialogue. A Mr Hobday has asked my father if he has any Dutch antiques in the house. And he replies, "Well . . . there *is* my mother." My grandmother lower down gives a roar of anger. But at this point we are approaching the door which being twenty feet high we will be able to pass through only if the pyramid turns sideways. Without discussing it the whole family ignores the opening and walks slowly through the pale pink rose-coloured walls into the next room.

A FINE ROMANCE

THE COURTSHIP

When my father finished school, his parents decided to send him to university in England. So leaving Ceylon by ship Mervyn Ondaatje arrived at Southampton. He took his entrance exams for Cambridge and, writing home a month later, told his parents the good news that he had been accepted at Queen's College. They sent him the funds for three years of university education. Finally he had made good. He had been causing much trouble at home and now seemed to have pulled himself out of that streak of bad behaviour in the tropics.

It was two and a half years later, after several modest letters about his successful academic career, that his parents discovered he had not even passed the entrance exam and was living off their money in England. He had rented extravagant rooms in Cambridge and simply eliminated the academic element of university, making close friends among the students, reading contemporary novels, boating, and making a name for himself as someone who knew exactly what was valuable and interesting in the Cambridge circles of the 1920s. He had a good time, becoming briefly engaged to a Russian countess, even taking a short trip to Ireland supposedly to fight against the Rebels when the university closed down for its vacation. No one knew about this Irish adventure except an aunt who was sent a photograph of him posing slyly in uniform.

On hearing the distressing news, his parents decided to confront him personally, and so his mother and father and sister Stephy packed their trunks and left for England by ship. In any case my father had just twenty-four more days of high living at Cambridge before his furious family arrived unannounced at his doors. Sheepishly he invited them in, being able to offer them only champagne at eleven in the morning. This did not impress them as he had hoped, while the great row which my grandfather had looked forward to for weeks and weeks was deflected by my father's useful habit of retreating into almost total silence, of never trying to justify any of his crimes, so that it was difficult to argue with him. Instead he went out at dinnertime for a few hours and came back to announce that he had become engaged to Kaye Roseleap—his sister Stephy's closest English friend. This news stilled most of the fury against him. Stephy moved onto his side and his parents were impressed by the fact that Kaye leapt from the notable Roseleaps of Dorset. On the whole everybody was pleased and the following day they all caught the train to the country to stay with the Roseleaps, taking along my father's cousin Phyllis.

During the week in Dorset my father behaved impeccably. The in-laws planned the wedding, Phyllis was invited to spend the summer with the Roseleaps, and the Ondaatjes (including my father) went back to Ceylon to wait out the four months before the marriage.

Two weeks after he arrived in Ceylon, my father came home one evening to announce that he was engaged to a Doris Gratiaen. The postponed argument at Cambridge now erupted on my grandfather's lawn in Kegalle. My father was calm and unconcerned with the various complications he seemed to have created and did not even plan to write to the Roseleaps. It was Stephy who wrote, setting off a chain reaction in the mails, one letter going to Phyllis whose holiday plans were terminated. My father continued with his technique of trying to solve one problem by creating another. The next day he returned home saying he had joined the Ceylon Light Infantry.

I am not sure how long he had known my mother before the engagement. He must have met her socially now and then before his Cambridge years, for one of his closest friends was Noel Gratiaen, my mother's brother. About this time, Noel returned to Ceylon, sent down from Oxford at the end of his first year for setting fire to his room. This in fact was common behaviour, but he had gone one step further, trying to put out the fire by throwing flaming sofas and armchairs out of the window onto the street and then dragging and hurling them into the river— where they sank three boats belonging to the Oxford rowing team. It was probably while visiting Noel in Colombo that my father first met Doris Gratiaen.

At that time Doris Gratiaen and Dorothy Clementi-Smith would perform radical dances in private, practising daily. Both women were about twenty-two and were greatly influenced by rumours of the dancing of Isadora Duncan. In a year or so they would perform in public. There is a reference to them in Rex Daniels' journals:

A garden party at the Residency Grounds. . . . Bertha and I sat next to the Governor and Lady Thompson. A show had been organized for them made up of various acts. First on was a ventriloquist from Trincomalee whose act was not vetted as he had arrived late. He was drunk and began to tell insulting jokes about the Governor. The act was stopped and was followed by Doris Gratiaen and Dorothy Clementi-Smith who did an item called "Dancing Brass Figures". They wore swimsuits and had covered themselves in gold metallic paint. It was a very beautiful dance but the gold paint had an allergic effect on the girls and the next day they were covered in a terrible red rash.

My father first saw them dance in the gardens of Deal Place. He would drive down from his parents' home in Kegalle to Colombo, stay at the Ceylon Light Infantry quarters, and spend his days with Noel watching the two girls practise. It is said he was enchanted with *both* girls, but Noel married Dorothy while my father became engaged to Noel's sister. More to keep my father company than anything else, Noel too had joined the Ceylon Light Infantry. This engagement of my father's was not as popular as the Roseleap one. He bought Doris Gratiaen a huge emerald engagement ring which he charged to his father's account. His father refused to pay and my father threatened to shoot himself. Eventually it was paid for by the family.

My father had nothing to do in Kegalle. It was too far away from Colombo and his new friends. His position with the Light Infantry was a casual one, almost a hobby. Often, in the midst of a party in Colombo, he would suddenly remember he was the duty officer that night and with a car full of men and women planning a midnight swim at Mount Lavinia, he would roll into the barracks, step out in his dress suit, inspect the guard, leap back into the car full of laughing and drunken friends and depart. But in Kegalle he was frustrated and lonely. Once he was given the car and asked to go and buy some fish. *Don't* forget the fish! his mother said. Two days later his parents got a telegram from Trincomalee, miles away in the north end of the island, to say he had the fish and would be back soon.

His quiet life in Kegalle was interrupted, however, when Doris Gratiaen wrote to break off the engagement. There were no phones, so it meant a drive to Colombo to discover what was wrong. But my grandfather, furious over the Trincomalee trip, refused him the car. Finally he got a lift with his father's brother Aelian. Aelian was a gracious and genial man and my father was bored and frantic. The combination almost proved disastrous. My father had never driven to Colombo directly in his life. There was a pattern of resthouses to be stopped at and so Aelian was forced to stop every ten miles and have a drink, too polite to refuse his young nephew. By the time they got to Colombo my father was very drunk and Aelian was slightly drunk and it was too late to visit Doris Gratiaen anyway. My father forced his Uncle to stay at the CLI mess. After a large meal and more drink my father announced that now he must shoot himself because Doris had broken off the engagement. Aelian, especially as he was quite drunk too, had a terrible time trying to hide every gun in the Ceylon Light Infantry building. The next day the problems were solved and the engagement was established once more. They were married a year later.

APRIL 11, 1932

"I remember the wedding. . . . They were to be married in Kegalle and five of us were to drive up in Ern's Fiat. Half way between Colombo and Kegalle we recognised a car in the ditch and beside it was the Bishop of Colombo who everyone knew was a terrible driver. He was supposed to marry them so we had to give him a lift.

"First of all his luggage had to be put in carefully because his vestments couldn't be crushed. Then his mitre and sceptre and those special shoes and whatnot. And as we were so crowded and a bishop couldn't sit on anyone's lap—and as no one could really sit on a bishop's lap, we had to let *him* drive the Fiat. We were all so squashed and terrified for the rest of the trip!"

HONEYMOON

The Nuwara Eliya Tennis Championships had ended and there were monsoons in Colombo. The headlines in the local papers said, "Lindberg's Baby Found—A Corpse!" Fred Astaire's sister, Adele, got married and the 13th President of the French Republic was shot to death by a Russian. The lepers of Colombo went on a hunger strike, a bottle of beer cost one rupee, and there were upsetting rumours that ladies were going to play at Wimbledon in shorts.

In America, women were still trying to steal the body of Valentino from his grave, and a woman from Kansas divorced her husband because he would not let her live near the Valentino mausoleum. The famous impressario, C. B. Cochran, claimed "the ideal modern girl—the Venus of today—should be neither thin nor plump, but should have the lines of a greyhound." It was rumoured that pythons were decreasing in Africa.

Charlie Chaplin was in Ceylon. He avoided all publicity and was only to be seen photographing and studying Kandyan dance. The films at the local cinemas in Colombo were "Love Birds," "Caught Cheating," and "Forbidden Love." There was fighting in Manchuria.

HISTORICAL
RELATIONS

The early twenties had been a busy and expensive time for my grandparents. They spent most of the year in Colombo and during the hot months of April and May moved to Nuwara Eliya. In various family journals there are references made to the time spent "up-country" away from the lowland heat. Cars would leave Colombo and perform the tiring five-hour journey, the radiators steaming as they wound their way up into the mountains. Books and sweaters and golf clubs and rifles were packed into trunks, children were taken out of school, dogs were bathed and made ready for the drive.

Nuwara Eliya was a different world. One did not sweat there and only those who had asthma tried to avoid these vacations. At an elevation of 6000 feet the families could look forward to constant parties, horse racing, the All Ceylon Tennis Tournament, and serious golf. Although the best Sinhalese tennis players competed up-country, they would move back to Colombo if they had to play champions from other nations—as the excessive heat could be guaranteed to destroy the visitors. And so, while monsoon and heat moved into deserted Colombo homes, it was to Nuwara Eliya that my grandparents and their circle of friends would go. They danced in large living rooms to the music of a Bijou-Moutrie piano while the log fires crackled in every room, or on quiet evenings read books on the moonlit porch, slicing open the pages as they progressed through a novel.

The gardens were full of cypress, rhododendrons, fox-gloves, arum-lilies and sweet pea; and people like the van Langenbergs, the Vernon Dickmans, the Henry de Mels and the Philip Ondaatjes were there. There were casual tragedies. Lucas Cantley's wife Jessica almost died after being shot by an unknown assailant while playing croquet with my grandfather. They found 113 pellets in her. "And poor Wilfred Batholomeusz who had large teeth was killed while out hunting when one of his companions mistook him for a wild boar." Most of the men belonged to the CLI reserves and usually borrowed guns when going on vacation.

It was in Nuwara Eliya that Dick de Vos danced with his wife Etta, who fell flat on the floor; she had not danced for years. He picked her up, deposited her on a cane chair, came over to Rex Daniels and said, "Now you know why I gave up dancing and took to drink." Each morning the men departed for the club to play a game of billiards. They would arrive around eleven in buggy carts pulled by bulls and play until the afternoon rest hours while the punkah, the large cloth fan, floated and waved above them and the twenty or so bulls snorted in a circle around the clubhouse. Major Robinson, who ran the prison, would officiate at the tournaments.

During the month of May the circus came to Nuwara Eliya.

Once, when the circus lights failed, Major Robinson drove the fire engine into the tent and focussed the headlights on the trapeze artist, who had no intention of continuing and sat there straddling his trapeze. At one of these touring circuses my Aunt Christie (then only twenty-five) stood up and volunteered to have an apple shot off her head by "a total stranger in the circus profession." That night T. W. Roberts was bitten in the leg by a dog while he danced with her. Later the dog was discovered to be rabid, but as T.W. had left for England nobody bothered to tell him. Most assume he survived. They were all there. Piggford of the police, Paynter the planter, the Finnellis who were Baptist missionaries—"she being an artist and a very good tap dancer."

This was Nuwara Eliya in the twenties and thirties. Everyone was vaguely related and had Sinhalese, Tamil, Dutch, British and Burgher blood in them going back many generations. There was a large social gap between this circle and the Europeans and English who were never part of the Ceylonese community. The English were seen as transients, snobs and racists, and were quite separate from those who had intermarried and who lived here permanently. My father always claimed to be a Ceylon Tamil, though that was probably more valid about three centuries earlier. Emil Daniels summed up the situation for most of them when he was asked by one of the British governors what his nationality was—"God alone knows, your excellency."

The era of grandparents. Philip Ondaatje was supposed to have the greatest collection of wine glasses in the Orient; my other grandfather, Willy Gratiaen, dreamt of snakes. Both my grandmothers lived cautiously, at least until their husbands died. Then they blossomed, especially Lalla who managed to persuade all those she met into chaos. It was Lalla who told us that the twenties were "so whimsical, so busy—that we were always tired."

THE WAR BETWEEN
MEN AND WOMEN

Years later, when Lalla was almost a grandmother, she was standing in the rain at the Pettah market on her way to a party. Money was not so easily available and she did not own a car. When the bus arrived she herded herself in with the rest and, after ten minutes of standing in the aisle, found a seat where three could sit side by side. Eventually the man next to her put his arm behind her shoulder to give them all more room.

Gradually she began to notice the shocked faces of the passengers facing her across the aisle. At first they looked disapprovingly and soon began whispering to each other. Lalla looked at the man next to her who had a smug smile on his face. He seemed to be enjoying himself. Then she looked down and saw that his hand had come over her left shoulder and was squeezing her breast. She smiled to herself.

She had not felt a thing. Her left breast had been removed five years earlier and he was ardently fondling the sponge beneath her gown.

FLAMING YOUTH

Francis de Saram had the most extreme case of alcoholism in my father's generation and, always the quickest, was the first to drink himself into the grave. He was my father's and Noel's closest friend and the best man at several weddings he tried to spoil. Unambitious, and generous, he lost all his teeth young —something he could never remember doing. When he got into a fight he would remove his false teeth and put them in his back pocket. He was in love for a while with Lorna Piachaud and started fights all over her wedding reception. He even attacked his own wife and then, overcome with guilt, decided to drown himself in a section of the Kandy Lake that was only twelve inches deep. While he crawled around on his hands and knees, H——consoled Francis' wife as well as he could "and took as much as he could get." If Francis was the extreme alcoholic,

H——was the great rake, his tumescent heart notorious all over Colombo.

Francis and his friends discovered that the cheapest drinks could be found on ships, where alcohol was duty free. Pretending to visit departing relatives, they would board vessels in the harbour and stumble off gangplanks in the early hours of the morning. They were usually ordered out of the lounge when Noel, unable to play a single tune, started thrashing out one of his spontaneous concerts on the piano. Once, when asked to prove who they knew on board, my father opened the first cabin door and claimed a sleeping man as his friend. My father was wearing a tie from his 'Cambridge' days and the sleeper, noticing this, groggily vouched for him. They coaxed the sleeper to the bar and my father managed to remember all the Cambridge names, recalling even the exploits of the notorious Sharron K——, who caused havoc with the population of three colleges.

> One night Mervyn came to our house and told Vernon, "We're all going to Gasanawa, get dressed." It was one in the morning. Vernon went off to find his clothes and returned to find Mervyn asleep in his bed. He couldn't be moved. You see he just needed a place to sleep.

Gasanawa was the rubber estate where Francis worked and it became the base for most of their parties. Twenty or thirty people would leap into their cars after a tennis tournament or during a boring evening and if the men were already drunk some of the women drove. They all poured out at Gasanawa where they slept in cabins that Francis had built for just such moments. Whenever he was sober, Francis tried to make the estate a perfect place for parties. He lived on gin, tonic-water, and canned meat. He was in the middle of building a tennis court when his boss ordered him to build a proper road into the estate. This took three years because Francis in his enthusiasm built it three times as wide as the main road in Colombo.

People's memories about Gasanawa, even today, are mythic. "There was a lovely flat rock in front of the bungalow where we danced to imported songs such as 'Moonlight Bay' and 'A Fine Romance.'" "A Fine Romance" was always my mother's favourite song. In her sixties I would come across her in the kitchen half singing, *We should be like a couple of hot tomatoes/but you're as cold as yesterday's mashed potatoes.*

So many songs of that period had to do with legumes, fruit and drink. "Yes, we have no bananas," "I've got a lovely bunch of coconuts," "Mung beans on your collar," "The Java Jive." . . . Dorothy Clementi-Smith would sing the solo verses to "There is a tavern in the town" while the others would drunkenly join in on the chorus. Even the shy Lyn Ludowyck betrayed his studies and came out there once, turning out to be a superb mimic, singing both male and female parts from Italian operas which the others had never heard of—so they all thought at first that he was singing a Sinhalese baila.

But for the most part it was the tango that was perfected on that rock at Gasanawa. Casually dressed couples, coated in a thin film of sweat, swirled under the moon to "Rio Rita" by John Bowles on the gramophone, wound up time and again by the drunk Francis. Francis could only dance the tango solo so that he wouldn't do damage to women's feet, for which he had too much respect. He would put on "I kiss your little hand, Madame" and mime great passion for an invisible partner, kissing the mythical hand, pleading to the stars and jungle around him to console him in an unrequited abstract love. He was a great dancer but with a limited endurance. He usually collapsed at the end of his performance, and a woman would sit beside him bathing his head and face with cool water while the others continued dancing.

The parties lasted until the end of the twenties when Francis lost his job over too splendid a road. He was lost to them all by 1935. He was everyone's immaculate, gentle friend, the most forgiven and best-dressed among them, whispering to someone a few seconds before he died, while holding a fish in his hand, "A man *must* have clothes for every occasion."

The waste of youth. Burned purposeless. They forgave that and understood that before everything else. After Francis died there was nowhere really to go. What seemed to follow was a rash of marriages. There had been good times. "Women fought each other like polecats over certain men."

THE BABYLON
STAKES

"The Wall Street crash had a terrible effect on us. Many
of the horses had to be taken over by the military."

The only occupation that
could hope to avert one
from drink and romance was gambling. In India only the aristoc-
racy gambled; in Ceylon the bankers and lime-burners and
fishmongers and the leisured class would spend their afternoons,
shoulder to shoulder, betting compulsively. The rulers of the
country genuinely believed that betting eliminated strikes; men
had to work in order to gamble.

If it was not horses it was crows. A crippled aunt, who could
not get to the track, began the fashion of betting on which crow
would leave a wall first. This proved so popular that the government considered putting a bounty on crows. In any case, soon
after the time Gertie Garvin trained a pet crow, bird-gambling
proved to be untrustworthy. But the real stars were involved
with racing: horses such as "Mordenis," jockeys like "Fordyce,"
the trainer "Captain Fenwick." There were racetracks all over the

island. If you sat in the grandstand all bets were five rupees. Then there was the two-rupee enclosure and finally, in the middle of the track, the 'gandhi enclosure' where the poorest stood. "From the grandstand you could watch them leaving like ants a good hour before the last race, having lost all their money."

The most dangerous track profession was starter of the race, and one of the few who survived was Clarence de Fonseka, who was famous for knowing every horse in the country by sight. As starter, he positioned himself at the far end of the track. And to forestall threats of death from the crowd in the gandhi enclosure, Clarence kept his fastest horse near him at all times. If a popular horse lost, the mob would race across the field to the starting post to tear him apart. Clarence would then leap onto his horse and gallop down the track in solitary splendour.

Racing concerned everyone. During the whole month of August my mother would close down her dancing school and go to the races. So would my grandmother, Lalla. Her figure at the races is ingrained in several people's memories: a large hat at a rakish angle that she wore with no consideration for anyone behind her, one hand on her hip, one hand on her hat, and a blue jacaranda blossom pinned to the shoulder of her dusty black dress, looking off into the drama of the one-hundred-yard stretch with the intensity of one preparing for the coming of the Magi. When the races were over, groups would depart for dinner, dance till early morning, go swimming and have a breakfast at the Mount Lavinia Hotel. Then to bed till noon when it was time for the races once more. The culmination of the season was the Governor's Cup stakes. Even during the war the August races were not to be postponed. Ceylon could have been invaded during the late afternoon as most of the Light Infantry was at the race track during these hours.

Many of my relatives owned a horse or two, which languished in comfort for much of the year and got trotted out for the August race meet. My grandmother's horse, 'Dickman Delight,' refused to step out of the stable if it was at all muddy. She would bet vast sums on her horse knowing that one day he would surprise everyone and win. The day this eventually happened, my grandmother was up north. She received a telegram in the early morning which read: "Rain over Colombo" so she put her money on another horse. Dickman Delight galloped to victory on dry turf. Japanese planes had attacked Galle Face Green in Colombo and the telegram should have read: "Raid over Colombo." Dickman Delight never won again.

Most people tried to own a horse, some even pooled their money, each "owning a leg." The desire was not so much to have horse-sense but to be involved with the ceremonial trappings. Percy Lewis de Soysa, for instance, took great care selecting his colours, which were gold and green. In his youth, while success-fully entertaining a woman at a Cambridge restaurant, he had ordered a bottle of champagne and at the end of the evening whispered to her that when he eventually owned a horse his racing colours would be taken from the label of the bottle. 'Searchlight Gomez' chose his colours, pink and black, after a certain lady's underwear and was proud of it.

There were races all year long. The Monsoon Meet in May, the Hakgalle Stakes in February, the Nuwara Eliya Cup in August. Some of the horses had become so inbred that jockeys could no longer insure themselves. The Babylon Stakes was banned after one horse, 'Forced Potato,' managed to bite a jockey and then leapt the fence to attack as many as it could in the jeering gandhi enclosure. But the jockeys had their perks. Gambling was so crucial to the economy of certain households that semi–respectable women slept with jockeys to get closer to "the horse's mouth."

If the crowd or the horses did not cause trouble, *The Searchlight*, a magazine published by the notorious Mr. Gomez, did. "One of those scurrilous things," it attacked starters and trainers and owners and provided gossip to be carefully read between races. Nobody wished to appear in it and everyone bought it. It sold for five cents but remained solvent, as the worst material could be toned down only with bribes to the editor. 'Searchlight Gomez,' went to jail once, and that for too good a joke. Every January issue featured the upcoming events for the year. One year he listed, under October 3rd, Hayley and Kenny's Annual Fire. This blatant but accurate reference to the way fire insurance was used to compensate for sagging trade was not appreciated and he was sued.

The Gasanawa group tried to take in all the races. In December they drove down to the Galle Gymkhana, stopping on the way to order oysters and have a swim at Ambalangoda. "Sissy," Francis' sister, "was always drowning herself because she was an exhibitionist." The men wore tweed, the women wore their best crinolines. After the races they would return to Ambalangoda, pick up the oysters "which we swallowed with wine if we lost or champagne if we won." Couples then paired off casually or with great complexity and danced in a half-hearted manner to the portable gramophone beside the cars. Ambalangoda was the centre for devil dances and exorcism rites, but this charmed group was part of another lost world. The men leaned their chins against the serene necks of the women, danced a waltz or two, slid oysters into their partner's mouths. The waves on the beach collected champagne corks. Men who had lost fortunes laughed frantically into the night. A woman from the village who was encountered carrying a basket of pineapples was persuaded to trade that for a watch removed from a wrist. Deeper inland at midnight, the devil dances began, drums portioned the night. Trucks carrying horses to the next meet glared their headlights as they passed the group by the side of the road. The horses, drummers, everyone else, seemed to have a purpose. The devil dances cured sickness, catarrh, deafness, aloneness. Here the gramophone accompanied a seduction or an arousal, it spoke of meadows and "little Spanish towns" or "a small hotel," a "blue room."

A hand cupped the heel of a woman who wished to climb a tree to see the stars more clearly. The men laughed into their tumblers. They all went swimming again with just the modesty of the night. An arm touched a face. A foot touched a stomach. They could have almost drowned or fallen in love and their lives would have been totally changed during any one of those evenings.

Then, everyone very drunk, the convoy of cars would race back to Gasanawa in the moonlight crashing into frangipani, almond trees, or slipping off the road to sink slowly up to the door handles in a paddy field.

TROPICAL GOSSIP

"Darling, come here quickly. There's trouble behind the tennis court. I think Frieda's fainted. Look—Craig is pulling her up."

"No, darling, leave them alone."

It seems that most of my relatives at some time were attracted to somebody they shouldn't have been. Love affairs rainbowed over marriages and lasted forever—so it often seemed that marriage was the greater infidelity. From the twenties until the war nobody really had to grow up. They remained wild and spoiled. It was only during the second half of my parents' generation that they suddenly turned to the real world. Years later, for instance, my uncle Noel would return to Ceylon as a Q.C. to argue for the lives of friends from his youth who had tried to overthrow the government.

But earlier, during their flaming youth, this energy formed complex relationships, though I still cannot break the code of how "interested in" or "attracted" they were to each other. Truth disappears with history and gossip tells us in the end nothing of personal relationships. There are stories of elopements, unrequited love, family feuds, and exhausting vendettas, which everyone was drawn into, had to be involved with. But nothing is said of the closeness between two people: how they grew in the shade of each other's presence. No one speaks of that exchange of gift and character—the way a person took on and recognized in himself the smile of a lover. Individuals are seen only in the context of these swirling social tides. It was almost impossible for a couple to do anything without rumour leaving their shoulders like a flock of messenger pigeons.

Where is the intimate and truthful in all this? Teenager and Uncle. Husband and lover. A lost father in his solace. And why do I want to know of this privacy? After the cups of tea, coffee, public conversations . . . I want to sit down with someone and talk with utter directness, want to talk to all the lost history like that deserving lover.

KEGALLE (i)

My paternal grandfather—
Philip—was a strict, aloof
man. Most people preferred his brother Aelian who was good-
natured and helpful to everyone. Both were lawyers but my
grandfather went on to make huge sums of money in land deals
and retired as he said he would at the age of forty. He built the
family home, 'Rock Hill,' on a prime spot of land right in the
centre of the town of Kegalle.

"Your great uncle Aelian was a very generous man," says
Stanley Suraweera. "I wanted to learn Latin and he offered to
tutor me from four until five every morning. I'd go to his house
by cart every day and he would be up, waiting for me." In later
years Aelian was to have several heart attacks. In one hospital he
was given so much morphine that he became addicted to it.

My grandfather lived at Rock Hill for most of his life and
ignored everybody in Kegalle social circles. He was immensely

wealthy. Most people considered him a snob, but with his family he was a very loving man. The whole family kissed each other goodnight and good morning, a constant tradition in the house —no matter what chaos my father was causing at the time. Family arguments were buried before bedtime and buried once more first thing in the morning.

So here was 'Bampa,' as we called him, determined to be a good father and patriarch, spreading a protective wing over his more popular brother Aelian, and living in his empire—acres of choice land in the heart of Kegalle. He was dark and his wife was very white, and a rival for my grandmother's hand remarked that he hoped the children would be striped. The whole family lived in terror of him. Even his strong-willed wife could not blossom till after his death. Like some other Ondaatjes, Bampa had a weakness for pretending to be 'English' and, in his starched collars and grey suits, was determined in his customs. My brother, who was only four years old then, still remembers painfully strict meals at Rock Hill with Bampa grinding his teeth at one end of the table—as if his carefully built ceremonies were being evaded by a weak-willed family. It was only in the afternoons when, dressed in sarong and vest, he went out for walks over his property (part of a mysterious treatment for diabetes), that he seemed to become a real part of the landscape around him.

Every two years he would visit England, buy crystal, and learn the latest dances. He was a perfect dancer. Numerous aunts remember him inviting them out in London and taking great pleasure in performing the most recent dance steps with a natural ease. Back home there was enough to worry about. There was Aelian, who was continually giving his money away to ecclesiastical causes, the cousin who was mauled to death by his underfed racehorse, and four star-crossed sisters who were secret drinkers.

Most Ondaatjes liked liquor, sometimes to excess. Most of them were hot tempered—though they blamed diabetes for this whenever possible. And most were genetically attracted to a family called Prins and had to be talked out of marriage—for the Prins brought bad luck wherever they went.

My grandfather died before the war and his funeral was spoken about with outrage and envy for months afterwards. He thought he had organized it well. All the women wore long black dresses and imported champagne was drunk surreptitiously from teacups. But his hope of departing with decorum collapsed before he was put into the ground. His four sisters and my recently liberated grandmother got into a loud argument over whether to pay the men two or three rupees to carry the coffin up the steep slopes to the cemetery. Awkward mourners who had come from Colombo waited as silent as my supine grandfather while the argument blazed from room to room and down the halls of Rock Hill. My grandmother peeled off her long black gloves in fury and refused to proceed with the ceremony, then slid them on with the aid of a daughter when it seemed the body would never leave the house. My father, who was overseeing the cooling of the champagne, was nowhere in sight. My mother and Uncle Aelian retired in a fit of giggles to the garden under the mangosteen tree. All this occurred on the afternoon of September 12, 1938. Aelian died of his liver problems in April of 1942.

*   *   *

For the next decade Rock Hill was seldom used by my family and my father was not to return to it for some years. By that time my parents were divorced and my father had lost various jobs. Bampa had willed the land to his grandchildren but my father, whenever he needed to, would sell or give away sections of land so that houses were gradually built up along the perimeter of the estate. My father returned alone to Kegalle in the late forties and took up farming. He lived quite simply at that time, separate from the earlier circle of friends, and my sister Gillian and I spent most of our holidays with him. By 1950 he had married again and was living with his wife and his two children from his second marriage, Jennifer and Susan.

He ended up, in those later years, concentrating on chickens. His dipsomania would recur every two months or so. Between bouts he would not touch a drink. Then he would be offered one, take it, and would not or could not stop drinking for three or four days. During that time he could do *nothing* but drink. Humorous and gentle when sober, he changed utterly and would do anything to get alcohol. He couldn't eat, had to have a bottle on him at all times. If his new wife Maureen had hidden a bottle, he would bring out his rifle and threaten to kill her. He knew, even when sober, that he would need to drink again, and so buried bottles all around the estate. In the heart of his drunkenness he would remember where the bottles were. He would go into the fowl run, dig under chicken straw, and pull out a half bottle. The cement niches on the side of the house held so many bottles that from the side the building resembled a wine cellar.

He talked to no one on those days, although he recognized friends, was aware of everything that was going on. He had to be at the peak of his intelligence in order to remember exactly where the bottles were so he could outwit his wife and family. Nobody could stop him. If Maureen managed to destroy the bottles of gin he had hidden he would drink methylated spirits. He drank until he collapsed and passed out. Then he would waken and drink again. Still no food. Sleep. Get up and have one more shot and then he was finished. He would not drink again for about two months, not until the next bout.

The day my father died, Stanley Suraweera, now a Proctor at Kegalle, was in Court when a messenger brought him the note: *Mervyn has dropped dead. What shall I do? Maureen.*

*　　*　　*

We had spent three days in Upcot in beautiful tea country with my half-sister Susan. On the way back to Colombo we drove through the Kadugannawa Pass and stopped at Kegalle. The old wooden bridge that only my father drove over without fear ("God loves a drunk" he would say to anyone who sat by him white with terror) had been replaced with a concrete one.

What to us had been a lovely spacious house was now small and dark, fading into the landscape. A Sinhalese family occupied Rock Hill. Only the mangosteen tree, which I practically lived in as a child during its season of fruit, was full and strong. At the back, the kitul tree still leaned against the kitchen—tall, with tiny yellow berries which the polecat used to love. Once a week it would climb up and spend the morning eating the berries and come down drunk, would stagger over the lawn pulling up flowers or come into the house to up-end drawers of cutlery and serviettes. Me and my polecat, my father said after one occasion when their drunks coincided, my father lapsing into his songs— baila or heartbreaking Rodgers and Hart or his own version of "My Bonnie Lies over the Ocean"—

> My whiskey comes over the ocean
> My brandy comes over the sea
> But my beer comes from F.X. Pereira

So F.X. Pereira for me.
F.X. . . . F.X. . . .
F.X. Pereira for me, for me. . . .

He emerged out of his bedroom to damn whoever it was that was playing the piano—to find the house empty—Maureen and the kids having left, and the polecat walking up and down over the keys breaking the silence of the house, oblivious to his human audience; and my father wishing to celebrate this companionship, discovering all the bottles gone, unable to find anything, finally walking up to the kerosene lamp hanging in the centre of the room at head level, and draining *that* liquid into his mouth. He and his polecat.

Gillian remembered some of the places where he hid bottles. *Here* she said, *and here.* Her family and my family walked around the house, through the depressed garden of guava trees, plantains, old forgotten flowerbeds. Whatever "empire" my grandfather had fought for had to all purposes disappeared.

DON'T TALK TO ME
ABOUT MATISSE

TABULA ASIAE

On my brother's wall in Toronto are the false maps. Old portraits of Ceylon. The result of sightings, glances from trading vessels, the theories of sextant. The shapes differ so much they seem to be translations—by Ptolemy, Mercator, François Valentyn, Mortier, and Heydt—growing from mythic shapes into eventual accuracy. Amoeba, then stout rectangle, and then the island as we know it now, a pendant off the ear of India. Around it, a blue-combed ocean busy with dolphin and sea-horse, cherub and compass. Ceylon floats on the Indian Ocean and holds its naive mountains, drawings of cassowary and boar who leap without perspective across imagined 'desertum' and plain.

At the edge of the maps the scrolled mantling depicts ferocious slipper-footed elephants, a white queen offering a necklace to natives who carry tusks and a conch, a Moorish king who stands amidst the power of books and armour. On the south-west corner of some charts are satyrs, hoof deep in foam, listening to the sound of the island, their tails writhing in the waves.

The maps reveal rumours of topography, the routes for invasion and trade, and the dark mad mind of travellers' tales appears throughout Arab and Chinese and medieval records. The island seduced all of Europe. The Portuguese. The Dutch. The English. And so its name changed, as well as its shape,—Serendip, Ratnapida ("island of gems"), Taprobane, Zeloan, Zeilan, Seyllan, Ceilon, and Ceylon—the wife of many marriages, courted by invaders who stepped ashore and claimed everything with the power of their sword or bible or language.

This pendant, once its shape stood still, became a mirror. It pretended to reflect each European power till newer ships arrived and spilled their nationalities, some of whom stayed and intermarried—my own ancestor arriving in 1600, a doctor who cured the residing governor's daughter with a strange herb and was rewarded with land, a foreign wife, and a new name which was a Dutch spelling of his own. Ondaatje. A parody of the ruling language. And when his Dutch wife died, marrying a Sinhalese woman, having nine children, and remaining. Here. At the centre of the rumour. At this point on the map.

ST. THOMAS' CHURCH

In Colombo a church faces west into the sea. We drive along Reclamation Street through markets and boutiques. The church ahead of us is painted a pale dirty blue. Below us, an oil-tanker dwarfs the harbour and the shops. We get out, followed by the children. A path about twelve feet wide bordered by plantain trees. The gothic doors give a sense, as all church doors do, of being wheeled open. Inside are wooden pews and their geometrical shadows and stone floors that whisper against the children's bare feet. We spread out.

After all these generations the coming darkness makes it necessary to move fast in order to read the brass plaques on the walls. The first ones are too recent, 19th century. Then, by the communion rail, I see it—cut across the stone floor. To kneel on the floors of a church built in 1650 and see your name chiseled in large letters so that it stretches from your fingertips to your elbow in some strange way removes vanity, eliminates the personal. It makes your own story a lyric. So the sound which came immediately out of my mouth as I half-gasped and called my sister spoke all that excitement of smallness, of being overpowered by stone.

What saved me was the lack of clarity. The slab was five feet long, three feet wide, a good portion of it had worn away. We remained on our knees in that fading light, asked the children to move their shadows, and peered sideways to try to catch the faint ridge of letters worn away by the traffic of feet. The light leaned into the chiseled area like frail sand. To the right of that slab was another; we had been standing on it totally unaware, as if in someone's rifle sight. Gillian wrote on a brown envelope as I read

Sacred to the memory of Natalia Asarrapa—wife of Philip Jurgen Ondaatje. Born 1797, married 1812, died 1822, age 25 years.

She was fifteen! That can't be right. Must be. Fifteen when she married and twenty-five when she died. Perhaps that was the first wife—before he married Jacoba de Melho? Probably another branch of the family.

We carry six ledgers out of the church into the last of the sunlight and sit on the vicarage steps to begin reading. Lifting the ancient pages and turning them over like old, skeletal leaves. The black script must have turned brown over a hundred years ago. The thick pages foxed and showing the destruction caused by silverfish, scars among the immaculate recordings of local history and formal signatures. We had not expected to find more than one Ondaatje here but the stones and pages are full of them. We had been looking for the Reverend Jurgen Ondaatje—a translator and eventual chaplain in Colombo from 1835 until 1847. It seems, however, as if every Ondaatje for miles around flocked

168

here to be baptised and married. When Jurgen died his son Simon took his place and was the last Tamil Colonial Chaplain of Ceylon.

Simon was the oldest of four brothers. Every Sunday morning they came to this church in carriages with their wives and children and after the service retired to the vicarage for drinks and lunch. Just before the meal, talk would erupt into a violent argument and each brother would demand to have his carriage brought round, climb into it with his hungry family and ride off to his own home, each in a different direction.

For years they tried but were never able to have a meal together. Each of them was prominent in his own field and was obviously too didactic and temperamental to agree with his brothers on any subject of discussion. There was nothing one could speak about that would not infringe on another's area of interest. If the subject was something as innocent as flowers, then Dr. William Charles Ondaatje, who was the Ceylonese Director of the Botanical Gardens, would throw scorn on any opinion and put the others in their place. He had introduced the olive to Ceylon. Finance or military talk was Matthew Ondaatje's area, and law or scholarship exercised Philip de Melho Jurgen's acid tongue. The only one who had full freedom was the Reverend Simon who said whatever he felt like during the sermon, knowing his brothers could not interrupt him. No doubt he caught hell as soon as he entered the vicarage next door for what he hoped would be a peaceful lunch. Whenever a funeral or baptism occurred, however, all the brothers would be there. The church records show Simon's name witnessing them all in a signature very like my father's.

We stand outside the church in twilight. The building has stood here for over three hundred years, in the palm of monsoons, through seasonal droughts and invasions from other countries. Its grounds were once beautiful. Lights begin to come on slowly below us in the harbour. As we are about to get into the Volks, my niece points to a grave and I start walking through the brush in my sandals. "Watch out for snakes!" God. I make a quick leap backwards and get into the car. Night falls quickly during the five minute drive back to the house. Sit down in my room and transcribe names and dates from the various envelopes into a notebook. When I finish there will be that eerie moment when I wash my hands and see very clearly the deep grey colour of old paper dust going down the drain.

MONSOON
NOTEBOOK (i)

To jungles and gravestones.
. . . Reading torn 100-year-
old newspaper clippings that come apart in your hands like wet
sand, information tough as plastic dolls. Watched leopards sip
slowly, watched the crow sitting restless on his branch peering
about with his beak open. Have seen the outline of a large fish
caught and thrown in the curl of a wave, been where nobody
wears socks, where you wash your feet before you go to bed,
where I watch my sister who alternatively reminds me of my
father, mother and brother. Driven through rainstorms that flood
the streets for an hour and suddenly evaporate, where sweat falls
in the path of this ballpoint, where the jak fruit rolls across your
feet in the back of the jeep, where there are eighteen ways of
describing the smell of a durian, where bullocks hold up traffic
and steam after the rains.

Have sat down to meals and noticed the fan stir in all the

spoons on the dining table. And driven that jeep so often I didn't have time to watch the country slide by thick with event, for everything came directly to me and passed me like snow. The black thick feather of bus exhaust everyone was sentimental against, the man vomiting out of a window, the pig just dead having his hairs burnt off on the Canal Road and old girlfriends from childhood who now towel their kids dry on the other side of the SSC pool, and my watch collecting sea under the glass and gleaming with underwater phosphorus by my bed at night, the inside of both my feet blistering in my first week from the fifteen-cent sandals and the obsessional sarong buying in Colombo, Kandy, Jaffna, Trincomalee, the toddy drink I got subtly smashed on by noon so I slept totally unaware of my dreams. And women and men with naked feet under the dinner table, and after the party the thunderstorm we walked through for five seconds from porch to car, thoroughly soaked and by the time we had driven ten minutes—without headlights which had been stolen that afternoon at the pool—we were dry just from the midnight heat inside the vehicle and the ghosts of steam cruising disorganized off the tarmac roads, and the man sleeping on the street who objected when I woke him each of us talking different languages, me miming a car coming around the corner and hitting him and he, drunk, perversely making me perform this action for him again and again, and I got back into the car fully wet once more and again dry in five miles. And the gecko on the wall waving his tail stiffly his jaws full of dragonfly whose wings symmetrically disappeared into his mouth—darkness filling the almost transparent body, and a yellow enamel-assed spider crossing the bidet and the white rat my daughter claims she saw in the toilet at the Maskeliya tennis club.

I witnessed everything. One morning I would wake and just

smell things for the whole day, it was so rich I had to select senses. And still everything moved slowly with the assured fateful speed of a coconut falling on someone's head, like the Jaffna train, like the fan at low speed, like the necessary sleep in the afternoon with dreams blinded by toddy.

TONGUE

In the early afternoon several children and I walk for an hour along the beach—from the foot of the garden at Uswetakeiyawa, past the wrecks, to the Pegasus Reef Hotel. After twenty minutes, with sun burning just the right side of our faces and bodies, climbing up and down the dunes, we are exhausted, feel drunk. One of my children talking about some dream she had before leaving Canada. Spray breaking and blazing white. Mad dog heat. On our left the cool dark of village trees. Crabs veer away from our naked steps. I keep counting the children, keep feeling that one is missing. We look down, away from the sun. So that we all suddenly stumble across the body.

From the back it looks like a crocodile. It is about eight feet long. The snout however is blunt, not pointed, as if a crocodile's nose has been chopped off and the sharp edges worn smooth by tides. For a moment I actually believe this. I don't want the others going too close in case it is not dead. It has a double row of pointed scales on its tail, and the grey body is covered in yellow spots—with black centres so they form yellow rings. He looks fat and bulky. No one from the village about ten yards away seems to have noticed him. I realize it is a kabaragoya. In English a sub-aquatic monitor. He is dangerous and can whip you to death with his tail. This creature must have been washed out to sea by a river and then drifted back onto the beach.

Kabaragoyas and thalagoyas are common in Ceylon and are seldom found anywhere else in the world. The kabaragoya is large, the size of an average crocodile, and the thalagoya smaller —a cross between an iguana and a giant lizard. Sir John Maundeville, one of the first travellers to write of Ceylon, speaks of their "schorte thyes and grete Nayles." And Robert Knox says of the kabaragoya that "he hath a blew forked tongue like a string, which he puts forth and hisseth and gapeth." The kabaragoya is in fact a useful scavenger and is now protected by law as it preys on fresh water crabs that undermine and ruin the bunds of paddy fields. The only thing that will scare it is a wild boar.

The thalagoya, on the other hand, will eat snails, beetles, centipedes, toads, skinks, eggs and young birds, and is not averse to garbage. It is also a great climber, and can leap forty feet from a tree to the ground, breaking its fall by landing obliquely with its chest, belly and tail. In Kegalle the thalagoyas would climb trees and leap onto the roof or into the house.

The thalagoya has a rasping tongue that "catches" and hooks objects. There is a myth that if a child is given thalagoya tongue to eat he will become brilliantly articulate, will always speak beautifully, and in his speech be able to "catch" and collect wonderful, humorous information.

There is a way to eat the tongue. The thalagoya is killed by placing it on the ground, doubling its head under the throat, and striking the nape with a clenched fist. The tongue should be sliced off and eaten as soon as possible after the animal dies. You take a plantain or banana, remove the skin and cut it lengthwise in half, place the grey tongue between two pieces of banana making a sandwich, and then swallow the thing without chewing, letting it slide down the throat whole. Many years later this will result in verbal brilliance, though sometimes this will be combined with bad behaviour (the burning of furniture, etc.). I am not sure what other side effects there are apart from possible death.

My Uncle Noel was given a thalagoya tongue. He spat half of it out, got very sick and nearly died. His mother, Lalla, who had a habit of throwing herself dangerously into such local practices, had insisted he eat it. In any case her son did become a brilliant lawyer and a great story teller, from eating just *part* of the tongue. My father, who was well aware of the legend, suggested we eat some when we were in the Ambalantota resthouse. One had just been killed there, having fallen through the roof. All the children hid screaming in the bathroom until it was time to leave.

The thalagoya has other uses. It has the only flesh that can be kept down by a persistently vomiting patient and is administered to pregnant women for morning sickness. But as children we knew exactly what thalagoyas and kabaragoyas were good for. The kabaragoya laid its eggs in the hollows of trees between the months of January and April. As this coincided with the Royal-Thomian cricket match, we would collect them and throw them into the stands full of Royal students. These were great weapons because they left a terrible itch wherever they splashed on skin. We used the thalagoya to scale walls. We tied a rope around its neck and heaved it over a wall. Its claws could cling to any surface, and we pulled ourselves up the rope after it.

About six months before I was born my mother observed a pair of kabaragoyas "in copula" at Pelmadulla. A reference is made to this sighting in *A Coloured Atlas of Some Vertebrates from Ceylon, Vol. 2,* a National Museums publication. It is my first memory.

SWEET LIKE A CROW

for Hetti Corea, 8 years old

The Sinhalese are beyond a doubt one of the least musical
people in the world. It would be quite impossible to have
less sense of pitch, line, or rhythm"

PAUL BOWLES

Your voice sounds like a scorpion being pushed
through a glass tube
like someone has just trod on a peacock
like wind howling in a coconut
like a rusty bible, like someone pulling barbed wire
across a stone courtyard, like a pig drowning,
a vattacka being fried
a bone shaking hands
a frog singing at Carnegie Hall.
Like a crow swimming in milk,
like a nose being hit by a mango
like the crowd at the Royal-Thomian match,
a womb full of twins, a pariah dog
with a magpie in its mouth
like the midnight jet from Casablanca
like Air Pakistan curry,
a typewriter on fire, like a spirit in the gas

which cooks your dinner,
like a hundred pappadans being crunched, like someone
uselessly trying to light 3 *Roses* matches in a dark room,
the clicking sound of a reef when you put your head into the sea,
a dolphin reciting epic poetry to a sleepy audience,
the sound of a fan when someone throws brinjals at it,
like pineapples being sliced in the Pettah market
like betel juice hitting a butterfly in mid-air
like a whole village running naked onto the street
and tearing their sarongs, like an angry family
pushing a jeep out of the mud, like dirt on the needle,
like 8 sharks being carried on the back of a bicycle
like 3 old ladies locked in the lavatory
like the sound I heard when having an afternoon sleep
and someone walked through my room in ankle bracelets.

THE KARAPOTHAS

"This Ceylon part of the journey goes wearily! wearily!
Tired out by being constantly disturbed all night— noisy
sea, and noisier soda-bottle-popping planters, and the
early dawn with crows and cocks.

The brown people of this island seem to me odiously
inquisitive and bothery-idiotic. All the while the savages
go on grinning and chattering to each other.

. . . The roads are intensely picturesque. Animals, apes,
porcupine, hornbill, squirrel, pidgeons, and figurative
dirt!"

From the journals of Edward Lear in Ceylon, 1875

"After all, Taormina, Ceylon, Africa, America—as far as
we go, they are only the negation of what we ourselves
stand for and are: and we're rather like Jonahs running
away from the place we belong.

. . . Ceylon is an experience—but heavens, not a perma-
nence."

D.H. Lawrence

"All jungles are evil."

Leonard Woolf

* * *

I sit in a house on Buller's Road. I am the foreigner. I am the prodigal who hates the foreigner. Looking out on overgrown garden and the two dogs who bark at everything, who fling themselves into the air towards bird and squirrel. Ants crawl onto the desk to taste whatever is placed here. Even my glass, which holds just ice water, has brought out a dozen who wade into the rim of liquid the tumbler leaves, checking it for sugar. We are back within the heat of Colombo, in the hottest month of the year. It is delicious heat. Sweat runs with its own tangible life down a body as if a giant egg has been broken onto our shoulders.

The most comfortable hours are from 4 A.M. until about nine in the morning; the rest of the day heat walks the house as an animal hugging everybody. No one moves too far from the circumference of the fan. Rich Sinhalese families go up-country during April. Most of the events in the erotic literature of Asia, one suspects, must take place in the mountains, for sex is almost impossible in Colombo except in the early morning hours, and very few have been conceived during this month for the last hundred years.

This is the heat that drove Englishmen crazy. D. H. Lawrence was in Ceylon for six weeks in 1922 as a guest of the Brewsters who lived in Kandy. Even though Kandy is several degrees cooler than Colombo, his cantankerous nature rose to the surface like sweat. He found the Sinhalese far too casual and complained about "the papaw-stinking buddhists." On his first day the

Brewsters took him for a walk around Kandy Lake. Achsah and Earl Brewster describe how Lawrence pulled out his silver watch and noticed that it had stopped. He went into a rage, heaving and pulling to break the chain, and threw the watch into the lake. The silver timepiece floated down and joined more significant unrecovered treasure buried by Kandyan kings.

Heat disgraces foreigners. Yesterday, on the road from Kandy to Colombo we passed New Year's festivities in every village—grease pole climbing, bicycle races with roadside crowds heaving buckets of water over the cyclists as they passed—everyone joining in the ceremonies during the blazing noon. But my kids, as we drove towards lowland heat, growing belligerent and yelling at each other to shut up, shut up, shut up.

Two miles away from Buller's Road lived another foreigner. Pablo Neruda. For two years during the thirties, he lived in Wellawatte while working for the Chilean Embassy. He had just escaped from Burma and Josie Bliss of "The widower's tango" and in his *Memoirs* writes mostly about his pet mongoose. An aunt of mine remembers his coming to dinner and continually breaking into song, but many of his dark claustrophobic pieces in *Residence on Earth* were written here, poems that saw this landscape governed by a crowded surrealism—full of vegetable oppressiveness.

Ceylon always did have too many foreigners . . . the 'Karapothas' as my niece calls them—the beetles with white spots who never grew ancient here, who stepped in and admired the landscape, disliked the "inquisitive natives" and left. They came originally and overpowered the land obsessive for something as delicate as the smell of cinnamon. Becoming wealthy with spices. When ships were still approaching, ten miles out at sea, captains would spill cinnamon onto the deck and invite passengers on board to *smell Ceylon* before the island even came into view.

"From Seyllan to Paradise is forty miles," says a legend, "the sound of the fountains of Paradise is heard there." But when Robert Knox was held captive on the island in the 17th century he remembered his time this way: "Thus was I left Desolate, Sick and in Captivity, having no earthly comforter, none but only He who looks down from Heaven to hear the groaning of the prisoners."

The leap from one imagination to the other can hardly be made; no more than Desdemona could understand truly the Moor's military exploits. We own the country we grow up in, or we are aliens and invaders. Othello's talent was a decorated sleeve she was charmed by. This island was a paradise to be sacked. Every conceivable thing was collected and shipped back to Europe: cardamons, pepper, silk, ginger, sandalwood, mustard oil, palmyrah root, tamarind, wild indigo, deers' horns, elephant tusks, hog lard, calamander, coral, seven kinds of cinnamon, pearl and cochineal. *A perfumed sea.*

And if this was paradise, it had a darker side. My ancestor, William Charles Ondaatje, knew of at least fifty-five species of poisons easily available to his countrymen, none of it, it seems, used against the invaders. Varieties of arsenic, juices from the centipede, scorpion, toad and glow-worm, jackal and "mungoose," ground blue peacock stones—these could stun a man into death in minutes. "Croton seeds are used as a means to facilitate theft and other criminal intentions," he wrote in his biological notebooks. In his most lyrical moment, in footnote 28 of his report on the Royal Botanic Gardens, William Charles steps away from the formal paper, out of the latinized garden, and, with the passion of a snail or bird, gifts us his heart.

> Here are majestic palms with their towering stems and graceful
> foliage, the shoe flower, the eatable passion flower. Here the
> water lily swims the rivers with expanded leaves—a prince of
> aquatic plants! The Aga-mula-naeti-wala, *creeper without begin-
> ning or end,* twines around trees and hangs in large festoons
> . . . and curious indeed these are from having neither leaves nor
> roots. Here is the winged thunbergia, the large snouted justicia,
> the mustard tree of Scripture with its succulent leaves and infi-
> nitesimal berries. The busy acacia with its sweet fragrance
> perfumes the dreary plains while other sad and un-named
> flowers sweeten the night with their blossoms which are shed in
> the dark.

The journals delight in the beauty and the poisons, he invents
"paper" out of indigenous vegetables, he tests local medicines and
poisons on dogs and rats. "A man at Jaffna committed suicide by
eating the *neagala* root. . . . A concoction of the plumbago is
given to produce abortion." Casually he lists the possible weapons around him. The karapothas crawled over them and admired
their beauty.

The island hid its knowledge. Intricate arts and customs and
religious ceremonies moved inland away from the new cities.
Only Robert Knox, held captive by a Kandyan king for twenty
years, wrote of the island well, learning its traditions. His memoir, *An Historical Relation,* was used by Defoe as a psychological
source for the ever inquisitive Robinson Crusoe. "If you peer
into the features of Crusoe you will see something of the man
who was not the lonely inhabitant of a desert island but who
lived in an alien land among strangers, cut away from his own

countrymen . . . and striving hard not only to return but also to employ profitably the single talent that had been given him."

Apart from Knox, and later Leonard Woolf in his novel, *A Village in the Jungle,* very few foreigners truly knew where they were.

*   *   *

I still believe the most beautiful alphabet was created by the Sinhalese. The insect of ink curves into a shape that is almost sickle, spoon, eyelid. The letters are washed blunt glass which betray no jaggedness. Sanskrit was governed by verticals, but its sharp grid features were not possible in Ceylon. Here the Ola leaves which people wrote on were too brittle. A straight line would cut apart the leaf and so a curling alphabet was derived from its Indian cousin. Moon coconut. The bones of a lover's spine.

When I was five—the only time in my life when my handwriting was meticulous—I sat in the tropical classrooms and learned the letters ඝ , and ඨ, repeating them page after page. How to write. The self-portrait of language. ඏ . Lid on a cooking utensil that takes the shape of fire. Years later, looking into a biology textbook, I came across a whole page depicting the small bones in the body and recognised, delighted, the shapes and forms of the first alphabet I ever copied from Kumarodaya's first grade reader.

At St Thomas' College Boy School I had written 'lines' as punishment. A hundred and fifty times. කොප්ප්ටන් නිවෙසෙහි වහලයට නැගී පොල්ගෙඩි විසි නොකරමි. I must not throw coconuts off the roof of Copplestone House. බාර්තබේ පියතුමාගේ තාරයේ උඩරවලට සිසිදා මුතු නොකරමි. We must not urinate again on Father Bar-

185

nabus' tires. A communal protest this time, the first of my socialist tendencies. The idiot phrases moved east across the page as if searching for longitude and story, some meaning or grace that would occur *blazing* after so much writing. For years I thought literature was punishment, simply a parade ground. The only freedom writing brought was as the author of rude expressions on walls and desks.

In the 5th Century B.C. graffiti poems were scratched onto the rock face of Sigiriya—the rock fortress of a despot king. Short verses to the painted women in the frescoes which spoke of love in all its confusions and brokenness. Poems to mythological women who consumed and overcame mundane lives. The phrases saw breasts as perfect swans; eyes were long and clean as horizons. The anonymous poets returned again and again to the same metaphors. Beautiful *false compare.* These were the first folk poems of the country.

When the government rounded up thousands of suspects during the Insurgency of 1971, the Vidyalankara campus of the University of Ceylon was turned into a prison camp. The police weeded out the guilty, trying to break their spirit. When the university opened again the returning students found hundreds of poems written on walls, ceilings, and in hidden corners of the campus. Quatrains and free verse about the struggle, tortures, the unbroken spirit, love of friends who had died for the cause. The students went around for days transcribing them into their notebooks before they were covered with whitewash and lye.

*   *   *

I spend hours talking with Ian Goonetileke, who runs the library at Peredeniya, about writers in Ceylon. He shows me a book he put together on the Insurgency. Because of censorship it had to be published in Switzerland. At the back of the book are ten photographs of charcoal drawings done by an insurgent on the walls of one of the houses he hid in. The average age of the insurgents was seventeen and thousands were killed by police and army. While the Kelani and Mahaveli rivers moved to the sea, heavy with bodies, these drawings were destroyed so that the book is now the only record of them. The artist is anonymous. The works seem as great as the Sigiriya frescoes. They too need to be eternal.

He also shows me the poetry of Lakdasa Wikkramasinha, one of his close friends who drowned recently at Mount Lavinia. A powerful and angry poet. Lakdasa was two years ahead of me at St. Thomas's College and though I never knew him we had studied in the same classrooms and with the same teachers.

As I leave his house, Ian returns to the beautiful George Keyt drawings which fill his study and the books he has to publish in other countries in order to keep the facts straight, the legends uncovered. He is a man who knows history is always present, is the last hour of his friend Lakdasa blacking out in the blue sea at Mount Lavinia where the tourists go to sunbathe, is the burned down wall that held those charcoal drawings whose passionate conscience should have been cut into rock. The voices I didn't know. The visions which are anonymous. And secret.

This morning in the house on Buller's Road I read the poetry of Lakdasa Wikkramasinha.

> *Don't talk to me about Matisse . . .*
> *the European style of 1900, the tradition of the studio*
> *where the nude woman reclines forever*
> *on a sheet of blood*

Talk to me instead of the culture generally—
how the murderers were sustained
by the beauty robbed of savages: to our remote
villages the painters came, and our white-washed
mud-huts were splattered with gunfire.

HIGH FLOWERS

The slow moving of her cotton
in the heat.
                    Hard shell of foot.
She chops the yellow coconut
the colour of Anuradhapura stone.

The woman my ancestors ignored
sits at the doorway chopping coconut
cleaning rice.

Her husband moves
in the air between trees.
The curved knife at his hip.
In high shadows
of coconut palms

he grasps a path of rope above his head
and another below him with his naked foot.
He drinks the first sweet mouthful
from the cut flower, then drains it
into a narrow-necked pot
and steps out to the next tree.

Above the small roads of Wattala,
Kalutara, the toddy tapper walks
collecting the white liquid for tavern vats.
Down here the light
storms through branches
and boils the street.
Villagers stand in the shadow and drink
the fluid from a coned leaf.
He works fast to reach his quota
before the maniac monsoon.
The shape of knife and pot
do not vary from 18th Century museum prints.

In the village,
a woman shuffles rice
in a cane mat.
Grit and husk separate
are thrown to the sun.

From his darkness among high flowers
to this room contained by mud walls
everything that is important occurs in shadow—
her discreet slow moving his dreams of walking
from tree to tree without ropes.
It is not vanity which allows him this freedom
but skill and habit, the curved knife

his father gave him, it is the coolness up there
—for the ground's heat has not yet risen—
which makes him forget necessity.

Kings.   Fortresses.   Traffic in open sun.

Within a doorway the woman
turns in the old pleasure of darkness.

In the high trees above her
shadows eliminate
the path he moves along.

TO COLOMBO

Returning from Sigiriya   hills
in their high green   the grey
animal fortress rock   claws of stone
rumours of wild boar

                    pass

paddy terraces
bullocks   brown men
who rise knee deep like the earth
out of the earth

Sunlight   Sunlight

stop for the cool *kurumba*
scoop the half formed white
into our mouths

                    remove

tarpaulin walls of the jeep
to receive lowland air

                    on a bench behind sunlight
                  the woman   the coconuts   the knife

WOMEN LIKE YOU

(the communal poem—Sigiri Graffiti, 5th century)

They do not stir
these ladies of the mountain
do not give us
the twitch of eyelids.

           The king is dead.

They answer no one
take the hard
rock as lover.
Women like you
make men pour out their hearts

               'Seeing you I want
               no other life'

'The golden skins have
caught my mind'

who came here
out of the bleached land
climbed this fortress
to adore the rock
and with the solitude of the air
behind them
            carved an alphabet
whose motive was perfect desire

wanting these portraits of women
to speak
and caress.

Hundreds of small verses
by different hands
became one
habit of the unrequited.

Seeing you
I want no other life
and turn around
to the sky
and everywhere below
jungle, waves of heat
secular love

Holding the new flowers
a circle of
first finger and thumb
which is a window

to your breast

pleasure of the skin
earring   earring
curl
of the belly
            and then
stone mermaid
stone heart
dry as a flower
on rock
you long eyed women
the golden
drunk swan breasts
lips
the long long eyes

we stand against the sky

I bring you

a flute
from the throat
of a loon

so talk to me
of the used heart

THE CINNAMON
PEELER

If I were a cinnamon peeler
I would ride your bed
and leave the yellow bark dust
on your pillow.

Your breasts and shoulders would reek
you could never walk through markets
without the profession of my fingers
floating over you. The blind would
stumble certain of whom they approached
though you might bathe
under rain gutters, monsoon.

Here on the upper thigh
at this smooth pasture
neighbour to your hair
or the crease

that cuts your back. This ankle.
You will be known among strangers
as the cinnamon peeler's wife.

I could hardly glance at you
before marriage
never touch you
—your keen nosed mother, your rough brothers.
I buried my hands
in saffron, disguised them
over smoking tar,
helped the honey gatherers. . .

                    *

When we swam once
I touched you in water
and our bodies remained free,
you could hold me and be blind of smell.
You climbed the bank and said

                    this is how you touch other women
the grass cutter's wife, the lime burner's daughter.
And you searched your arms
for the missing perfume
                    and knew

                    what good is it
to be the lime burner's daughter
left with no trace
as if not spoken to in the act of love
as if wounded without the pleasure of a scar.

You touched
your belly to my hands
in the dry air and said
I am the cinnamon
peeler's wife. Smell me.

KEGALLE (ii)

The family home of Rock Hill was littered with snakes, especially cobras. The immediate garden was not so dangerous, but one step further and you would see several. The chickens that my father kept in later years were an even greater magnet. The snakes came for the eggs. The only deterrent my father discovered was ping-pong balls. He had crates of ping-pong balls shipped to Rock Hill and distributed them among the eggs. The snake would swallow the ball whole and be unable to digest it. There are several paragraphs on this method of snake control in a pamphlet he wrote on poultry farming.

The snakes also had the habit of coming into the house and at least once a month there would be shrieks, the family would run around, the shotgun would be pulled out, and the snake would be blasted to pieces. Certain sections of the walls and floors showed the scars of shot. My stepmother found one coiled asleep on her desk and was unable to approach the drawer to get the key to open the gun case. At another time one lay sleeping on the large radio to draw its warmth and, as nobody wanted to destroy the one source of music in the house, this one was watched carefully but left alone.

Most times though there would be running footsteps, yells of fear and excitement, everybody trying to quiet everybody else, and my father or stepmother would blast away not caring what was in the background, a wall, good ebony, a sofa, or a decanter. They killed at least thirty snakes between them.

After my father died, a grey cobra came into the house. My stepmother loaded the gun and fired at point blank range. The gun jammed. She stepped back and reloaded but by then the snake had slid out into the garden. For the next month this snake would often come into the house and each time the gun would misfire or jam, or my stepmother would miss at absurdly short range. The snake attacked no one and had a tendency to follow my younger sister Susan around. Other snakes entering the house were killed by the shotgun, lifted with a long stick and flicked into the bushes, but the old grey cobra led a charmed life. Finally one of the old workers at Rock Hill told my stepmother what had become obvious, that it was my father who had come to protect his family. And in fact, whether it was because the chicken farm closed down or because of my father's presence in the form of a snake, very few other snakes came into the house again.

*   *   *

The last incident at Rock Hill took place in 1971, a year before the farm was sold. 1971 was the year of the Insurgence. The rebels against the government consisted of thousands from every walk of life—but essentially the young. The age of an insurgent ranged from fifteen to twenty. They were a strange mixture of innocence and determination and anarchy, making home-made bombs with nails and scraps of metal and at the same time delighted and proud of their uniforms of blue trousers with a stripe down the side, and tennis shoes. Some had never worn tennis shoes before. My cousin Rhunie was staying at the Ambepussa resthouse with the Chitrasena dance troupe when fifty insurgents marched up the road in formation chanting "we are hungry we are hungry," ransacked the place for food, but did not touch any one there because they were all fans of the dance company.

The insurgents were remarkably well organized and general belief is that they would have taken over the country if one group hadn't mixed up the dates and attacked the police station in Wellawaya a day too soon. The following day every police station and every army barrack and every radio station was to be hit simultaneously. Some gangs hid out in the jungle reserves at Wilpattu and Yala where they survived by shooting and eating the wildlife. A week before the uprising they had broken into local government offices, gone through the files and found the location of every registered weapon in the country. The day after the revolt broke out, a gang of twenty marched from house to house in Kegalle collecting weapons and finally came up the hill to Rock Hill.

They had ransacked several houses already, stripping them of everything—food, utensils, radios and clothing, but this group of 17-year-olds was extremely courteous to my stepmother and her children. My father had apparently donated several acres of Rock Hill towards a playground several years earlier and many of these insurgents had known him well.

They asked for whatever weapons the house had and my stepmother handed over the notorious shotgun. They checked their files and saw a rifle was also listed. It turned out to be an air rifle, wrongly categorized. I had used it often as a ten-year-old, ankle deep in paddy fields, shooting at birds, and if there were no birds, at the fruit of trees. While all this official business was going on around the front porch, the rest of the insurgents had put down their huge collection of weapons, collected from all over Kegalle, and persuaded my younger sister Susan to provide a bat and a tennis ball. Asking her to join them, they proceeded to play a game of cricket on the front lawn. They played for most of the afternoon.

ECLIPSE
PLUMAGE

LUNCH
CONVERSATION

Wait a minute, wait a minute! When did all this happen, I'm trying to get it straight . . .

Your mother was nine, Hilden was there, and your grandmother Lalla and David Grenier and his wife Dickie.

How old was Hilden?

Oh, in his early twenties.

But Hilden was having dinner with my mother and you.

Yes, says Barbara. And Trevor de Saram. And Hilden and your mother and I were quite drunk. It was a wedding lunch, Babette's

I think, I can't remember all those weddings. I know Hilden was moving with a rotten crowd of drinkers then so he was drunk quite early and we were all laughing about the drowning of David Grenier.

I didn't say a word.

Laughing at Lalla, because Lalla nearly drowned too. You see, she was caught in a current and instead of fighting it she just relaxed and went with it out to sea and eventually came back in a semi-circle. Claimed she passed ships.

And then Trevor got up in a temper and challenged Hilden to a duel. He couldn't *stand* everyone laughing, and Hilden and Doris (your mother) being drunk, two of them flirting away he thought.

But *why?,* your mother asked Trevor.

Because he is casting aspersions on you . . .

Nonsense, I love aspersions. And everyone laughed and Trevor stood there in a rage.

And then, said Barbara, I realized that Trevor had been in love with your mother, your father always *said* there was a secret admirer. Trevor couldn't stand Hilden and her having a good time in front of him.

Nonsense, said your mother. It would have been incest. And besides (watching Hilden and Trevor and aware of the fascinated dinner table audience), both these men are after my old age pension.

What happened, said Hilden, was that I drew a line around Doris in the sand. A circle. And threatened her, "don't you dare step out of that circle or I'll thrash you."

Wait a minute, wait a minute, *when* is this happening?

Your mother is nine years old, Hilden says. And out in the sea near Negombo David Grenier is drowning. I didn't want her to go out.

You were in love with a nine year old?

Neither Hilden nor Trevor were *ever* in love with our mother, Gillian whispers to me. People always get that way at weddings, always remembering the past in a sentimental way, pretending great secret passions which went unsaid . . .

No No No. Trevor *was* in love with your mother.

Rot!

I was in my twenties, Hilden chimes in. Your mother was nine. I simply didn't want her going into the water while we tried to rescue David Grenier. Dickie, his wife, had fainted. Lalla—your mother's mother—was caught in the current and out at sea, I was on the shore with Trevor.

Trevor was there too you see.

Who is Hilden? asks Tory.

I am Hilden . . . your host!

Oh.

Anyway . . . there seems to be three different stories that you're telling.

No, *one,* everybody says laughing.

One when your mother was nine. Then when she was sixty-five and drinking at the wedding lunch, and obviously there is a period of unrequited love suffered by the silent Trevor who never stated his love but always fought with anyone he thought was insulting your mother, even if in truth she was simply having a good time with them the way she was with Hilden, when she was sixty-five.

Good God, I was there with them both, says Barbara, and *I'm* married to Hilden.

So where is my grandmother?

She is now out at sea while Hilden dramatically draws a circle round your mother and says "Don't you *dare* step out of that!" Your mother watches David Grenier drowning. Grenier's wife —who is going to marry three more times including one man who went crazy—is lying in the sand having fainted. And your mother can see the bob of her mother's head in the waves now and then. Hilden and Trevor are trying to retrieve David

Grenier's body, carefully, so as not to get caught in the current themselves.

My mother is nine.

Your mother is nine. And this takes place in Negombo.

OK

So an hour later my grandmother, Lalla, comes back and entertains everyone with stories of how she passed ships out there and they tell her David Grenier is dead. And nobody wants to break the news to his wife Dickie. Nobody could. And Lalla says, alright, she will, for Dickie is her sister. And she went and sat with Dickie who was still in a faint in the sand, and Lalla, wearing her elaborate bathing suit, held her hand. Don't shock her, says Trevor, whatever you do break it to her gently. My grandmother waves him away and for fifteen minutes she sits alone with her sister, waiting for her to waken. She doesn't know what to say. She is also suddenly very tired. She hates hurting anybody.

The two men, Hilden and Trevor, will walk with her daughter, my mother, about a hundred yards away down the beach, keeping their distance, waiting until they see Dickie sitting up. And then they will walk slowly back towards Dickie and my grandmother and give their sympathies.

Dickie stirs. Lalla is holding her hand. She looks up and the first words are, "How is David? Is he alright?" "Quite well, darling," Lalla says. "He is in the next room having a cup of tea."

AUNTS

How I have used them.
... They knit the story to-
gether, each memory a wild thread in the sarong. They lead me
through their dark rooms crowded with various kinds of furniture—teak, rattan, calamander, bamboo—their voices whispering over tea, cigarettes, distracting me from the tale with their
long bony arms, which move over the table like the stretched feet
of storks. I would love to photograph this. The thin muscle on
the upper arms, the bones and veins at the wrist that almost
become part of the discreet bangle, all disappearing into the river
of bright sari or faded cotton print.

My aunt Dolly stands five foot tall, weighing seventy pounds.
She has not stopped smoking since the age of fifteen and her
80-year-old brain leaps like a spark plug bringing this year that
year to life. Always repeating the last three words of your
question and then turning a surprising corner on her own. In the

large house whose wings are now disintegrating into garden and bush she moves frail as Miss Havisham. From outside the house seems incapable of use. I climb in through the window that frames her and she greets me with "I never thought I'd see you again," and suddenly all these journeys are worth it, just to be able to hug this thin woman who throws her cane onto the table in order to embrace me.

She and her brother Arthur were my father's close friends all his life. He knew that, whatever he had done, Arthur would be there to talk him out of madness, weakness, aloneness. They introduced most of the children of our generation to the theatre, dressing us up in costumes for *The Mikado, A Midsummer Night's Dream*—all of which Dolly made herself. Although her family was not excessive in their affairs, they shielded anyone who was in the midst of a passion. "Affairs were going on all around us, even when we were children . . . so we were well trained."

Today is one of Dolly's deaf days but the conversation rolls with the pure joy of the meeting. "Oh I looked after you several times when you were in Boralesgamuwa, do you remember?" "Yes, yes." "WHAT?" *"Yes."* The frailty does not stop her stories though she pauses now and then to say, "God if you quote me I'm dead. I'll be caught for libel and *killed*. . . . You see they liked their flirtations. All the wives met their beaux in the Cinnamon Gardens, that's where they went to flirt, then they'd come here and use us as an alibi. Your grandmother Lalla for instance had lots of relationships. We could never keep up with her. We almost had to write the names down to remember who she was seeing. My advice you see is to get on with everybody—no matter what they do."

The conversation is continually halted by a man lying just below the ceiling hammering nails into it—hoping to keep it

213

propped up for a few more years. Outside loud chickens fill in the spaces between Dolly's words. Eyes squint in the smoke. "I wish I could see you properly but my glasses are being fixed this week."

As I prepare to leave she walks with me, half deaf and blind, under several ladders in her living room that balance paint and workmen, into the garden where there is a wild horse, a 1930 car splayed flat on its axles and hundreds of flowering bushes so that her eyes swim out into the dark green and unfocussed purple. There is very little now that separates the house from the garden. Rain and vines and chickens move into the building. Before I leave, she points to a group photograph of a fancy dress party that shows herself and my grandmother Lalla among the crowd. She has looked at it for years and has in this way memorized everyone's place in the picture. She reels off names and laughs at the facial expressions she can no longer see. It has moved tangible, palpable, into her brain, the way memory invades the present in those who are old, the way gardens invade houses here, the way her tiny body steps into mine as intimate as anything I have witnessed and I have to force myself to be gentle with this frailty in the midst of my embrace.

THE PASSIONS
OF LALLA

My Grandmother died in the blue arms of a jacaranda tree. She could read thunder.

She claimed to have been born outdoors, abruptly, during a picnic, though there is little evidence for this. Her father—who came from a subdued line of Keyts—had thrown caution to the winds and married a Dickman. The bloodline was considered eccentric (one Dickman had set herself on fire) and rumours about the family often percolated across Colombo in hushed tones. "People who married the Dickmans were afraid."

There is no information about Lalla growing up. Perhaps she was a shy child, for those who are magical break from silent structures after years of chrysalis. By the time she was twenty she was living in Colombo and tentatively engaged to Shelton de Saram—a very good looking and utterly selfish man. He desired the good life, and when Frieda Donhorst arrived from England "with a thin English varnish and the Donhorst checkbook" he promptly married her. Lalla was heartbroken. She went into fits of rage, threw herself on and pounded various beds belonging to her immediate family, and quickly married Willie Gratiaen—a champion cricketer—on the rebound.

Willie was also a broker, and being one of the first Ceylonese to work for the English firm of E. John and Co. brought them most of their local business. The married couple bought a large house called "Palm Lodge" in the heart of Colombo and here, in the three acres that came with the house, they began a dairy. The dairy was Willie's second attempt at raising livestock. Fond of eggs, he had decided earlier to import and raise a breed of black chicken from Australia. At great expense the prize Australorp eggs arrived by ship, ready for hatching, but Lalla accidentally cooked them all while preparing for a dinner party.

Shortly after Willie began the dairy he fell seriously ill. Lalla, unable to cope, would run into neighbours' homes, pound on their beds, and promise to become a Catholic if Willie recovered. He never did and Lalla was left to bring up their two children.

She was not yet thirty, and for the next few years her closest friend was her neighbor, Rene de Saram, who also ran a dairy. Rene's husband disliked Lalla and disliked his wife's chickens. Lalla and the chickens would wake him before dawn every morning, especially Lalla with her loud laughter filtering across the garden as she organized the milkers. One morning Rene woke to silence and, stepping into the garden, discovered her husband tying the beaks of all the chickens with little pieces of string, or in some cases with rubber bands. She protested, but he prevailed and soon they saw their chickens perform a dance of death, dying of exhaustion and hunger, a few managing to escape along Inner Flower Road, some kidnapped by a furious Lalla in the folds of her large brown dress and taken to Palm Lodge where she had them cooked. A year later the husband lapsed into total silence and the only sounds which could be heard from his quarters were barkings and later on the cluck of hens. It is believed he was the victim of someone's charm. For several weeks he clucked, barked, and chirped, tearing his feather pillows into snowstorms, scratching at the expensive parquet floors, leaping from first-storey windows onto the lawn. After he shot himself, Rene was left at the age of thirty-two to bring up their children. So both Rene and Lalla, after years of excessive high living, were to have difficult times—surviving on their wits and character and beauty. Both widows became the focus of the attention of numerous bored husbands. Neither of them was to marry again.

Each had thirty-five cows. Milking began at four-thirty in the morning and by six their milkmen would be cycling all over town to deliver fresh milk to customers. Lalla and Rene took the law into their own hands whenever necessary. When one of their cows caught Rinderpest Fever—a disease which could make government officials close down a dairy for months—Rene took the army pistol which had already killed her husband and personally shot it dead. With Lalla's help she burnt it and buried it in her garden. The milk went out that morning as usual, the tin vessels clanking against the handlebars of several bicycles.

Lalla's head milkman at this time was named Brumphy, and when a Scot named McKay made a pass at a servant girl Brumphy stabbed him to death. By the time the police arrived Lalla had hidden him in one of her sheds, and when they came back a second time she had taken Brumphy over to a neighbour named Lillian Bevan. For some reason Mrs. Bevan approved of everything Lalla did. She was sick when Lalla stormed in to hide Brumphy under the bed whose counterpane had wide lace edges that came down to the floor. Lalla explained that it was only a minor crime; when the police came to the Bevan household and described the brutal stabbing in graphic detail Lillian was terrified as the murderer was just a few feet away from her. But she could never disappoint Lalla and kept quiet. The police watched the house for two days and Lillian dutifully halved her meals and passed a share under the bed. "I'm proud of you darling!" said Lalla when she eventually spirited Brumphy away to another location.

However, there was a hearing in court presided over by Judge E. W. Jayawardene—one of Lalla's favourite bridge partners. When she was called to give evidence she kept referring to him as "My Lord My God." E.W. was probably one of the ugliest men in Ceylon at the time. When he asked Lalla if Brumphy was good-looking—trying humorously to suggest some motive for her protecting him—she replied, "Good looking? Who can say, My Lord My God, some people may find *you* good looking." She was thrown out of court while the gallery hooted with laughter and gave her a standing ovation. This dialogue is still in the judicial records in the Buller's Road Court Museum. In any case she continued to play bridge with E. W. Jayawardene and their sons would remain close friends.

Apart from rare appearances in court (sometimes to watch other friends give evidence), Lalla's day was carefully planned. She would be up at four with the milkers, oversee the dairy, look after the books, and be finished by 9 A.M. The rest of the day would be given over to gallivanting—social calls, lunch parties, visits from admirers, and bridge. She also brought up her two children. It was in the garden at Palm Lodge that my mother and

218

Dorothy Clementi-Smith would practise their dances, quite often surrounded by cattle.

*   *   *

For years Palm Lodge attracted a constant group—first as children, then teenagers, and then young adults. For most of her life children flocked to Lalla, for she was the most casual and irresponsible of chaperones, being far too busy with her own life to oversee them all. Behind Palm Lodge was a paddy field which separated her house from "Royden," where the Daniels lived. When there were complaints that hordes of children ran into Royden with muddy feet, Lalla bought ten pairs of stilts and taught them to walk across the paddy fields on these "boruka-kuls" or "lying legs." Lalla would say "yes" to any request if she was busy at bridge so they knew when to ask her for permission to do the most outrageous things. Every child had to be part of the group. She particularly objected to children being sent for extra tuition on Saturdays and would hire a Wallace Carriage and go searching for children like Peggy Peiris. She swept into the school at noon yelling "PEGGY!!!," fluttering down the halls in her long black clothes loose at the edges like a rooster dragging its tail, and Peggy's friends would lean over the bannisters and say "Look, look, your mad aunt has arrived."

As these children grew older they discovered that Lalla had very little money. She would take groups out for meals and be refused service as she hadn't paid her previous bills. Everyone went with her anyway, though they could never be sure of eating. It was the same with adults. During one of her grand dinner parties she asked Lionel Wendt who was very shy to carve the meat. A big pot was placed in front of him. As he removed the lid a baby goat jumped out and skittered down the table. Lalla had been so involved with the joke—buying the kid that morning and finding a big enough pot—that she had forgotten about the real dinner and there was nothing to eat once the shock and laughter had subsided.

In the early years her two children, Noel and Doris, could hardly move without being used as part of Lalla's daily theatre. She was constantly dreaming up costumes for my mother to wear to fancy dress parties, which were the rage at the time. Because of Lalla, my mother won every fancy dress competition for three years while in her late teens. Lalla tended to go in for animals or sea creatures. The crowning achievement was my mother's appearance at the Galle Face Dance as a lobster—the outfit bright red and covered with crustaceans and claws which grew out of her shoulder blades and seemed to move of their own accord. The problem was that she could not sit down for the whole evening but had to walk or waltz stiffly from side to side with her various beaux who, although respecting the imagination behind the outfit, found her beautiful frame almost unapproachable. Who knows, this may have been Lalla's ulterior motive. For years my mother tended to be admired from a distance. On the ballroom floor she stood out in her animal or shell fish beauty but claws and caterpillar bulges tended to deflect suitors from thoughts of seduction. When couples paired off to walk along Galle Face Green under the moonlight it would, after all, be embarrassing to be seen escorting a lobster.

When my mother eventually announced her engagement to my father, Lalla turned to friends and said, "What do you *think,* darling, she's going to marry an Ondaatje . . . she's going to marry a *Tamil!*" Years later, when I sent my mother my first book of poems, she met my sister at the door with a shocked face and in exactly the same tone and phrasing said, "What do you *think*, Janet" (her hand holding her cheek to emphasize the tragedy), "Michael has become a *poet!*" Lalla continued to stress the Tamil element in my father's background, which pleased him enormously. For the wedding ceremony she had two marriage chairs decorated in a Hindu style and laughed all through the ceremony. The incident was, however, the beginning of a war with my father.

Eccentrics can be the most irritating people to live with. My mother, for instance, strangely, *never* spoke of Lalla to me. Lalla was loved most by people who saw her arriving from the distance like a storm. She did love children, or at least loved company of any kind—cows, adults, babies, dogs. She always had to be surrounded. But being "grabbed" or "contained" by anyone drove her mad. She would be compassionate to the character of children but tended to avoid holding them on her lap. And she could not abide having grandchildren hold her hands when she took them for walks. She would quickly divert them into the entrance of the frightening maze in the Nuwara Eliya Park and leave them there, lost, while she went off to steal flowers. She was always determined to be physically selfish. Into her sixties she would still complain of how she used to be "pinned down" to breast feed her son before she could leave for dances.

*   *   *

With children grown up and out of the way, Lalla busied herself with her sisters and brothers. "Dickie" seemed to be marrying constantly; after David Grenier drowned she married a de Vos, a Wombeck, and then an Englishman. Lalla's brother Vere attempted to remain a bachelor all his life. When she was flirting with Catholicism she decided that Vere should marry her priest's sister—a woman who *had* planned on becoming a nun. The sister also had a dowry of thirty thousand rupees, and both Lalla and Vere were short of money at the time, for both enjoyed expensive drinking sessions. Lalla masterminded the marriage, even though the woman wasn't good-looking and Vere liked good-looking women. On the wedding night the bride prayed for half an hour beside the bed and then started singing hymns, so Vere departed, foregoing nuptial bliss, and for the rest of her life the poor woman had a sign above her door which read "Unloved. Unloved. Unloved." Lalla went to mass the following week, having eaten a huge meal. When refused mass she said, 'Then I'll resign," and avoided the church for the rest of her life.

A good many of my relatives from this generation seem to have tormented the church sexually. Italian monks who became enamoured of certain aunts would return to Italy to discard their robes and return to find the women already married. Jesuit fathers too were falling out of the church and into love with the de Sarams with the regularity of mangoes thudding onto dry lawns during a drought. Vere also became the concern of various religious groups that tried to save him. And during the last months of his life he was "held captive" by a group of Roman Catholic nuns in Galle so that no one knew where he was until the announcement of his death.

Vere was known as "a sweet drunk" and he and Lalla always drank together. While Lalla grew loud and cheerful, Vere became excessively courteous. Drink was hazardous for him, however, as he came to believe he escaped the laws of gravity while under the influence. He kept trying to hang his hat on walls where there was no hook and often stepped out of boats to walk home. But drink quietened him except for these few excesses. His close friend, the lawyer Cox Sproule, was a different matter. Cox was charming when sober and brilliant when drunk. He would appear in court stumbling over chairs with a mind clear as a bell, winning cases under a judge who had pleaded with him just that morning not to appear in court in such a condition. He hated the English. Unlike Cox, Vere had no profession to focus whatever talents he had. He did try to become an auctioneer but being both shy and drunk he was a failure. The only job that came his way was supervising Italian prisoners during the war. Once a week he would ride to Colombo on his motorcycle, bringing as many bottles of alcohol as he could manage for his friends and his sister. He had encouraged the prisoners to set up a brewery, so that there was a distillery in every hut in the prison camp. He remained drunk with the prisoners for most of the war years. Even Cox Sproule joined him for six months when he was jailed for helping three German spies escape from the country.

What happened to Lalla's other brother, Evan, no one knows. But all through her life, when the children sent her money, Lalla would immediately forward it on to Evan. He was supposedly a thief and Lalla loved him. "Jesus died to save sinners," she said, "and I will die for Evan." Evan manages to escape family memory, appearing only now and then to offer blocs of votes to any friend running for public office by bringing along all his illegitimate children.

*   *   *

By the mid-thirties both Lalla's and Rene's dairies had been wiped out by Rinderpest. Both were drinking heavily and both were broke.

We now enter the phase when Lalla is best remembered. Her

children were married and out of the way. Most of her social life had been based at Palm Lodge but now she had to sell the house, and she burst loose on the country and her friends like an ancient monarch who had lost all her possessions. She was free to move wherever she wished, to do whatever she wanted. She took thorough advantage of everyone and had bases all over the country. Her schemes for organizing parties and bridge games exaggerated themselves. She was full of the "passions," whether drunk or not. She had always loved flowers but in her last decade couldn't be bothered to grow them. Still, whenever she arrived on a visit she would be carrying an armful of flowers and announce, "Darling, I've just been to church and I've stolen some flowers for you. These are from Mrs. Abeysekare's, the lilies are from Mrs. Ratnayake's, the agapanthus is from Violet Meedeniya, and the rest are from *your* garden." She stole flowers compulsively, even in the owner's presence. As she spoke with someone her straying left hand would pull up a prize rose along with the roots, all so that she could appreciate it for that one moment, gaze into it with complete pleasure, swallow its qualities whole, and then hand the flower, discarding it, to the owner. She ravaged some of the best gardens in Colombo and Nuwara Eliya. For some years she was barred from the Hakgalle Public Gardens.

Property was there to be taken or given away. When she was rich she had given parties for all the poor children in the neighbourhood and handed out gifts. When she was poor she still organized them but now would go out to the Pettah market on the morning of the party and steal toys. All her life she had given away everything she owned to whoever wanted it and so now felt free to take whatever she wanted. She was a lyrical socialist. Having no home in her last years, she breezed into houses for weekends or even weeks, cheated at bridge with her closest friends, calling them "damn thieves," "bloody rogues." She only played cards for money and if faced with a difficult contract would throw down her hand, gather the others up, and proclaim "the rest are mine." Everyone knew she was lying but it didn't matter. Once when my brother and two sisters who were very young were playing a game of "beggar-my-neighbour" on the porch, Lalla came to watch. She walked up and down beside them, seemingly very irritated. After ten minutes she could stand it no longer, opened her purse, gave them each two rupees, and said, "Never, *never* play cards for love."

She was in her prime. During the war she opened up a boarding house in Nuwara Eliya with Muriel Potger, a chain smoker who did all the work while Lalla breezed through the rooms saying, "Muriel, for godsake, we can't breathe in this place!"— being more of a pest than a help. If she had to go out she would say, "I'll just freshen up" and disappear into her room for a stiff drink. If there was none she took a quick swig of eau de cologne to snap her awake. Old flames visited her constantly throughout her life. She refused to lose friends; even her first beau, Shelton de Saram, would arrive after breakfast to escort her for walks. His unfortunate wife, Frieda, would always telephone Lalla first and would spend most afternoons riding in her trap through the Cinnamon Gardens or the park searching for them.

Lalla's great claim to fame was that she was the first woman in Ceylon to have a mastectomy. It turned out to be unnecessary but she always claimed to support modern science, throwing herself into new causes. (Even in death her generosity exceeded the physically possible for she had donated her body to six hospitals). The false breast would never be still for long. She was an energetic person. It would crawl over to join its twin on the right hand side or sometimes appear on her back, "for dancing" she smirked. She called it her Wandering Jew and would yell at the grandchildren in the middle of a formal dinner to fetch her tit as she had forgotten to put it on. She kept losing the contraption to servants who were mystified by it as well as to the dog, Chindit, who would be found gnawing at the foam as if it were tender chicken. She went through four breasts in her lifetime. One she left on a branch of a tree in Hakgalle Gardens to dry out after a rainstorm, one flew off when she was riding behind Vere on his motorbike, and the third she was very mysterious about, almost embarrassed though Lalla was never embarrassed. Most believed it had been forgotten after a romantic assignation in Trincomalee with a man who may or may not have been in the Cabinet.

*　　*　　*

Children tell little more than animals, said Kipling. When Lalla came to Bishop's College Girls School on Parents' Day and pissed behind bushes—or when in Nuwara Eliya she simply stood with her legs apart and urinated—my sisters were so embarrassed and ashamed they did not admit or speak of this to each other for over fifteen years. Lalla's son Noel was most appalled by her. She, however, was immensely proud of his success, and my Aunt Nedra recalls seeing Lalla sitting on a sack of rice in the fish market surrounded by workers and fishermen, with whom she was having one of her long daily chats, pointing to a picture of a bewigged judge in *The Daily News* and saying in Sinhalese that *this* was *her* son. But Lalla could never be just a mother; that seemed to be only one muscle in her chameleon nature, which had too many other things to reflect. And I am not sure what my mother's relationship was to her. Maybe they were too similar to even recognize much of a problem, both having huge compassionate hearts that never even considered revenge or small-mindedness, both howling and wheezing with laughter over the frailest joke, both carrying their own theatre on their backs. Lalla remained the centre of the world she moved through. She had been beautiful when young but most free after her husband died and her children grew up. There was some sense of divine right she felt she and everyone else had, even if she had to beg for it or steal it. This overbearing charmed flower.

*   *   *

In her last years she was searching for the great death. She never found, looking under leaves, the giant snake, the fang which would brush against the ankle like a whisper. A whole generation grew old or died around her. Prime Ministers fell off horses, a jellyfish slid down the throat of a famous swimmer. During the forties she moved with the rest of the country towards Independence and the 20th century. Her freedom accelerated. Her arms still flagged down strange cars for a lift to the Pettah market where she could trade gossip with her friends and place bets in the "bucket shops." She carried everything she really needed with her, and a friend meeting her once at a train station was appalled to be given as a gift a huge fish that Lalla had carried doubled up in her handbag.

She could be silent as a snake or flower. She loved the thunder; it spoke to her like a king. As if her mild dead husband had been transformed into a cosmic umpire, given the megaphone of nature. Sky noises and the abrupt light told her details of careers, incidental wisdom, allowing her to risk everything because the thunder would warn her along with the snake of lightning. She would stop the car and swim in the Mahaveli, serene among currents, still wearing her hat. Would step out of the river, dry in the sun for five minutes and climb back into the car among the shocked eyeballs of her companions, her huge handbag once more on her lap carrying four packs of cards, possibly a fish.

In August 1947, she received a small inheritance, called her brother Vere, and they drove off to Nuwara Eliya on his motorcycle. She was 68 years old. These were to be her last days. The boarding house she had looked after during the war was empty and so they bought food and booze and moved in to play "Ajoutha"—a card game that normally takes at least eight hours. It was a game the Portuguese had taught the Sinhalese in the 15th century to keep them quiet and preoccupied while they invaded the country. Lalla opened the bottles of Rocklands Gin (the same brand that was destroying her son-in-law) and Vere prepared the Italian menus, which he had learned from his prisoners of war. In her earlier days in Nuwara Eliya, Lalla would have been up at dawn to walk through the park—inhabited at that hour only by nuns and monkeys—walk round the golf-course where gardeners would stagger under the weight of giant python-like hoses as they watered the greens. But now she slept till noon, and in the early evening rode up to Moon Plains, her arms spread out like a crucifix behind Vere.

Moon Plains. Drowned in blue and gold flowers whose names she had never bothered to learn, tugged by the wind, leaning in angles for miles and miles against the hills 5000 feet above sea level. They watched the exit of the sun and the sudden appearance of the moon half way up the sky. Those lovely accidental moons —a horn a chalice a thumbnail—and then they would climb onto the motorcycle, the 60-year-old brother and the 68-year-old sister, who was his best friend forever.

Riding back on August 13, 1947, they heard the wild thunder and she knew someone was going to die. Death, however, not to be read out there. She gazed and listened but there seemed to be no victim or parabola end beyond her. It rained hard during the last mile to the house and they went indoors to drink for the rest of the evening. The next day the rains continued and she refused Vere's offer of a ride knowing there would be death soon. "Cannot wreck this perfect body, Vere. The police will spend hours searching for my breast thinking it was lost in the crash." So they played two-handed Ajoutha and drank. But now she could not sleep at all, and they talked as they never had about husbands, lovers, his various possible marriages. She did not mention her readings of the thunder to Vere, who was now almost comatose on the bluebird print sofa. But she could not keep her eyes closed like him and at 5 A.M. on August 15, 1947, she wanted fresh air, needed to walk, a walk to Moon Plains, no motorcycle, no danger, and she stepped out towards the still dark night of almost dawn and straight into the floods.

For two days and nights they had been oblivious to the amount of destruction outside their home. The whole country was mauled by the rains that year. Ratmalana, Bentota, Chilaw, Anuradhapura, were all under water. The forty-foot-high Peredeniya Bridge had been swept away. In Nuwara Eliya, Galways's Land Bird Sanctuary and the Golf Course were ten feet under water. Snakes and fish from the lake swam into the windows of the Golf Club, into the bar, and around the indoor badminton court. Fish were found captured in the badminton nets when the flood receded a week later. Lalla took one step off the front porch and was immediately hauled away by an arm of water, her handbag bursting open. 208 cards moved ahead of her like a disturbed nest as she was thrown downhill still comfortable and drunk, snagged for a few moments on the railings of the Good Shepherd Convent and then lifted away towards the town of Nuwara Eliya.

It was her last perfect journey. The new river in the street moved her right across the race course and park towards the bus station. As the light came up slowly she was being swirled fast, "floating" (as ever confident of surviving this too) alongside branches and leaves, the dawn starting to hit flamboyant trees as she slipped past them like a dark log, shoes lost, false breast lost. She was free as a fish, travelling faster than she had in years, fast as Vere's motorcycle, only now there was this *roar* around her. She overtook Jesus lizards that swam and ran in bursts over the water, she was surrounded by tired half-drowned fly-catchers screaming *tack tack tack tack,* frogmouths, nightjars forced to keep awake, brain-fever birds and their irritating ascending scales, snake eagles, scimitar-babblers, they rode the air around Lalla wishing to perch on her unable to alight on anything except what was moving.

What was moving was rushing flood. In the park she floated over the intricate fir tree hedges of the maze—which would always continue to terrify her grandchildren—its secret spread out naked as a skeleton for her. The symmetrical flower beds also began to receive the day's light and Lalla gazed down at them with wonder, moving as lazily as that long dark scarf which trailed off her neck brushing the branches and never catching. She would always wear silk, as she showed us, her grandchildren, would pull the scarf like a fluid through the ring removed from her finger, pulled sleepily through, as she moved now, awake to the new angle of her favourite trees, the Syzygium, the Araucaria Pine, over the now unnecessary iron gates of the park, and through the town of Nuwara Eliya itself and its shops and stalls where she had haggled for guavas, now six feet under water, windows smashed in by the weight of all this collected rain.

Drifting slower she tried to hold onto things. A bicycle hit her across the knees. She saw the dead body of a human. She began to see the drowned dogs of the town. Cattle. She saw men on roofs fighting with each other, looting, almost surprised by the quick dawn in the mountains revealing them, not even watching her magic ride, the alcohol still in her—serene and relaxed.

Below the main street of Nuwara Eliya the land drops suddenly and Lalla fell into deeper waters, past the houses of 'Cranleigh' and 'Ferncliff.' They were homes she knew well, where she had played and argued over cards. The water here was rougher and she went under for longer and longer moments coming up with a gasp and then pulled down like bait, pulled under by something not comfortable any more, and then there was the great blue ahead of her, like a sheaf of blue wheat, like a large eye that peered towards her, and she hit it and was dead.

THE
PRODIGAL

HARBOUR

I arrived in a plane but love the harbour. Dusk. And the turning on of electricity in ships, portholes of moon, the blue glide of a tug, the harbour road and its ship chandlers, soap makers, ice on bicycles, the hidden anonymous barber shops behind the pink dirt walls of Reclamation Street.

One frail memory dragged up out of the past—going to the harbour to say goodbye to a sister or mother, dusk. For years I loved the song, "Harbour lights," and later in my teens danced disgracefully with girls, humming "Sea of Heartbreak."

There is nothing wise about a harbour, but it is real life. It is as sincere as a Singapore cassette. Infinite waters cohabit with flotsam on this side of the breakwater and the luxury liners and Maldive fishing vessels steam out to erase calm sea. Who was I saying goodbye to? Automatically as I travel on the tug with my brother-in-law, a pilot in the harbour, I sing "the lights in the harbour don't shine for me . . ." but I love it here, skimming out into the night anonymous among the lazy commerce, my nieces dancing on the breakwater as they wait, the lovely swallowing of thick night air as it carves around my brain, blunt, cleaning itself with nothing but this anonymity, with the magic words. *Harbour. Lost ship. Chandler. Estuary.*

MONSOON
NOTEBOOK (ii)

The bars across the windows did not always work. When bats would invade the house at dusk, the beautiful long-haired girls would rush to the corner of rooms and hide their heads under dresses. The bats suddenly drifting like dark squadrons through the house—for never more than two minutes—arcing into the halls over the uncleared dining room table and out along the verandah where the parents would be sitting trying to capture the cricket scores on the BBC with a shortwave radio.

Wildlife stormed or crept into homes this way. The snake either entered through the bathroom drain for remnants of water or, finding the porch doors open, came in like a king and moved in a straight line through the living room, dining room, the kitchen and servant's quarters, and out the back, as if taking the most civilized short cut to another street in town. Others moved in permanently; birds nested above the fans, the silverfish slid into steamer trunks and photograph albums—eating their way through portraits and wedding pictures. What images of family life they consumed in their minute jaws and took into their bodies no thicker than the pages they ate.

And the animals also on the periphery of rooms and porches, their sounds forever in your ear. During our visit to the jungle, while we slept on the verandah at 3 A.M., night would be suddenly alive with disturbed peacocks. A casual movement from one of them roosting in the trees would waken them all and, so fussing, sounding like branches full of cats, they would weep weep loud into the night.

One evening I kept the tape recorder beside my bed and wakened by them once more out of a deep sleep automatically pressed the machine on to record them. Now, and here, Canadian February, I write this in the kitchen and play that section of cassette to hear not just peacocks but all the noises of the night behind them—inaudible then because they were always there like breath. In this silent room (with its own unheard hum of fridge, fluorescent light) there are these frogs loud as river, gruntings, the whistle of other birds brash and sleepy, but in that night so modest behind the peacocks they were unfocussed by the brain —nothing more than darkness, all those sweet loud younger brothers of the night.

HOW I WAS BATHED

We are having a formal dinner. String hoppers, meat curry, egg rulang papadams, potato curry. Alice's date chutney, seeni sambol, mallung and brinjals and iced water. All the dishes are on the table and a good part of the meal is spent passing them around to each other. It is my favourite meal—anything that has string hoppers and egg rulang I eat with a lascivious hunger. For dessert there is buffalo curd and jaggery sauce—a sweet honey made from the coconut, like maple syrup but with a smoky taste.

In this formal setting Gillian begins to describe to everyone present how I used to be bathed when I was five. She had heard the story in detail from Yasmine Gooneratne, who was a prefect with her at Bishop's College for Girls. I listen intently, making sure I get a good portion of the egg rulang.

The first school I went to was a girls' school in Colombo which accepted young boys of five or six for a couple of years.

The nurse or ayah in charge of our cleanliness was a small, muscular and vicious woman named Maratina. I roamed with my pack of school friends, usually filthy from morning to night, and every second evening we were given a bath. The bathroom was a sparse empty stone room with open drains in the floor and a tap to one side. We were marched in by Maratina and ordered to strip. She collected our clothes, threw them out of the room, and locked the door. The eight of us were herded terrified into one corner.

Maratina filled a bucket with water and flung the contents towards our cowering screaming bodies. Another bucket was filled and hurled towards us hard as a police hose. Then she strode forward, grabbed a child by the hair, pulled him over to the centre, scrubbed him violently with carbolic soap and threw him towards the opposite side of the room. She plucked another and repeated the soaping. Totally in control of the squirming bodies she eventually scrubbed us all, then returned to the bucket and thrashed water over our soapy nakedness. Bleary-eyed, our bodies tingling and reeling, our hair curved back from the force of the throw, we stood there shining. She approached with a towel, dried us fast and brutally, and threw us out one by one to get into our sarongs and go to bed.

The guests, the children, everyone is laughing and Gillian is no doubt exaggerating Yasmine's account in her usual style, her long arms miming the capture and scrub of five-year-olds. I am dreaming and wondering why this was never to be traumatically remembered. It is the kind of event that should have surfaced as the first chapter of an anguished autobiographical novel. I am thinking also of Yasmine Gooneratne, now teaching at a university in Australia, whom I met just last year at an International Writers' Conference in New Delhi. We talked then mostly about

Gillian who had also been at university with her. Why did *she* not tell me the story—this demure woman in a sari who was once "bath prefect" at Bishop's College Girl's School, who officiated over the cleansing of my lean five-year-old nakedness?

WILPATTU

April 8th

From Anuradhapura we drive towards the Wilpattu Jungle, through the small town of Nochiyagama. "That's it," I tell my daughter, "that'll be a good name for a child of yours." *Nochi*. Once we reach Wilpattu a tracker-guide is assigned to us. He will live with us during the next few days and be with us whenever we take treks out in the jeep to look for animals. We now have an hour's journey to the middle of the jungle. It is a slow ten-mile-an-hour drive on bad roads of red clay and sand.

5 P.M. Manikappolu Utu. A large wooden house on stilts, and fresh "elephant droppings" around the place, which turn out to be buffalo shit. We empty the jeep of all the food we have brought and begin to change out of sweat-soaked clothes. On the porch is a muted light and long cane chairs. A delicate rain begins

pattering on the tin roof then suddenly veers into a thunder shower which whitens the landscape. To the left of the house is a large pond, almost a lake, where water lilies float closed at this hour, now being pounded bouncing under the rain. The girls are out there in their dresses getting wet and suddenly the rest of us decide this is the only chance for a bath that we will have here and walk out into the storm. Nine of us holding up our arms for all the rain we can reach.

We are slightly drunk with this place—the beautiful house, the animals which are appearing now, and this tough cold rain turning the hard-baked earth into red mud. All of us are in our solitude. Not really concerned about the others, just revelling in a private pleasure. It is like communal sleep. The storm falters then starts up again, wilder than ever. The bungalow's cook and the tracker watch from the doorways of the house not quite believing what is happening to this strange mixture of people— Sinhalese, Canadian, and one quiet French girl—who are now soaping themselves with a bar of soap and throwing it around like a foaming elixir so everyone is suddenly white, as if in a petticoat, and now trying even harder to catch the rain everywhere, bending over to let it land on our backs and shoulders. Some move under the warmer rain of the trees, some sit as if it was Sunday afternoon on a bench by the pond of water lilies and crocodiles, and the others wade ankle-deep in swirling mud by the jeep. On the other side of the pond there are about thirty deer—as if in a dry universe. And storks on the bank whose reflections are being shattered.

Then a new burst of energy. A *val oora*—a large filthy black wild boar has appeared majestically out of the trees with tusks that turn his quiet face into hare-lipped deformity. He watches, making us aware of each other half-soaped, happy and ridiculous, dresses heavy with rain, sarongs above the knees. All of us—the lilies, the trees with their wind drunk hair, this magnificent val oora who is now the centre of the storm—celebrating the elimination of heat. He moves straight-thighed, stiff, but with a lunging walk, keeping his polite distance.

Wild black pig in a white rainstorm, concerned about this invasion, this metamorphosis of soap, this dented Volkswagen, this jeep. He can take his pick, any one of us. If I am to die soon I would choose to die now under his wet alphabet of tusk, while I am cool and clean and in good company.

*   *   *

April 11th

Last morning in Wilpattu. Everyone packing and arguing in the hushed early light. Where is the torch? My Leyden shirt? Whose towel is this? Last night, right off the porch, a leopard tracked and waited for a chance to pounce on one of the deer that stayed around the house. Our dinner was interrupted by screams from the deer, and we were soon all outside using the flashlights to pick out the red eye of the leopard, the green eyes of the deer and later the red eye of the crocodile who had come to watch. Everyone lasciviously waiting for a kill.

Once, when there was nobody staying in this bungalow except the cook, a leopard paced up and down the porch. This is the porch onto which we have moved all the beds and slept these last three nights, telling each other ghost stories and feeling absolutely secure in the jungle heat. At one of the other bungalows guests have to sleep behind closed doors, for a bear comes regularly each

244

night, climbs the stairs slowly as if exhausted, and sleeps on whatever free bed is available.

On this last morning I leave the others and go downstairs to find my soap which I left on a railing after one of our rain baths. It has rained every day from five thirty until six, hard perfect thunderstorms. No sign of the soap. I ask the cook and the tracker and they both give the same answer. The wild pig has taken it. *My* wild pig. That repulsively exotic creature in his thick black body and the ridge of non-symmetrical hair running down his back. This thing has walked off with my bar of Pears Transparent Soap? Why not my copy of Rumi poetry? Or Merwin translations? That soap was aristocratic and kept me feeling good all through the filthy hotels of Africa, whenever I could find a shower. The tracker and cook keep giving me evidence that it is the pig. He constantly removes things after taking a small bite, once even took a handbag. As the pig comes to the back door for garbage daily I am beginning to believe them. What does this wild pig want soap for? Visions begin to form of the creature returning to his friends with Pears Transparent Soap and then all of them bathing and scrubbing their armpits in the rain in a foul parody of us. I can see their mouths open to catch drops of water on their tongues, washing their hooves, standing complacently under the drain spout, and then moving in Pears fragrance to a dinner of Manikappolu garbage.

With me irritated at this loss we leave Wilpattu, the jeep following the Volkswagen. My eyes are peeled for a last sight of the oora, my soap caught in his tusk and his mouth foaming.

KUTTAPITIYA

The last estate we lived on as children was called Kuttapitiya and was famous for its gardens. Walls of flowers—ochre,
lavender, pink—would flourish and die within a month, followed by even more exaggerated and inbred colours. My father
was superintendent of a tea and rubber plantation and each morning at 5 A.M. a drummer began his slow rhythmic beat, an alarm
clock for all those who worked there. He played for half an hour
and slowly and lazily we rose into the pale blue mornings. At
breakfast we could watch the flamboyant tree and lavender-
cotton catch fire. House and garden were perched high above the
mist which filled the valley below like a mattress, cutting us off
from the real world. My mother and father lived there for the
longest period of their marriage.

Looking down off the edge of the garden we could see the road
to Pelmadulla wind and disappear like a lethargic dark yellow

snake into overhanging foliage. Everything seemed green below us. Where we stood, the muted purple leaves of orchid fell at the gentlest breeze onto someone's shadow. It was the perfect place for children who were allowed to go wild. My brother borrowing a pakispetti box, attaching wheels, and bumping down the steep slopes—a dangerous training for his future bobsledding. Having our hair cut on the front lawn by a travelling barber. And daily arguments over Monopoly, cricket, or marital issues that blazed and died on the privacy of this mountain.

And there was Lalla too, like a bee attracted to the perfume of any flower, who came up every other week solely to ransack the garden and who departed with a car full of sprigs and branches. With hardly any room to move or stretch, she rode back to Colombo, still as a corpse in a flower-packed hearse.

In his last years my father was a founding member of "The Ceylon Cactus and Succulent Society" and this interest began during his time in Kuttapitiya—all because of his devious and defensive nature. He loved ordered gardens and hated to see beds ravaged by Lalla's plundering. Gradually the vegetation at Kuttapitiya took on a prickly character. He began with roses, then Lalla wore gloves, and so he progressed to the cactus. The landscape turned grey around us. He welcomed the thorn bush, experimented with gnarled Japanese fig trees, retreated to pragmatic vegetables or spears of the succulent. His appreciation of growing things became more subtle, turned within a more limited spectrum and gradually Lalla's visits tapered away. Her journeys were in any case made solely for the effect of arriving at friends' houses in Colombo bearing soft rain-grown flowers.

This left the family alone once more. We had everything. It was and still is the most beautiful place in the world. We drove up, my family, Gillian's family, from the south coast, dusty, with headaches, tired, up a terrible stone broken road and stopped at the big bungalow. And my daughter turned to me on the edge of the lawn where I had my first haircuts and said, "If we lived here it would be perfect." "Yes," I said.

TRAVELS IN CEYLON

Ceylon falls on a map and its outline is the shape of a tear. After the spaces of India and Canada it is so small. A miniature. Drive ten miles and you are in a landscape so different that by rights it should belong to another country. From Galle in the south to Colombo a third of the way up the coast is only seventy miles. When houses were built along the coastal road it was said that a chicken could walk between the two cities without touching ground. The country is cross-hatched with maze-like routes whose only escape is the sea. From a ship or plane you can turn back or look down at the disorder. Villages spill onto streets, the jungle encroaches on village.

The Ceylon Road and Rail Map resembles a small garden full of darting red and black birds. In the middle of the 19th century, a 17-year-old English officer was ordered to organize the building of a road from Colombo to Kandy. Workers tore paths out of the sides of mountains and hacked through jungle, even drilled a huge hole through a rock on the hairpin bend of the Kadugannawa Pass. It was finished when the officer was thirty-six. There was a lot of this sort of casual obsession going on at that time.

My father, too, seemed fated to have an obsession with trains all his life. Rail trips became his nemesis. If one was to be blind drunk in the twenties and thirties, one somehow managed it on public transport, or on roads that would terrify a sober man with mountain passes, rock cuts, and precipices. Being an officer in the Ceylon Light Infantry, my father was allowed free train passes and became notorious on the Colombo-Trincomalee run.

He began quietly enough. In his twenties he pulled out his army pistol, terrified a fellow officer—John Kotelawala—under his seat, walked through the swaying carriages and threatened to kill the driver unless he stopped the train. The train halted ten miles out of Colombo at seven-thirty in the morning. He explained that he expected this trip to be a pleasant one and he wanted his good friend Arthur van Langenberg who had missed the train to enjoy it with him.

The passengers emptied out to wait on the tracks while a runner was sent back to Colombo to get Arthur. After a two-hour delay Arthur arrived, John Kotelawala came out from under his seat, everyone jumped back on, my father put his pistol away, and the train continued on to Trincomalee.

I think my father believed that he owned the railway by birthright. He wore the railway as if it was a public suit of clothes. Trains in Ceylon lack privacy entirely. There are no individual compartments, and most of the passengers spend their time walking through carriages, curious to see who else is on board. So people usually knew when Mervyn Ondaatje boarded the train, with or without his army revolver. (He tended to stop trains more often when in uniform.) If the trip coincided with his days of dipsomania the train could be delayed for hours. Messages would be telegraphed from one station to another to arrange for a relative to meet and remove him from the train. My uncle Noel was usually called. As he was in the Navy during the war, a naval jeep would roar towards Anuradhapura to pick up the major from the Ceylon Light Infantry.

When my father removed all his clothes and leapt from the train, rushing into the Kadugannawa tunnel, the Navy finally refused to follow and my mother was sent for. He stayed in the darkness of that three-quarter-mile-long tunnel for three hours stopping rail traffic going both ways. My mother, clutching a suit of civilian clothing (the Army would not allow her to advertise his military connections), walked into that darkness, finding him and talking with him for over an hour and a half. A moment only Conrad could have interpreted. She went in there alone, his clothes in one arm—but no shoes, an oversight he later complained of—and a railway lantern that he shattered as soon as she reached him. They had been married for six years.

They survived that darkness. And my mother, the lover of Tennyson and early Yeats, began to realize that she had caught onto a different breed of dog. She was to become tough and valiant in a very different world from then on, determined, when they divorced, never to ask him for money, and to raise us all on her own earnings. They were both from gracious, genteel families, but my father went down a path unknown to his parents and wife. She followed him and coped with him for fourteen years, surrounding his behaviour like a tough and demure breeze. Talking him out of suicide in a three-quarter-mile-long tunnel, for god's sake! She walked in armed with clothes she had borrowed from another passenger, and a light, and her knowledgeable love of all the beautiful formal poetry that existed up to the 1930s, to meet her naked husband in the darkness, in the black slow breeze of the Kadugannawa tunnel, unable to find him until he rushed at her, grabbed that lantern and dashed it against the wall before he realized who it was, who had come for him.

"It's me!"

Then a pause. And, "How *dare* you follow me!"

"I followed you because no one else would follow you."

If you look at my mother's handwriting from the thirties on, it has changed a good deal from her youth. It looks wild, drunk, the letters are much larger and billow over the pages, almost as if she had changed hands. Reading her letters we thought that the blue aerograms were written in ten seconds flat. But once my sister saw her writing and it was the most laboured process, her tongue twisting in her mouth. As if that scrawl was the result of great discipline, as if at the age of thirty or so she had been blasted, forgotten how to write, lost the use of a habitual style and forced herself to cope with a new dark unknown alphabet.

*   *   *

Resthouses are an old tradition in Ceylon. The roads are so dangerous that there is one every fifteen miles. You can drive in to relax, have a drink or lunch or get a room for the night. Between Colombo and Kandy people stop at the Kegalle resthouse; from Colombo to Hatton, they stop at the Kitulgala resthouse. This was my father's favourite.

It was on his travels by road that my father waged war with a certain Sammy Dias Bandaranaike, a close relative of the eventual Prime Minister of Ceylon who was assassinated by a Buddhist monk.

It is important to understand the tradition of the Visitors' Book. After a brief or long stay at a resthouse, one is expected to write one's comments. The Bandaranaike-Ondaatje feud began and was contained within the arena of such visitors' books. What happened was that Sammy Dias Bandaranaike and my father happened to visit the Kitulgala resthouse simultaneously. Sammy Dias, or so my side of the feud tells it, was a scrounger for complaints. While most people wrote two or three curt lines, he would have spent his whole visit checking every tap and shower to see what was wrong and would have plenty to say. On this occasion, Sammy left first, having written half a page in the Kitulgala resthouse visitors' book. He bitched at everything, from the service to the badly made drinks, to the poor rice, to the bad beds. Almost an epic. My father left two hours later and wrote two sentences, "No complaints. Not even about Mr. Bandaranaike." As most people read these comments, they were as public as a newspaper advertisement, and soon everyone including Sammy had heard about it. And everyone but Sammy was amused.

A few months later they both happened to hit the resthouse in Avissawella for lunch. They stayed there only an hour ignoring each other. Sammy left first, wrote a half-page attack on my father, and complimented the good food. My father wrote one and a half pages of vindictive prose about the Bandaranaike family, dropping hints of madness and incest. The next time they came together, Sammy Dias allowed my father to write first and, after he had left, put down all the gossip he knew about the Ondaatjes.

This literary war broke so many codes that for the first time in Ceylon history pages had to be ripped out of visitors' books. Eventually one would write about the other even when the other was nowhere near the resthouse. Pages continued to be torn out, ruining a good archival history of two semi-prominent Ceylon families. The war petered out when neither Sammy Dias nor my father was allowed to write their impressions of a stay or a meal. The standard comment on visitors' books today about "constructive criticism" dates from this period.

*   *   *

My father's last train ride (he was banned from the Ceylon Railways after 1943) was his most dramatic. The year I was born he was a major with the Ceylon Light Infantry and was stationed away from my mother in Trincomalee. There were fears of a Japanese attack and he became obsessed with a possible invasion. In charge of Transport he would wake up whole battalions and rush them to various points of the harbour or coastline, absolutely certain that the Japanese would not come by plane but by ship. Marble Beach, Coral Beach, Nilaveli, Elephant Point, Frenchman's Pass, all suddenly began to glow like firelies from army jeeps sent there at three in the morning. He began to drink a lot, moved onto a plateau of constant alcohol, and had to be hospitalized. Authorities decided to send him back to a military hospital in Colombo under the care of John Kotelawala, once more the unfortunate travelling companion. (Sir John Kotelawala, for he was eventually to become Prime Minister.) Somehow my father smuggled bottles of gin onto the train and even before they left Trinco he was raging. The train sped through tunnels, scrubland, careened around sharp bends, and my father's fury imitated it, its speed and shake and loudness, he blew in and out of carriages, heaving bottles out of the windows as he finished them, getting John Kotelawala's gun.

More drama was taking place off the train as his relatives tried to intercept it before he reached Colombo. For some reason it was crucial that he be taken to hospital by a member of the family rather than under military guard. His sister, my Aunt Stephy, drove to meet the train at Anuradhapura, not quite sure what his condition was but sure that she was his favourite sister. Unfortunately she arrived at the station in a white silk dress, a white feathered hat, and a long white pair of gloves—perhaps to impress John Kotelawala who was in charge of her brother and who was attracted to her. Her looks gathered such a crowd and caused such an uproar that she was surrounded and couldn't reach the carriage when the train slowed into the station. John Kotelawala glanced at her with wonder—this slight, demure, beautiful woman in white on the urine-soaked platform—while he struggled with her brother who had begun to take off his clothes.

"Mervyn!"

"Stephy!"

Shouted as they passed each other, the train pulling out, Stephy still being mobbed, and an empty bottle crashing onto the end of the platform like a last sentence.

John Kotelawala was knocked out by my father before he reached Galgamuwa. He never pressed charges. In any case my father took over the train.

He made it shunt back and forth ten miles one way, ten miles another, so that all trains, some full of troops, were grounded in the south unable to go anywhere. He managed to get the driver of the train drunk as well and was finishing a bottle of gin every hour walking up and down the carriages almost naked, but keeping his shoes on this time and hitting the state of inebriation during which he would start rattling off wonderful limericks—thus keeping the passengers amused.

But there was another problem to contend with. One whole carriage was given over to high-ranking British officers. They had retired early and, while the train witnessed small revolutions among the local military, everyone felt that the anarchic events should be kept from the sleeping foreigners. The English thought Ceylon trains were bad enough, and if they discovered that officers in the Ceylon Light Infantry were going berserk and upsetting schedules they might just leave the country in disgust. Therefore, if anyone wished to reach the other end of the train, they would climb onto the roof of the "English carriage" and tiptoe, silhouetted by the moon above them, to the next compartment. My father, too, whenever he needed to speak with the driver, climbed out into the night and strolled over the train, clutching a bottle and revolver and greeting passengers in hushed tones who were coming the other way. Fellow officers who were trying to subdue him would never have considered waking up the English. They slept on serenely with their rage for order in the tropics, while the train shunted and reversed into the night and there was chaos and hilarity in the parentheses around them.

Meanwhile, my Uncle Noel, fearful that my father would be charged, was waiting for the train at Kelaniya six miles out of Colombo, quite near where my father had stopped the train to wait for Arthur van Langenberg. So they knew him well there.

But the train kept shunting back and forth, never reaching Kela-niya, because at this point my father was absolutely certain the Japanese had mined the train with bombs, which would explode if they reached Colombo. Therefore, anyone who was without a military connection was put off the train at Polgahawela, and he cruised up and down the carriages breaking all the lights that would heat the bombs. He was saving the train and Colombo. While my Uncle Noel waited for over six hours at Kelaniya— the train coming into sight and then retreating once more to the north—my father and two officers under his control searched every piece of luggage. He alone found over twenty-five bombs and as he collected them the others became silent and no longer argued. There were now only fifteen people, save for the sleeping English, on the Trinco-Colombo train, which eventually, as night was ending and the gin ran out, drifted into Kelaniya. My father and the driver had consumed almost seven bottles since that morning.

My Uncle Noel put the bruised John Kotelawala in the back of the Navy jeep he had borrowed. And then my father said he couldn't leave the bombs on the train, they had to take them in the jeep and drop them into the river. He rushed back time and again into the train and brought out the pots of curd that passengers had been carrying. They were carefully loaded into the jeep alongside the prone body of the future Prime Minister. Before my Uncle drove to the hospital, he stopped at the Kelani-Colombo bridge and my father dropped all twenty-five pots into the river below, witnessing huge explosions as they smashed into the water.

SIR JOHN

Gillian and I drive south on the Galle Road, and just past Ratmalana Airport turn inland to the home of Sir John Kotelawala. The jeep dusty, covered in 3-in-1 Oil, moves through the long palatial driveway of red earth and into sudden greenery. A small man in white shirt and shorts, very thin legs, sits on the porch waiting for us. As we park he gets up slowly. We have been invited for breakfast with Sir John and it is 8:30 in the morning.

I have spoken to him on the phone but he seems to have forgotten why we are here, though he is expecting us at breakfast. Gillian and I give our names once more. Mervyn Ondaatje's children. You knew him in the Ceylon Light Infantry?

"Ahh!"

His diplomat's face is utterly shocked. "That one!" he says. "The fellow who got us into all that trouble!" and begins laughing. The last people in the world this millionaire and ex-Prime Minister probably expected to see were the children of Mervyn Ondaatje—the officer who got the D.T.'s in Trincomalee and took a notorious train ride to Colombo in 1943. This is probably the first time anyone has come not so much to see him, *the* Sir John Kotelawala, but because he happened to know for a few hectic months during the war a consistently drunk officer in the Ceylon Light Infantry.

After about ten minutes he still isn't over this bizarre motive for the visit. A servant brings him a cane basket full of fruit, and bread, and scones. Sir John says "come" and begins to stroll into the garden with the food under his arm. I gather we are to have breakfast under the trees. As we usually eat at seven in the morning, Gillian and I are both starving. He walks slowly towards a series of aquariums on the other side of the pool and driveway. "My fish from Australia," he says, and begins to feed them from the basket. I lift my head to see a peacock on the roof spreading his tail.

"Hell of a lot of trouble that one caused." What? "You know he jumped out of the train when it was going full speed . . . luckily we were passing a paddy field and he fell into it. When the train stopped he just climbed aboard again covered with mud." It is a Victorian dream. We are on the lawn, my sister Gillian, this frail and powerful man, and we are surrounded by four or five peacocks who are consuming my scones, leaning in jerks towards the basket he holds. And interspersed among the peacocks as if imitating them are sprinklers which throw off tails of white, keeping the birds company. Now it is time to feed the sambhur deer and jungle fowl.

In the next half hour we ease him back into the story three times and, his memory finally alive to the forties, he remembers more and more. All through his narrative he never calls my father by his name, christian or surname, just "this chap," or "that fellow." He is enjoying the story now. I've heard it from three or four other points of view and can remind him of certain bones —the pots of curd, etc.

"I was the commanding officer, you see. He had been drinking for months. Then one night at two in the morning he drives into the base in his jeep. He says the Japanese have invaded. He's found one. Well I didn't think so, but I climbed into the jeep and drove off with him. There was a man five yards out in the surf standing there like a statue. This fellow says, 'There he is.' He had found him two hours earlier coming ashore, halted him, fired his pistol into the water between the man's legs and said, stay there, stay right there, *do not move* till I get back, and jumped into the jeep and came to get us at the base. I put the jeep lights on him and we could see right away he was a Tamil. So then I knew.

"Next morning I took him with me to Colombo by train. He played hell on the way."

The sambhur has eaten all the bananas, so we go back in, join Sir John's doctor and the doctor's wife and sit down in an open dining room to the real breakfast.

Sir John's breakfasts are legendary, always hoppers and fish curry, mangoes and curd. A breeze blows magically under the table, a precise luxury, and I stretch my feet to its source as I tear apart the first hopper. My sandal is wrenched off and goes flying down under the length of the table, luckily not in the direction of Sir John. My foot tingling. While everyone else eats I lean back and look underneath and there is a small portable fan a few inches from my toes ready to tear into flesh this time. I could have lost a toe during one of these breakfasts searching for my father.

Sir John is talking about someone else now, delighting in some scandal about "one of the best liars we have." The open windows that come down to within six inches of the floor have no glass. A crow steps up as if to make an announcement, moves away and then the peacock climbs in and steps down to the light brown parquet floor. His feet give a slight click at each step. No one has seen this wonder, it seems, but me. Sir John reaches for a hopper, tears off the brittle edges of the dough, and taking the soft delicious centre, holds it out and the peacock he has not even looked at but hears, perhaps just senses, takes a final step forward, declines his neck and accepts the hopper walking away to a less busy part of the dining room, eating as he walks.

While we eat, an amateur theatre group from Colombo which is producing *Camelot* receives permission to be photographed on the grounds. The dream-like setting is now made more surreal by Sinhalese actors wearing thick velvet costumes, pointed hats, and chain mail in this terrible May heat. A group of black knights mime festive songs among the peacocks and fountains. Guinevere kisses Arthur beside the tank of Australian fish.

The photographers outside, the idea of *Camelot,* all remind Sir John of his political tribulations. For he claims that if anything lost him elections it was the grandness of the house and his parties —pictures of which appeared in the newspapers. He tells us of one of the most scandalous photographs organized by the Opposition. A demure young couple visited him along with a third friend who had a camera. They asked if he minded their taking some photographs and he gave them permission. The photographer took several pictures of the couple. Suddenly the man dropped to his knees, lifted up the woman's sari and started chewing away at her upper thigh. Sir John who was watching casually a few yards away rushed forward and asked what was happening. The man on his knees unburied his head and grinned at him saying, "snake bite, sir," and returned to the thigh of the woman.

A week later three photographs appeared in the newspapers of this blatantly sexual act with Sir John also in the picture chatting casually to the woman whose face was in the throes of ecstasy.

PHOTOGRAPH

My Aunt pulls out the album and there is the photograph I have been waiting for all my life. My father and mother together. May 1932.

They are on their honeymoon and the two of them, very soberly dressed, have walked into a photographic studio. The photographer is used to wedding pictures. He has probably seen every pose. My father sits facing the camera, my mother stands beside him and bends over so that her face is in profile on a level with his. Then they both begin to make hideous faces.

My father's pupils droop to the south-west corner of his sockets. His jaw falls and resettles into a groan that is half idiot, half shock. (All this emphasized by his dark suit and well-combed hair.) My mother in white has twisted her lovely features and stuck out her jaw and upper lip so that her profile is in the posture of a monkey. The print is made into a postcard and sent through the mails to various friends. On the back my father has written *"What we think of married life."*

Everything is there, of course. Their good looks behind the tortured faces, their mutual humour, and the fact that both of them are hams of a very superior sort. The evidence I wanted that they were absolutely perfect for each other. My father's tanned skin, my mother's milk paleness, and this theatre of their own making.

It is the only photograph I have found of the two of them together.

WHAT WE THINK
OF MARRIED LIFE

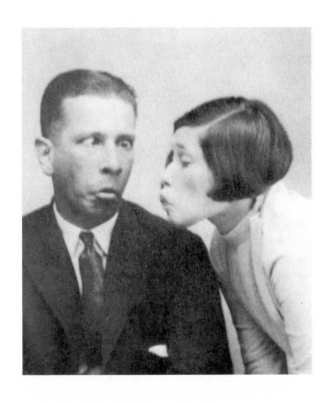

TEA COUNTRY

"The thing about Mum was —she was a terrifically social person. And he came down to Colombo and swooped her up and took her to the tea estate. OK. They were in love, happy with each other, they had kids. But later there was nothing for her to do there."

Tea country. The sleepy green landscape that held her captive. And now, 40 years later, in early May, on the verge of monsoon weather, I have come here to visit my half-sister Susan and her husband Sunil. The green pattern of landscape and life-style almost unchanged.

The one hundred mile drive from Colombo took us five hours. The gearshift was giving trouble, the horn was fading, and the engine heated up so fast we had to stop every twenty minutes to cool off and refill the radiator. We came along a road that climbed five thousand feet in thirty miles. Eventually the transmission broke in second gear, and the last miles were driven praying we wouldn't have to stop, not for oncoming trucks and buses, not for the numerous May Day parades along the mountain roads. The car stalled a mile away from the house and we walked under the thunder clouds that made the dark tea bushes brighter, through the lines of pluckers, Sunil carrying his Colombo whiskey and Susan and I some bags of food.

In a wet shirt and with a headache it was good to walk. Twenty degrees cooler up here than in Colombo. And a sourceless light that seems to brighten the landscape from underneath, as if yellow flowers in the garden are leaking into wet air. Dampness hangs over the house, while three of us and one servant rattle around this huge long bungalow from which all furniture has been sent to be upholstered save for a few cane chairs, and where the loudest noise is the excited breathing of two dogs.

An hour later I am standing in the hall with Susan when I hear a pistol shot. Blue waves of flame. The house—hit by lightning, hit at the fuse-box on the wall just above my head. I am so shaken I act calmly for the rest of the afternoon. Lightning has never touched this house before even though, perched on top of a tea estate, it seems an obvious target. The bolt is a signal for the end of quietness and the weather bursts open windows and steps into hallways. During the long evening we play scrabble, shouting out scores, almost unable to be heard over the stereophonic field of the rain.

*　　*　　*

We wake to a silence. Now the long quiet mornings. Susan moves up and down halls to the kitchens, organizing meals, reorganizing after the chaos of the first monsoon storm (burned out fuse-boxes, knocked down telephone wires, chicken wires, dismantled gardens).

The dining room doors open to the wet lawn and the francisco bushes. Their blossoms, like torn blue and white paper, release perfume into this room. When the dogs bark, eight or so parakeets swerve out of the guava tree and disappear over the cliff of the hill. Across the valley, a waterfall stumbles down. In a month or two the really hard rains will come for eighteen hours a day and that waterfall will once again become tough as a glacier and wash away the road. But now it looks as delicate as the path of a white butterfly in a long-exposed photograph.

I can leave this table, walk ten yards out of the house, and be surrounded by versions of green. The most regal green being the tea bush which is regal also in its symmetrical efficient planting. Such precision would be jungle in five years if left alone. In the distance the tea pickers move, in another silence, like an army. The roads weave and whorl away—bright yellow under the grey sky. The sun, invisible, struggles up somewhere. This is the colour of landscape, this is the silence, that surrounded my parents' marriage.

"WHAT WE THINK
OF MARRIED LIFE"

She is very gentle, Susan, my half-sister. Almost utterly humble. So sitting here with Susan and Sunil I find myself surprised they are younger than me. She has this calmness and quietness as opposed to the anger and argument which I see in myself, my brother, and two sisters.

I have been thinking that if she has Ondaatje blood and no Gratiaen blood then obviously it is from my mother's side that we got a sense of the dramatic, the tall stories, the determination to now and then hold the floor. The ham in us. While from my father, in spite of his temporary manic public behaviour, we got our sense of secrecy, the desire to be reclusive.

My father loved books and so did my mother, but my father swallowed the heart of books and kept that knowledge and emotion to himself. My mother read her favourite poems out loud, would make us read plays together and acted herself, even running a small dance and theatre school that people still remember in Colombo. Her reading out loud demanded the whole room, and while young her grace and dancing caught everyone's attention. Later it was her voice, her stories with that husky wheezing laugh that almost drowned out the punch lines. She belonged to a type of Ceylonese family whose women would take the minutest reaction from another and blow it up into a tremendously exciting tale, then later use it as an example of someone's strain of character. If anything kept their generation alive it was this recording by exaggeration. Ordinary tennis matches would be mythologized to the extent that one player was so drunk that he almost died on the court. An individual would be eternally remembered for one small act that in five years had become so magnified he was just a footnote below it. The silence of the tea estates and no doubt my mother's sense of theatre and romance (fed by vociferous readings of J. M. Barrie and Michael Arlen) combined the edited delicacies of fiction with the last era of a colonial Ceylon.

My father's actions were minimal and more private. Although he tormented his own father's rules of decorum he simultaneously and almost secretly valued the elements of honour and gentleness. He reportedly couldn't stand his mother-in-law, Lalla, for what he saw as her crudeness, although the stories about my father are closer in style to those about Lalla than anyone else. While we used to love rushing around the house and estate at Lalla's insistence to catch the dog Chindit, who had run off with her false breast, my father would retire to a book or his office acutely embarrassed. Either that, or, and of this we were never sure, he would secretly train the dog to torment his mother-in-law by such acts. We know he encouraged Chindit to fart whenever possible in her vicinity and by raising his eyebrows would surreptitiously make us feel it was she who made us recoil to the other end of the room.

My father's dramatic nature pleased only himself and sometimes the four of us. Or he would tell a hilarious joke in everyone's presence that would convulse just my mother and himself.

My mother loved, *always* loved, even in her last years long after their divorce, his secretive and slightly crooked humour. It bound them together probably more than anything. They were in a world to themselves, genial with everyone but sharing a code of humour. And if there was to be drama in their lives my father preferred it to be just between the two of them. My mother on the other hand would somehow select the one action that would be remembered by everyone in the vicinity of the tea estate and would reach Colombo in twenty-four hours. On one of the last occasions that my mother left my father, after the tirade that was brief, loud, alcoholically one-sided, she told him she was leaving him at 11:00 P.M. She bundled us all up and, after my father grabbed the car key and threw it into the darkness of a hundred tea bushes, she got four servants and with each of us on a pair of shoulders, marched off through tea estate and dense jungle in utter darkness to a neighbouring home five miles away.

It was she who instilled theatre in all of us. She was determined that we would each be as good an actor as she was. Whenever my father would lapse into one of his alcoholic states, she would send the three older children (I would be asleep—too young, and oblivious) into my father's room where by now he could hardly talk let alone argue. The three of them, well coached, would perform with tears streaming, "Daddy, don't drink, daddy, if you love us, don't drink," while my mother waited outside and listened. My father, I hope, too far gone to know the extent of the wars against him. These moments embarrassed my older brother and sister terribly; for days after they felt guilty and miserable. Gillian, the youngest of the three, threw herself with eagerness into these one-act plays and when they returned to the living room my mother would pat her on the back and say, "Well done Gillian—you were by *far* the best."

Her motive was to cure my father of manic alcoholic consumption. Those were moments of total war as far as she was concerned. During all the months of soberness the two of them were equals, very close and full of humour, but in his moments of darkness she drew on every play she had been in or had read and used it as a weapon, knowing that when my father sobered up this essentially shy man would be appalled to hear how my mother had over-reacted. Her behaviour in his drunken moments was there to shock him in his times of gentleness when he loved muted behaviour. Whatever plays my mother acted in publicly were not a patch on the real-life drama she directed and starred in during her married life. If Mervyn was to humiliate her she could embarrass him by retaliating with some grand gesture—whether it was a celebrated walk through the jungle or actually holding her breath until she fainted at the Kitulgala resthouse when she saw him beginning to drink too much, so that he had to stop and drive her home.

His victories came when he was sober. Then he would discover some outrageous thing she had done and begin to mend fences. Within a week, by his charm and wit, he would have made my mother's behaviour more ludicrous than his—a bomb to disturb a butterfly, till he seemed the more sane of the two. In this way an incident, which most had felt could never be surmounted and which no doubt would destroy the marriage, was cemented over. Rather than being jealous, my mother was never happier and for the next six months or so they were delightful company, wonderful parents. And then with the first drink, after which he could almost never stop, the wars would begin again.

Finally, when it all came to an end, she played her last scene with him. She arrived at the divorce court in a stunning white dress and hat (she had never worn a hat in her life before) and calmly asked for a divorce, demanding no alimony—nothing for her and nothing for the children. She got a job at The Grand Oriental Hotel, trained herself as a housekeeper-manager and supported us through schools by working in hotels in Ceylon and then England till she died. The easy life of the tea estate and the theatrical wars were over. They had come a long way in fourteen years from being the products of two of the best known and wealthiest families in Ceylon: my father now owning only a chicken farm at Rock Hill, my mother working in a hotel.

Before my mother left for England in 1949 she went to a fortune-teller who predicted that while she would continue to see each of her children often for the rest of her life, she would never see them all together again. This turned out to be true. Gillian stayed in Ceylon with me, Christopher and Janet went to England. I went to England, Christopher went to Canada, Gillian came to England, Janet went to America, Gillian returned to Ceylon, Janet returned to England, I went to Canada. Magnetic fields would go crazy in the presence of more than three Ondaatjes. And my father. Always separate until he died, away from us. The north pole.

DIALOGUES

(i)

"Once he nearly killed us. Not you. But the three older children. He was driving the Ford and he was drunk and taking the corners with great swerves— and you know those up-country roads. We began by cheering but soon we were terrified. Yelling at him to stop. Finally on one corner he almost went off the cliff. Two wheels had gone over the edge and the car hung there caught on the axle. Below us was a terrific plunge down the mountainside. We were in the back seat and once we calmed down, we looked in the front seat and saw that Daddy was asleep. He had passed out. But to us he was asleep and that seemed much worse. *Much* too casual.

As he had been driving he was on the right hand side—the side which was about to tilt over, so we all scrambled to the left.

But if we climbed into the front seat and got out then he would have gone over by himself. We didn't know what to do. We had passed some tea pluckers a few hundred yards back and the only hope was that they might be able to lift the car back onto the road. We decided the lightest one should go but Janet and Gillian got into a fight as to who was the lightest. They were both sensitive about their weight at the time. Finally Gillian went off and Janet and I tried to pull him towards the passenger seat.

When he wakened the car had already been lifted and moved to the centre of the road. He felt better, he said, started the car up and told us to hop in. But none of us would get into the car again."

(ii)

"I remember when Daddy lost his job. He had just been sacked and he was drinking. Mummy was in the front seat with him, you and I were in the back. And for the whole trip he kept saying "I'm ruined. I've ruined all of you. All of you." And he would weep. It was a terrible trip. And Mum kept comforting him and saying she would never leave him, she would never leave him. Do you remember that . . . ?"

(iii)

"When I left for England, god that was a terrible day for Mum. We were all at Kuttapitiya and she drove me down to Colombo. Left early in the morning. She had to move fast. He was drinking such a lot then and she couldn't leave him for too long. So when we boarded the ship, *The Queen of Bermuda,* that was about the time he was waking up and she had to get back before he got into trouble. She knew he had already begun his drinking as she said goodbye to me."

(iv)

"Remember all the pillows he had to sleep with? Remember how he used to make us massage his legs? Each of us had to do it for ten minutes. . . ."

(v)

"To us he was an utterly charming man, always gracious. When you spoke to him you knew you were speaking to the *real* Mervyn. He was always so open and loved those he visited. But none of us knew what he was like when he was drunk. So when your mother spoke of the reasons for the break-up it was a complete surprise. Oh I did see him drunk once and he was a bloody nuisance, but only once.

Anyway she told us things were rough. Their servant, Gopal, would not obey her and would continue to buy your father bottles. So we suggested the two of them go up to "Ferncliff" in Nuwara Eliya. They stayed there a week but that didn't work out and they returned to Kegalle. He had lost his job by then, so they were at home most of the time. Then your mother got typhoid. Para-typhoid, not the most serious kind, but she had it —and he wouldn't believe her. She said he hit her to make her get out of bed. Somehow she convinced Gopal how serious it was, and while he always obeyed your father he went into town and phoned us. We drove her down to Colombo and put her in Spittel's Nursing Home.

She never went back to him. When she was released she went and lived with Noel and Zillah at Horton Place.

Anyway, a few years later we decided to work on the lawn at "Ferncliff" which was turning brown. So we arranged to have some turf delivered from the Golf Club. And when we started digging we found about thirty bottles of Rocklands Gin buried in that front lawn by your father. . . ."

(vi)

"I don't know when this happened or how old I was. I was lying on a bed. It was night. The room was being thrown around and they were shouting. Like giants."

(vii)

"After leaving him she worked at the Mount Lavinia Hotel and then the Grand Oriental Hotel, that's called the Taprobane now. Then in the fifties she moved to England. She had a rough time during those early years in England, working at that boarding house in Lancaster Gate. She had one small room with just a gas ring. Noel's daughter, Wendy, was boarded at a private school at the time and she was wonderful. Every weekend she'd tell all her Cheltenham friends "Now we must go and visit Aunt Doris," and she'd drag these posh English school girls, about 6 or 7 of them, and they'd crowd into that small bed-sitter and cook crumpets over the gas ring."

(viii)

"I had some friends who played tennis. My best friends in London. And they were invited to Ceylon for a tournament. They were there for two weeks. When they came back to England I didn't contact them. Never answered their calls. You see I thought they would have found out what a disgraceful family I had come from. Mummy had drummed this story into us about what we had all been through there. I had this image that the Ondaatjes were absolute pariahs. I was twenty-five years old then. When I went back five years later to Ceylon to see Gillian I was still nervous and was totally surprised that everyone remembered him and all of us with such delight and love. . . ."

(ix)

"In the end he used to come to Colombo every two weeks to bring me eggs and fertilizer for my garden. He was subdued then, no longer the irrepressible Mervyn we used to know, very kind and quiet. He was happy just to sit here and listen to me gab away. . . . I never met his second wife, Maureen, until the day of his funeral."

(x)

"You know what I remember best is how sad his face was. I would be doing something and suddenly look up and catch his face naked. And full of sorrow. I don't know. Long after the divorce I wrote to him. I'd just been to my first dance and I complained about all the soppy songs the boys sang to us, especially one they played constantly, which went "Kiss me once and kiss me twice and kiss me once again. . . it's been a *long long* time," and he wrote back saying he just wished he could kiss us all once again.

. . . The sections you sent me made me very sad, remembering him and all those times. Of course I was always the serious one among us, with no sense of humour. I showed what you had written to someone and they laughed and said what a wonderful childhood we must have had, and I said it was a nightmare."

(xi)

"When I used to meet him years later he was always a fund of wonderful stories, never dirty, never mocked a woman. Anyway, one day I ran into him in the Fort and that night your mother, who was visiting Ceylon at the time, came to dinner. So, playing the devil's advocate, I told her who I had seen that morning and I said, *you* should see him. I remember she was very silent and looked down at her empty plate and around the room, somewhat surprised, and said, 'Why should I have to see him?' And I don't know why but I kept pushing it and then gradually she began to be interested. I think she almost gave in. I said I could easily reach him by phone, he could come over and join us. They were both in their sixties then, hadn't seen each other even once since the divorce. For old time's sake, Doris, I said, just to see each other. Then my wife thought I was being too cocky and made me change the subject and suggested we eat, that dinner was ready. But I know she was nearly persuaded to, I could tell that more than anything else. It was so close. . . ."

BLIND FAITH

During certain hours, at certain years in our lives, we see ourselves as remnants from the earlier generations that were destroyed. So our job becomes to keep peace with enemy camps, eliminate the chaos at the end of Jacobean tragedies, and with "the mercy of distance" write the histories.

Fortinbras. Edgar. Christopher, my sisters, Wendy, myself. I think all of our lives have been terribly shaped by what went on before us. And why of Shakespeare's cast of characters do I remain most curious about Edgar? Who if I look deeper into the metaphor, torments his father over an imaginary cliff.

Words such as *love, passion, duty,* are so continually used they grow to have no meaning—except as coins or weapons. Hard language softens. I never knew what my father felt of these "things." My loss was that I never spoke to him as an adult. Was he locked in the ceremony of being "a father"? He died before I even thought of such things.

I long for the moment in the play where Edgar reveals himself to Gloucester and it never happens. Look I am the son who has grown up. I am the son you have made hazardous, who still loves you. I am now part of an adult's ceremony, but I want to say I am writing this book about you at a time when I am least sure about such words. . . . Give me your arm. Let go my hand. Give me your arm. Give the word. "Sweet Marjoram" . . . a tender herb.

THE BONE

There is a story about my father I cannot come to terms with. It is one of the versions of his train escapade. In this one he had escaped from the train and run off naked into the jungle. ("Your father had a runaway complex," someone has already told me.) His friend Arthur was called to find him and persuade him back. When Arthur eventually tracked him down this is what he saw.

My father is walking towards him, huge and naked. In one hand he holds five ropes, and dangling on the end of each of them is a black dog. None of the five are touching the ground. He is holding his arm outstretched, holding them with one arm as if he has supernatural strength. Terrible noises are coming from him and from the dogs as if there is a conversation between them that is subterranean, volcanic. All their tongues hanging out.

They were probably stray dogs which my father had stumbled

on in jungle villages, he had perhaps picked them up as he walked along. He was a man who loved dogs. But this scene had no humour or gentleness in it. The dogs were too powerful to be in danger of being strangled. The danger was to the naked man who held them at arm's length, towards whom they swung like large dark magnets. He did not recognize Arthur, he would not let go of the ropes. He had captured all the evil in the regions he had passed through and was holding it.

Arthur cut the ropes and the animals splashed to the ground, writhing free and escaping. He guided my father back to the road and the car that his sister Stephy waited in. They put him in the back seat, his arm still held away from him, now out of the open car window. All the way to Colombo the lengths of rope dangled from his fist in the hot passing air.

THE CEYLON CACTUS
AND SUCCULENT SOCIETY

"THANIKAMA"

After the morning's drive to Colombo, after the meeting with Doris—tense, speaking in whispers in the hotel lobby—he would force himself to sit on the terrace overlooking the sea. Would sit in the sunlight drinking beers, which he ordered ice-cold, and finishing them before the sweat even evaporated from the surface of the bottle. Poured out the glasses of Nuwara Eliya beer. He sat there all afternoon, hoping she would notice him and come down to speak with him properly, truthfully. He wanted his wife to stop this *posing* at her work. Had to speak with her. He could hardly remember where the children were now. Two in school in England, one in Kegalle, one in Colombo . . . .

Till 5 o'clock, he sat out on the blue terrace with the blaze of sun on him—determined to be somewhere where they could be alone if she changed her mind and came down to him—not with the other guests and drinkers in the cool shadows of the lobby of the Mount Lavinia Hotel. He recalled everyone. Their crowd. Noel, Trevor, Francis who was dead now, Dorothy who ran riot. All burghers and Sinhalese families, separate from the Europeans. The memory of his friends was with him in the sun. He poured them out of the bottles into his glass tankard and drank. He remembered Harold Tooby from his schooldays and his years at Cambridge where the code was "you can always get away with more than you think you can get away with. . . . " Till Lionel Wendt accidentally told his father of the deception. Lionel always guilty over this, who gave him and Doris a painting by George Keyt for their wedding. He still had that in any case, and the wooden statue of a woman he had picked up at an auction which everyone else hated. Objects had stayed and people disappeared.

At five he got into the white Ford. She had not come down to him. And he drove to F. X. Pereira in the Ridgeway Building and bought cases of beer and gin to take back to Kegalle. Then he parked near the Galle Face Hotel, old haunt, and crossed the street to the bar where journalists and others from Lake House sat and talked politics, talked rubbish, talked about sport, which he was not at all interested in now. Did not mention Doris. Drank and laughed and listened, till eleven at night at which time they all went home to their wives. He walked down Galle Road and ate a meal at a Muslim restaurant, sitting alone in one of the frail wooden booths, the food so hot it would sear back the drunkenness and sleepiness, and then got into his car. This was 1947.

He drove along Galle Face Green where the Japanese had eventually attacked, by plane, and disappeared into the Fort whose streets were dark and quiet and empty. He loved the Fort at this hour, these Colombo nights, the windows of his car open and the breeze for the first time almost cool, no longer tepid, hitting his face with all the night smells, the perfume of closed boutiques. An animal crossed the road and he braked to a halt and watched it, strolling at its own speed for it was midnight and if a car would actually stop it could be trusted. This animal paused when it reached the pavement and looked back at the man in the white car—who still had not moved on. They gazed at each other and then the creature ran up the steps of the white building and into the post office which stayed open all night.

He thought, I could sleep here too. I could leave the car in the centre of Queen's Road and go in. Other cars would weave around the Ford. It would disturb no one for four or five hours. Nothing would change. He lifted his foot off the clutch, pressed the accelerator and moved on through the Fort towards Mutwal, passed the church of his ancestors—all priests and doctors and translators—which looked down on him through a row of plantain trees, looked down onto the ships in the harbour docked like enormous sinking jewels. He drove out of Colombo.

An hour later he could have stopped at the Ambepussa resthouse but continued on, the day's alcohol still in him though he had already stopped twice on the side of the road, urinated into darkness and mysterious foliage. Halted briefly at Warakapola where the dark villages held the future and gave a Tamil a lift, the man striking up a conversation about stars, and he, proud of that mutual ancestry, discussing Orion with him. The man was a cinnamon peeler and the smell filled the car, he did not want to stop, wanted to take him all the way past the spice gardens to Kegalle rather than letting him out a mile up the road. He drove on, the cinnamon blown out already by new smells from the night, drove dangerously, he couldn't quite remember if he was driving dangerously or not, just aware of the night breezes, the fall-out from spice gardens he skirted as if driving past vast kitchens. One of the lamps of his car was dead so he knew he was approaching stray walkers disguised as a motorcycle. He weaved up the Nelundeniya U-turns, then into the town of Kegalle. Over the bridge into Rock Hill.

For about ten minutes he sat in front of the house now fully aware that the car was empty but for his body, this corpse. Leaving the car door open like a white broken wing on the lawn, he moved towards the porch, a case of liquor under his arm. *Moonless.* The absence of even an edge of the moon. Into the bedroom, the bottle top already unscrewed. Tooby, Tooby, you should see your school friend now. The bottle top in my mouth as I sit on the bed like a lost ship on a white sea. And they sat years ago on deck-chairs, young, going to England. In the absurd English clothes they surprised each other with. And then during the heart of the marriage sailed to Australia serene over the dark mountains in the sea, the bed of the ocean like a dragon's back, ridges and troughs and the darkest eye of the Diamantina crater. This too was part of the universe, a feature of the earth. Kissed in the botanical gardens of Perth, took the Overland train east across the country just so they could say they had seen the Pacific. His Colombo suit fell off him now to the floor, onto its own pool of white and he got into bed. Thinking. What was he thinking about? More and more he watched himself do nothing, with nothing. At moments like this.

He saw himself with the bottle. Where was his book. He had lost it. What was the book. It was not Shakespeare, not those plays of love he wept over too easily. With dark blue bindings. You creaked them open and stepped into a roomful of sorrow. A mid-summer dream. All of them had moved at times with an ass's head, Titania Dorothy Hilden Lysander de Saram, a mongrel collection part Sinhalese part Dutch part Tamil part ass moving slowly in the forests with foolish and serious obsessions. No, he looked around the bare room, don't talk to me about Shakespeare, about "green hats."

The bottle was half empty beside him. He arose and lit the kerosene lamp. He wanted to look at his face, though the mirror was stained as if brown water and rust hung captive in the glass. He stepped towards the bathroom, the yellow pendulum of lamp beside his knees. With each swing he witnessed the state of the room and corridor. A glimpse of cobwebs quickly aging, undusted glass. No sweeper for weeks. And nature advanced. Tea bush became jungle, branches put their arms into the windows. If you stood still you were invaded. Wealth that was static quickly rotted. The paper money in your pocket, wet from your own sweat, gathered mould.

In the bathroom ants had attacked the novel thrown on the floor by the commode. A whole battalion was carrying one page away from its source, carrying the intimate print as if rolling a tablet away from him. He knelt down on the red tile, slowly, not wishing to disturb their work. It was page *189*. He had not got that far in the book yet but he surrendered it to them. He sat down forgetting the mirror he had been moving towards. Scared of the company of the mirror. He sat down with his back against the wall and waited. The white rectangle moved with the busy arduous ants. Duty, he thought. But that was just a fragment gazed at by the bottom of his eye. He drank. There. He saw the midnight rat.

MONSOON NOTEBOOK (iii)

A school exercise book. I write this at the desk of calamander looking out of the windows into dry black night. "Thanikama." "Aloneness." Birdless. The sound of an animal passing through the garden. Midnight and noon and dawn and dusk are the hours of danger, susceptibility to the "grahayas"—planetary spirits of malignant character. Avoid eating certain foods in lonely places, the devils will smell you out. Carry some metal. An iron heart. Do not step on bone or hair or human ash.

Sweat down my back. The fan pauses then begins again. At midnight this hand is the only thing moving. As discreetly and carefully as whatever animals in the garden fold brown leaves into their mouths, visit the drain for water, or scale the broken glass that crowns the walls. Watch the hand move. Waiting for it to say something, to stumble casually on perception, the shape of an unknown thing.

The garden a few feet away is suddenly under the fist of a downpour. Within half a second an easy dry night is filled with the noise of rain on tin, cement and earth—waking others slowly in the house. But I actually saw it, looking out into the blackness, saw the white downpour (reflected off the room's light) falling like an object past the window. And now the dust that has been there for months is bounced off the earth and pours, the smell of it, into the room. I get up, walk to the night, and breathe it in —the dust, the tactile smell of wetness, oxygen now being pounded into the ground so it is difficult to breathe.

FINAL DAYS
FATHER TONGUE

Jennifer:

The poultry farm was very big then. He had thousands of chickens. He had dual-purpose breeds—those that laid eggs but could also be eaten. The Light Sussex, the Rhode Island Reds, the Plymouth Rocks. And he was also the Visiting Agent for the region, inspecting estates and writing up reports on how they were run . . . I think he was one of the first Ceylonese to become a V.A. But the chickens took up most of his time. I designed a poster for the poultry farm and he got them printed up grandly. And we would dream up these advertisements together for the newspapers. Many were not allowed by the *Daily News* such as "Rock Hill Farms Will Teach your Grandmother to Suck Eggs!" He kept us all busy. I did the correspondence and Susan collected the eggs. It would have been easy to be cut off at Kegalle but he built a world for us there

—all those books and radio programmes. We would listen to "20 Questions"—my god we heard that every week and he loved it and I hated it.

During the day he would invent jobs for which he would pay us. Now and then he would announce "Beetle Week." We had to catch black coconut beetles, which he then fed to his fowls. Ten cents for the large ones, five cents for the small ones, and we would spend hours sorting them out and deciding if they were large or small. The whole day would be organized like this, with these games. For instance, *cats*. He loved most animals but was aloof from cats. However they always followed him. So if he went into town we would take bets on how many cats would come up to him. And although he disliked them I think he was quite proud of this trait in himself. Cats would cross the street if they saw him coming. When we got into the car he would have to get in first and we would then have to start throwing them out, have to stop them crawling back under his seat.

He loved our gullibility, our innocence, and his tricks on us would last for years. When he picked Suzie and me up from boarding school for a day he would take us to Elephant House and order cakes and cream buns and Lanka Colas. He had at one time said, "the more you eat the less I'll have to pay," and we believed him and for *his* sake ate as much as we could. It was only when Maureen came with him once and was appalled by our greed that we discovered the truth and we were almost slapped for our stupidity.

He could make children behave because he kept them interested. You, apparently, were a saint when Daddy was around but if he left the house you were hell. He missed you all terribly, he longed for you, but with us—his second family—he was just as loving. I wasn't his real daughter but I was probably closest to him in his last years. He brought me up like a princess and would defend me against everyone, even my strictest teachers. There was a Miss Kaula—a battleaxe. She was charmed by Daddy. She preened herself before he arrived and allowed him to upset all the visiting hours. He was amazingly protective. He would never let me stay with friends over the weekend, they would have to come and stay with us. And if there wasn't enough food to go around he would announce these signals such as "F.H.B.", which meant "Family Hold Back." We loved all those codes. The only time I saw him totally lost was when I begged him to take me to a movie. It was a "twist" movie. Joey D. and the Starlighters in *Peppermint Twist*. He was horrified by it. It was the future.

He could always laugh at himself. He was so big in the end, so large. He donated 313 rupees to the Rotary Club and when he was asked why it was that amount, he said because that was his weight. I think it was a glandular problem but he just didn't bother about it. When he took us for our first dance, it surprised me how light he was on his feet. He remembered all those waltzes and foxtrots from a long time ago. As we danced I saw our reflection in a mirror and he smiled and said, "Now you look like my tie." I was sixteen and tiny beside him. At my seventeenth birthday party we had to water the gin.

When he began drinking I would just get lost, that was easy to do at Rock Hill. He'd be insensible; and then, when he was getting better, he was like an angel and would do anything for you. . . . There was a song he used to sing when he was drunk, over and over. He had made it up and he sang it only when he was really drunk. Partly English and partly Sinhalese, a bit like a baila as it used brand names and street names and gibberish. It made no sense to anyone but it wasn't gibberish to him because he always sang exactly the same words each time.

His last days were very quiet. He would allow himself one cigarette a day. After dinner he would go out onto the verandah and sit for about an hour by himself or with me before his radio programmes came on. He would have his cigarette then. If I wanted permission to do something such as go for a dance I would ask him then, for at that moment he was most content with things. I remember there was quite a ceremony of course. I would bring him the round tin of cigarettes and the matches and he would light one and smoke it slowly. That would be around 8 o'clock in the evening.

*   *   *

V. C. de Silva:

He was brilliant at selling chickens. I don't know how he did it, but he would put on this official air and that helped. If I could get 15 rupees for a pullet, he would get 27.50. But there was a certain amount of gullibility in his dealings with adults and some abused his generosity. When he had money he would spend it.

I was considered one of his closest friends. I was also his medical adviser, and we talked poultry and dogs. After your mother left in 1947, I lived with your father for a month. I was the go-between, taking flowers to your mother in Colombo. Then in

1950 I was practicing in Kandy and he came to see me because he was vomiting blood. Then he and I and Archer Jayawardene became close friends. We would meet once a week at the *Daily News* bookshop in Kandy.

We never drank with him. If Archer and I arrived at Rock Hill he would give us a large glass of ice-cold milk. He would always be reading my medical books, my dog and poultry books; he would brood on these things. When he had the D.T.'s I would give him half a grain of morphine to sedate him for 12 hours and he would come out of it ok. Before he died there was a second bout of haemorrhaging—stomach this time. But death was due to a cerebral haemorrhage.

There were just two or three of us who were very close to him. As for Maureen, I think she knew I was too close a friend for her to like me. God, I learned a great deal from him. There was nothing about poultry he didn't know. Or dogs. He used to have a lot of faith in me so I loved him too.

*   *   *

Archer Jayawardene:

He was a founder of the Cactus and Succulent Society. We had a hundred members and once a year we would have lunch and tea at the Kandy Garden Club.

He loved organizing us. He suddenly decided to get us to dance in our old age. I think Maureen wanted to go to a New Year's Dance and he suggested that we all take dancing lessons. He hired

298

a teacher and we had to take lessons twice a week. He was wonderful at planning these things—picnics, trips to the Perahera. He loved the Perahera and always got into trouble during them. Once he ran over a policeman's foot. At the police station he fell asleep on the Inspector's desk and it took several men to move him.

But he spent most of his spare time reading or listening to that huge wireless on the front porch. He lived in another world I think. He was not interested in politics. Usually he never spoke about the past. But when the *coup* case was on he went down to Colombo to visit his old friends, Derek and Royce, in jail.

A year before he died he went into that terrible depression. V.C. de Silva and I would go there and he wouldn't speak to us. We were his closest friends and he ignored us. Just sat there completely still as if caught against something so he couldn't move. A cousin of mine was a psychiatrist and I drove him up from Colombo and I introduced him and before I had even stepped off the porch he was having a *hell* of a chat with that doctor.

His funeral was a tragi-comedy sort of business. First of all the coffin they brought was too small so they had to build a new one in the house. Then they couldn't get it out so they had to break the doors down. And the day of the funeral was a rainy day. He had bought this plot of land right at the top of a hill. We made that steep climb, carrying the coffin, slipping and falling to our knees on a thin muddy road.

He had not been well during that last year after the depression. He was content though. I think that both of us were impatient men. But the cactus and the gardening—you know—we had taught ourselves something. Now my wife and I have moved to this small house and the furniture still hasn't arrived, but I don't really care. The Buddhists say if you have things you only worry about them. I go cycling at three in the morning when the streets are empty . . . I'm really enjoying myself. I keep telling my wife we should get ready for the other life, the flying.

Two days before he died we were together. We were alone in the house. I can't remember what we said but we sat there for three hours. I too don't talk much. You know it is a most relaxed thing when you sit with a best friend and you know there is nothing you have to tell him, to empty your mind. We just stayed there together, silent in the dusk like this, and we were quite happy.

*   *   *

He would swing wildly, in those last years—not so much from sobriety to drink but from calmness to depression. But he was shy, he didn't want anyone else to be troubled by it, so he would be quiet most of the time. That was his only defense. To keep it within so the fear would not hurt others.

I keep thinking of the lines from Goethe . . . "Oh, who will heal the sufferings / Of the man whose balm turned poison?" I can only clarify this range in him by focussing on this metamorphosis. At the end he moved courteous among his few friends so they never realized, or could only guess at, his torn state, and by then he had already gone too far, was on the cliff. And how could his children know when he would write them his strange quirky notes, such as, "Dear Jenny—I am in the quite well. I hope you are in the same well. Love Daddy xxx" ?

His fantasies were awful. Paranoia took over during his downward swings. He personally shattered three hundred eggs. Dug a pit and threw them in beating them to pieces with a large staff so nothing would survive—all because he knew someone was trying to poison the family. This he did secretly so no one would worry.

When he could no longer hold all the information, the awareness of what was happening, he would turn to drink. Or, in the last year before he died, he broke down completely. Ceremonies darkened around him. His two closest friends were saddened, not just for what had happened to him but because it seemed he no longer trusted them. He was in the well of total silence. Sat on the verandah looking out onto coconut trees, the suspect chickens. He cooked himself an omelette and a cup of soup. At this point he did not drink. He sat catatonic, his eyes drifting over the lawn. It was too late to act secure, polite.

They found a doctor he would talk to and he was taken to a nursing home in Colombo. When the children came to visit him he was distant with them because he thought they were imitations. He longed to hold his children in his arms. You must understand all this was happening while his first family was in England or Canada or Colombo totally unaware of what was happening to him. That would always be the curse on us, the guilt we would be left with.

He came home after two weeks cheerful and positive. Years earlier, Archer and Doreen Jayawardene had mentioned to him that Rock Hill was a "see devi" place, meaning a home of contentment and peace. Now when he saw them again he said, "Isn't this a see devi place once more?" And for the first time he explained to his friends the state of his darkness:

When I saw you come (my father said), I saw poisonous gas around you. You walked across the lawn to me and you were wading through green gas as if you were crossing a river by foot and you were not aware of it. And I thought if I speak, if I point it out it will destroy you instantly. I was immune. It would not kill me but if I revealed this world to you you would suffer for you had no knowledge, no defenses against it. . . .

About a year later he delivered some eggs to the railway station and on the way back decided to visit his cousin Phyllis in Kandy. She remembers him driving in while she sat on the porch and she stood up. He waved but kept on going round the circle of driveway and left, still waving. An hour later she received a phone call from him. He said, "You must have thought me quite mad, but I realized as I was slowing down that I was getting a flat tire so I felt I should get home quickly." They laughed cheerfully at the incident and those were the last words they spoke to each other.

There is so much to know and we can only guess. Guess around him. To know him from these stray actions I am told about by those who loved him. And yet, he is still one of those books we long to read whose pages remain uncut. We are still unwise. It is not that he became too complicated but that he had reduced himself to a few things around him and he gave them immense meaning and significance. The behaviour of certain creatures he could theorize on for hours with V.C. de Silva. He kept journals about every one of the four hundred varieties of cactus and succulents—some of which he had never seen, others of which he had smuggled into the country via a friend. Important days were those when certain waterplants arrived from islands in the Pacific. He had come to love the specific variety of growing things and the information he was taught by them. There were the invented games with his children. There was the relearning of old songs from the past to delight them. They could be charmed by the silliness of lyrics from the thirties which had always moved him.

Courtesy. A modesty. In spite of the excess of his gestures earlier in his life he was in the end a miniaturist pleased by small things, the decent gestures among a small circle of family and friends. He made up lovely songs about every dog he had owned —each of them had a different tune and in the verses he celebrated their natures.

"You must get this book right," my brother tells me, "You can only write it once." But the book again is incomplete. In the end all your children move among the scattered acts and memories with no more clues. Not that we ever thought we would be able to fully understand you. Love is often enough, towards your stadium of small things. Whatever brought you solace we would have applauded. Whatever controlled the fear we all share we would have embraced. That could only be dealt with one day at a time—with that song we cannot translate, or the dusty green of the cactus you touch and turn carefully like a wounded child towards the sun, or the cigarettes you light.

LAST MORNING

Half an hour before light I am woken by the sound of rain. Rain on wall, coconut, and petal. This sound above the noise of the fan. The world already awake in the darkness beyond the barred windows as I get up and stand here, waiting for the last morning.

My body must remember everything, this brief insect bite, smell of wet fruit, the slow snail light, rain, rain, and underneath the hint of colours a sound of furious wet birds whose range of mimicry includes what one imagines to be large beasts, trains, burning electricity. Dark trees, the mildewed garden wall, the slow air pinned down by rain. Above me the fan's continual dazzling of its hand. When I turn on the light, the bulb on the long three-foot cord will sway to the electrical breeze making my shadow move back and forth on the wall.

But I do not turn on the light yet. I want this emptiness of a dark room where I listen and wait. There is nothing in this view that could not be a hundred years old, that might not have been here when I left Ceylon at the age of eleven. My mother looks out of her Colombo window thinking of divorce, my father wakes after three days of alcohol, his body hardly able to move from the stiffness in muscles he cannot remember exerting. It is a morning scenery well known to my sister and her children who leave for swimming practice before dawn crossing the empty city in the Volks, passing the pockets of open shops and their light-bulb light that sell newspapers and food. I stood like this in the long mornings of my childhood unable to bear the wait till full daylight when I could go and visit the Peiris family down the road in Boralesgamuwa; the wonderful, long days I spent there with Paul and Lionel and Aunt Peggy who would casually object to my climbing all over her bookcases in my naked and dirty feet. Bookcases I stood under again this week which were full of signed first editions of poems by Neruda and Lawrence and George Keyt. All this was here before I dreamed of getting married, having children, wanting to write.

Here where some ants as small as microdots bite and feel themselves being lifted by the swelling five times as large as their bodies. Rising on their own poison. Here where the cassette now starts up in the next room. During the monsoon, on my last morning, all this Beethoven and rain.

ACKNOWLEDGMENTS

A literary work is a communal act. And this book could not have been *imagined*, let alone conceived, without the help of many people.

The book is a composite of two return journeys to Sri Lanka, in 1978 and 1980. On each occasion I stayed for several months, travelling alone and then joined by my wife and children. My sister, Gillian, took many of the journeys of research with me all over the island. She, and my other sister, Janet, and my brother, Christopher, were central in helping me recreate the era of my parents. This is their book as much as mine. My own family too had to put up with compulsive questioning of everyone we met, hearing again and again long lists of confused genealogies and rumour.

Raw material came from many sources; and I would like to thank a larger group of relatives, friends and colleagues who helped me in my inquisitiveness: Alwin Ratnayake, Phyllis and Ned Sansoni, Ernest and Nalini McIntyre, Zillah Gratiaen, Pam Fernando, Wendy Partridge, Dolly van Langenberg, Susan and Sunil Perera, Jennifer Saravanamuttu, Archer and Doreen Jayawardene, V.C. de Silva, Peggy and Harold Peiris, Sylvia Fernando, Stanley

Suraweera, Hamish and Gill Sproule, Dhama Jagoda, Ian Goonetileke, Yasmine Gooneratne, Wimal Dissanayake, Jilska Vanderwall, Rex and Bertha Daniel, Irene Vanderwall, Rohan and Kamini de Soysa, Erica Perera, Clarence de Fonseka, Nesta Brohier, Nedra de Saram, Sam Kadirgamar, Dorothy Lowman, John Kotelawela, Irangenie "Chandi" Meedeniya, Barbara Sansoni, Trevor de Saram, Thea Wickramasuriya, Jenny Fonseka, Yolande Ilangakoon, Babe Jonklaas, Verna and Mary Vangeyzel, Audrey de Vos . . . and Shaan, Eggily, and Hetti Corea.

While all these names may give an air of authenticity, I must confess that the book is not a history but a portrait or "gesture." And if those listed above disapprove of the fictional air I apologize and can only say that in Sri Lanka a well-told lie is worth a thousand facts.

*   *   *

Thanks to the Canada Council and Ontario Arts Council and Glendon College, York University, for their support. And to the editors of *The Capilano Review, periodics, The Canadian Forum,* and *Brick,* who published sections from the work in progress.

*   *   *

Finally, special thanks to three friends who helped me at many stages with the manuscript: Daphne Marlatt, Stan Dragland, and Barrie Nichol, *"for my papers ware promiscuous and out of forme with severall inlargements and untutored narrative."*

Credits

The stanza from the poem, "Don't Talk to me about Matisse," comes from the book *O Regal Blood* by Lakdasa Wikkramasinha, published in Colombo in February 1975.

The lines from Goethe are from a translation by James Wright in his *Collected Poems*. Published by Wesleyan University Press, 1971.

"Sea of Heartbreak" by Don Gibson. Copyright MCMLX and MCMLXI by Shapiro, Berstein & Co., Inc., 10 East 53 Street, New York 10022. International Copyright Secured. All rights reserved. Used by permisson.

"It's Been a Long, Long Time" by Sammy Cahn & Jule Styne, published by Cahn Music Company and Morley Music Company.

"A Fine Romance" by Dorothy Fields & Jerome Kern. Copyright © 1936 T. B. Harms Company (c/o The Welk Music Group, Santa Monica, CA 90401) Copyright renewed. International Copyright Secured. All rights reserved. Used by permission.

The lines quoted in *The Karapothas* sequence linking Robinson Crusoe with Robert Knox's *An Historical Relation*, published by the Ceylon Historical Association.

The remarks by W. C. Ondaaje come from his "Report on the Royal Botanical Gardens, Peradeniya" which was published in Ceylon Almanc of 1853.

An exerpt from Rex Daniel's journal is used with his kind permission.

Photograph of the 1947 Nuwara Eliya flood courtesy of Dr Wickrema Weerasooriya.

Photograph of Sensation Rock from cave's *Book of Ceylon*

Every effort has been made to secure clearance for material used within this book.

In the Skin of a Lion

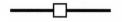

This book is in memory of Michel Lambeth,
Sharon Stevenson, and Bill and Michal Acres

And for Linda, and Sarah Sheard and David Young

I'd like to express my gratitude to The John Simon Guggenheim Foundation who gave me a grant during the writing of this book. Also to the Ontario Arts Council, the El Basha Restaurant, the Multicultural History Society of Ontario, and Glendon College, York University.

I would also like to thank Andrea Kristof, Margo Teasdale, George and Ruth Grant, Donya Peroff, Rick Halendby, Paul Thompson, and Lillian Petroff. Also Ian Redforth for his work on Finnish lumber-camp workers. A special thank you to Ellen Seligman.

This is a work of fiction and certain liberties have at times been taken with some dates and locales.

CONTENTS

1

2

3

The joyful will stoop with sorrow, and when
you have gone to the earth I will let my hair
grow long for your sake, I will wander through
the wilderness in the skin of a lion.

THE EPIC OF GILGAMESH

Never again will a single story be told
as though it were the only one.

JOHN BERGER

This is a story a young girl gathers in a car during the early hours of the morning. She listens and asks questions as the vehicle travels through darkness. Outside, the countryside is unbetrayed. The man who is driving could say, "In that field is a castle," and it would be possible for her to believe him.

She listens to the man as he picks up and brings together various corners of the story, attempting to carry it all in his arms. And he is tired, sometimes as elliptical as his concentration on the road, at times overexcited — "Do you see?" He turns to her in the faint light of the speedometer.

Driving the four hours to Marmora under six stars and a moon.

She stays awake to keep him company.

1

LITTLE SEEDS

IF HE IS AWAKE early enough the boy sees the men walk past the farmhouse down First Lake Road. Then he stands at the bedroom window and watches: he can see two or three lanterns between the soft maple and the walnut tree. He hears their boots on gravel. Thirty loggers, wrapped up dark, carrying axes and small packages of food which hang from their belts. The boy walks downstairs and moves to a window in the kitchen where he can look down the driveway. They move from right to left. Already they seem exhausted, before the energy of the sun.

Sometimes, he knows, this collection of strangers will meet the cows being brought in from a pasture barn for milking and there will be a hushed politeness as they stand to the side of the road holding up the lanterns (one step back and they will be in a knee-high snowdrift), to let the cows lazily pass them on the narrow road. Sometimes the men put their hands on the warm flanks of these animals and receive their heat as they pass. They put their thin-gloved hands on these black and white creatures, who are barely discernible in the last of the night's darkness. They must do this gently, without any sense of attack or right. They do not own this land as the owner of the cows does.

The holsteins pass the silent gauntlet of men. The farmer who follows the cows nods. He passes this strange community most mornings during the winter months, the companionship a silent comfort to him in the dark of five A.M. – for he has been rounding up cattle for over an hour to take them to the milking barns.

The boy who witnesses this procession, and who even dreams about it, has also watched the men working a mile away in the grey trees. He has heard their barks, heard their axes banging into the cold wood as if into metal, has seen a fire beside the creek where water is molecular and grey under the thin ice.

The sweat moves between their hard bodies and the cold clothes. Some die of pneumonia or from the sulphur in their lungs from the mills they work in during other seasons. They sleep in the shacks behind the Bellrock Hotel and have little connection with the town.

Neither the boy nor his father has ever been into those dark rooms, into a warmth which is the odour of men. A raw table, four bunks, a window the size of a torso. These are built each December and dismantled the following spring. No one in the town of Bellrock really knows where the men have come from. It takes someone else, much later, to tell the boy that. The only connection the loggers have with the town is when they emerge to skate along the line of river, on homemade skates, the blades made of old knives.

For the boy the end of winter means a blue river, means the disappearance of these men.

*   *   *

He longs for the summer nights, for the moment when he turns out the lights, turns out even the small cream funnel in the hall near the room where his father sleeps. Then the house is in darkness except for the bright light in the kitchen. He sits down at the long table and looks into his school geography book with the maps of the world, the white sweep of currents, testing the names to himself, mouthing out the exotic. *Caspian. Nepal. Durango.* He closes the book and brushes it with his palms, feeling the texture of the pebbled cover and its coloured dyes which create a map of Canada.

Later, he walks through the dark living room, his hand stretched out in front of him, and returns the book to a shelf. He stands in darkness, rubbing his arms to bring energy back into his body. He is forcing himself to stay awake, take his time. It is still hot and he is naked to the waist. He walks back into the bright kitchen and moves from window to window to search out the moths pinioned against the screens, clinging to brightness. From across the fields they will have seen this one lighted room and travelled towards it. A summer night's inquiry.

Bugs, plant hoppers, grasshoppers, rust-dark moths. Patrick gazes on these things which have navigated the warm air above the surface of the earth and attached themselves to the mesh with a muted thunk. He'd heard them as he read, his senses tuned to such noises. Years later at the Riverdale Library he will learn how the shining leaf-chafers destroy shrubbery, how the flower beetles feed on the juice of decaying wood or young corn. There will suddenly be order and shape to these nights. Having given them fictional names he will learn their formal titles as if perusing the guest list for a ball – the Spur-throated Grasshopper! The Archbishop of Canterbury!

Even the real names are beautiful. Amber-winged skimmer. Bush cricket. Throughout the summer he records their visits and sketches the repeaters. Is it the same creature? He crayons the orange wings of the geometer into his notebook, the lunar moth, the soft brown – as if rabbit fur – of the tussock moth. He will not open the screen and capture their pollened bodies. He did this once and the terrified thrash of the moth – a brown-pink creature who released coloured dust on his fingers – scared them both.

Up close they are prehistoric. The insect jaws munch. Are they eating something minute or is it subliminal – the way his father chews his tongue when in the fields. The kitchen light radiates through their porous wings; even those that are squat, like the peach-green aphid, appear to be constructed of powder.

Patrick pulls a double-ocarina from his pocket. Outside he will not waken his father, the noise will simply drift up into the arms of soft maple. Perhaps he can haunt these creatures. Perhaps they are not mute at all, it is just a lack of range in his hearing. (When he was nine his father discovered him lying on the ground, his ear against the hard shell of cow shit inside which he could hear several bugs flapping and knocking.) He knows the robust calls from the small bodies of cicadas, but he wants conversation – the language of damsel flies who need something to translate their breath the way he uses the ocarina to give himself a voice, something to leap with over the wall of this place.

Do they return nightly to show him something? Or does he haunt them? In the way he steps from the dark house and at the doorway of the glowing kitchen says to the empty fields, *I am here. Come and visit me.*

He was born into a region which did not appear on a map until 1910, though his family had worked there for twenty years and the land had been homesteaded since 1816.

In the school atlas the place is pale green and nameless. The river slips out of an unnamed lake and is a simple blue line until it becomes the Napanee twenty-five miles to the south, and, only because of logging, will eventually be called Depot Creek. "Deep Eau."

His father works for two or three farms, cutting wood, haying, herding cattle. The cows cross the river twice a day – in the morning they wander to the land south of the creek and in the afternoon they are rounded up for milking. In winter the animals are taken down the road to a pasture barn, though once a cow headed towards the river longing for back pasture.

They do not miss it for two hours and then his father guesses where it has gone. He runs towards the river yelling to the boy Patrick to follow with the field horses. Patrick is bareback on a horse leading the other by the rope, urging them on through the deep snow. He sees his father through the bare trees as he rides down the slope towards the swimming hole.

In mid-river, half-submerged in the ice, is the neighbouring farmer's holstein. There is no colour. The dry stalks of dead mulleins, grey trees, and the swamp now clean and white. His father with a rope around his shoulders creeps on his hands and knees across the ice towards the black and white shape. The cow heaves, splitting more ice, and cold water seeps up. Hazen Lewis pauses, calming the animal, then creeps on. He must get the rope under the body twice. Patrick moves forward slowly till he kneels on the other side of the cow. His father puts his left hand on the neck of the animal and plunges his right arm into the freezing water as low as he can go beneath the body. On the other side Patrick puts an arm in and waves it back and forth trying to come in contact with the rope. They cannot reach each other. Patrick lies on the ice so his arm and shoulder can go deeper, his wrist already starting to numb, and he thinks that soon he will not be able to feel the rope even if it brushes against him.

The cow shifts and water soaks into the boy's coat, through to his chest. His father pulls back and the two of them kneel on either side of the cow and swing their wet arms, beating them against their chests. They don't speak. They must work as quickly as possible. His father puts his ungloved hand against the cow's ear to collect the animal's heat. He lies down sideways on the ice and plunges his arm down again, the water inches from his face. Patrick, in a mirror image, swirls his hand under-water but again there is nothing to touch. "I'm going under now. You've got to get it fast," his father says, and Patrick sees his father's trunk twitch and his head go into the icy water. Patrick's hand clutches his father's other arm on top of the cow, holding it tightly.

Then Patrick puts his head into the water and reaches out. He touches his father's wrist under the cow. He dares not let go and moves his hand carefully until he grips the thick braided rope. He pulls at it but it won't move. He realizes his father in going down deeper has somehow got his body over the rope, that he's lying on it. Patrick will not let go, though he is run-ning out of air. His father gasps out of the water, lies on his back on the ice, and breathes hard past the ache in his eyes, then is suddenly aware of what he is lying on and rolls away, freeing the rope. Patrick pulls, using his foot now to jerk himself up out of the water, and he slithers over the ice away from the cow.

He sits up and sees his father and puts his arms up in a vic-tory gesture. His father is frantically trying to get water out of his ears and off his eyes before it freezes in the air and Patrick uses his dry sleeve and does the same, shrinking his hand back into the jacket, prodding the cloth into his ears. He can feel the ice on his chin and neck already forming but he doesn't worry about that. His father scuttles back to shore and returns with a second rope. This one he attaches to the first rope, and Patrick hauls it towards himself under the cow, so both ropes are now circled around the animal.

Patrick looks up – at the grey rock of the swimming hole, the oak towering over the dirty brush that spikes out of the snow. There is a clear blue sky. The boy feels as if he has not seen these things in years. Till this moment there was just his father, the black-and-white shape of the cow, and that terrible black water which cut into his eyes when he opened them down there.

His father attaches the ropes to the horses. The face of the half-submerged cow, a giant eye lolling, seems unconcerned. Patrick expects it to start chewing in complete boredom. He lifts its lip and puts his cold fingers against the gums to steal heat. Then he crawls to the bank.

Holding each of the horses by the halter he and his father yell encouragement to them. The horses do not even hesitate at the weight they are pulling. From the bank he sees the cow's tongue slide out, its complacent look for the first time replaced by concern as it is dragged towards the shoreline, breaking ice as it cuts a path. About ten feet from the bank where the ice is thicker the body tightens against the ropes. The horses stop. He and his father switch them, and they break into a trot. Then the whole cow magically emerges out of the ice and is dragged on its side, its four legs straight and hard in the air, dragged uncompromisingly onto the shore over the brown mulleins.

They let the horses go. He and his father try to untie the ropes on the cow but it is too difficult and his father brings out a knife and cuts the ropes away. The animal lies there snorting its steam into the cold air, then stumbles up and stands watching them. More than anything Patrick is surprised at his father who is obsessed with not wasting things. He has lectured the boy several times on saving rope. Always unknot. Never cut! Bringing out his knife and slicing the rope to pieces is an outrageous, luxurious act.

They begin to run back home, looking behind them to see if the cow is following. The boy gasps, "If she goes into the ice again I'm not doing a thing." "Neither am I," yells his father, laughing. By the time they reach their back kitchen, it is almost dark and they have pains in their stomachs.

In the house Hazen Lewis lights the naphtha lamp and builds a fire. The boy shivers during dinner and the father tells the boy he can sleep with him. In bed later on, they do not acknowledge each other apart from sharing the warmth under the blanket. His father lies so still Patrick doesn't know if he is asleep or awake. The boy looks towards the kitchen and its dying fire.

He imagines himself through the winter until he is a white midsummer shadow beside his father. In summer his father drips gasoline onto the caterpillar tents and sets them on fire. *Flof.* The grey cobweb skins collapse into flame. Caterpillars drop onto grass, the acrid burn smell is in the roof of the boy's mouth. Two of them meticulously search a field in the evening light. Patrick points to a nest his father has missed and they walk deeper into the pasture.

He is almost asleep. In the darkness another flame ignites then withers into nothing.

*   *   *

In the drive-shed Hazen Lewis outlined the boy's body onto the plank walls with green chalk. Then he tacked wires back and forth across the outline as if realigning the veins in his son's frame. Muscles of cordite and the spine a tributary of the black powder fuse. This is how the boy remembers his father, studying the outline which the boy has just stepped away from as the lit fuse smoulders up and blows out a section of plank where the head had been.

Hazen Lewis was an abashed man, withdrawn from the world around him, uninterested in the habits of civilization outside his own focus. He would step up to his horse and assume it, as if it were a train, as if flesh and blood did not exist.

In winter months Patrick carried meals into the acreage north of the creek where his father, solitary, cut timber all day, minute in those white halls. And then when Patrick was fifteen, his father made the one leap of his life. At some moment, chopping into hemlock, hearing only the axe and its pivoting echo, he must have imagined the trees and permafrost and maple syrup ovens erupting up in one heave, the snow shaken off every branch in the woods around him. He stopped in mid-afternoon, walked home, unlaced his bear paws, and put away the axe forever. He wrote away for books, travelled into Kingston for materials. The explosion he saw in the woods had been an idea as he tugged his axe out of the hemlock. He bought dynamite and blasting caps and fuses, drew diagrams on the walls of the drive-shed, then carried the explosives into the woods. He laid the charges against rock and ice and trees. The detonator cap spat a flame into the cartridge and his eyes watched the snow collapse out of branches from the shudder in the air. Whatever was dislodged became a graph showing him the radius of the tremor.

Before the spring breakup Hazen Lewis rode down to the Rathbun Timber Company headquarters. He demonstrated his talent, moving a log into precisely the location he said it would go, exploding a half-ton of shale, and was hired along with the river drivers. He had secured a role for himself in the industry that took place along the Depot Lakes and the Napanee River. When the company closed down some years later he moved over and worked as a dynamiter in the feldspar mine excavations around Verona and Godfrey, hired by the Richardson Mines. In all his life the longest speech was the one made to the Rathbun staff when he told them what he could do and that as far as he was concerned there were only two sensible jobs in logging – being a dynamiter and being a cook.

Along the chain of Depot Lakes – from First Depot to Fifth Depot – the loggers arrived in winter and disappeared into shanty camps, walking twenty miles into land they did not know. All February and March at the centre of the lakes the pyramids of logs grew, hauled there by sleds. Before daybreak the men were working – through the worst storms, in weather far below zero – and they finished at six. The double-handed crosscut saw brought down the pines. The pulp cutters, bent double, had to saw the stumps just above the ground. This was the worst job. Some used the swede saw. It cut spruce at twice the speed of the crosscut, and when they moved to the next camp they rolled up the narrow blade, making new handles in whatever forest they arrived at.

In April, with the melting of the lake ice, the river drives began. This was the easiest and most dangerous work. From Bellrock to Napanee men were stationed wherever the river narrowed. Bridges or split rocks had two or three men always there in case of a jam. If a jammed log did not get fished out in time, the weight of others would pile up behind it and the whole length of the river would be padlocked. At this point the river drivers could do nothing and a dispatcher was sent on horseback for the dynamiter. A twenty-foot log suddenly leaping out of the water and side-swiping a man, breaking his chest.

Hazen Lewis and his son rode up to the split rock. The large man walked around the logjam. He drilled in a plug of dynamite and lit the fuse. He got the boy to shout the warning and the logs went up into the air, onto the bank, and the river was free.

In difficult cases Patrick would remove his clothes and grease himself down with oil from the crankcase of the steam donkey. He dove into the ribbed water and swam among the logs. Every half-minute wherever he was he had to raise his hand to assure his father. Eventually the boy located the log his father had pointed to. He caught the charge thrown out to him, crimped the blasting cap onto the fuse with his teeth, and lit the powder.

He re-emerged from the water, walked back to the horses, and dried himself with the towels from the packsack, like his father not even turning around to watch. A river exploded behind him, the crows leafing up.

The drives lasted a month and he watched the men float by, riding the sawlogs with their large poles towards Yarker down to Napanee where the corralled logs were towed to the mills. He was always beside his father. Patrick lazed in a patch of sun by the bridge and they waited.

At noon the cook walked up First Lake Road with two dairy pails. One pail carried tea, the other contained thick pork sandwiches. The sound of the crows above the food was a signal, and men emerged from various bends in the river. When the meal was over the cook picked up two empty pails and stepped onto a log on the water's edge and floated back downstream to the camp. He stood up straight in mid-river, travelling at only the speed that the river wished. He would float under the bridge without altering his posture, though there was only an inch to spare, nodding to loggers on the bank, disheartened by the ever-present crows. He would step off at the camp at Goose Island with his shoes perfectly dry.

Hazen read his pamphlets. He dried the powdered cordite on a rock. He was sullen even in the company of his son. All his energy was with the fuse travelling at two minutes to the yard under floorboards, around the trunks of trees, and up into someone's pocket. He kept receiving that image in his mind. Could he do it? The fuse stitched into the cloth of the trouser leg. The man sleeping perhaps by a campfire, the fuse smouldering horizontal into his shirt pocket, blowing out the heart. In his preoccupations the fuse always zigzagged like a hound's nose along the ground, setting alight the ground cover till it was red lichen.

Hazen Lewis did not teach his son anything, no legend, no base of theory. The boy watched him prepare charges or pack equipment neatly back into his wooden case. His father wore no metal on him – not a watch or belt buckle. He was a man who with his few props had become self-sufficient, as invisible as possible. The explosions jostled logs out of the water unharmed. He left a track of half-inch holes in the granite all down the Depot Lakes system and along the Moira River system where he sometimes was hired. But these were as modest and minimal as they could be. A woodpecker's work. He never wore a hat. He was a big man, six-foot-six, a heavy body. He was a bad rider of horses and later on a bad driver of trucks. He could assemble river dynamite with his eyes closed. He was meticulous in washing his clothes every evening in case there were remnants, little seeds of explosive on his apparel. Patrick scorned this obsession. His father took off his shirt one evening and threw it onto the campfire. The shirt fizzed and sprayed sparks over the knees of the loggers. There were abrupt lessons like this.

It was strange for Patrick to realize later that he had learned important things, the way children learn from watching how adults angle a hat or approach a strange dog. He knew how much a piece of dynamite the size of a bullfrog could destroy. But he absorbed everything from a distance. The only moments his father was verbal was when calling square dances in the Yarker and Tamworth hotels during the log drives. He was always called on and he walked up to the stage as if it were a duty and broke into verses, swirling around the guitars and fiddles, dropping in a last phrase tight before he hit the wall of the rhyme. Taciturn about everything else, his father was taciturn in his square-dance calling. His words would slide noncommittal over the dance floor, the boy watching at the edge and mouthing the phrases to himself. Not a muscle moved in the large body of his father as he stood there calling *"Little red wagon the axle draggin'."*

The unemotional tongue. Patrick could see himself on stage striding up and down, his arms bent and cocky. *"Birdie fly out and the crow fly in – crow fly out and give birdie a spin,"* he would mutter to himself, later, in the daylight.

One winter night when he was eleven years old, Patrick walked out from the long kitchen. A blue moth had pulsed on the screen, bathed briefly in light, and then disappeared into darkness. He did not think it would go far. He picked up the kerosene lamp and went out. A rare winter moth. It was scuffing along the snow as if injured and he could follow it easily. In the back garden he lost it, the turquoise moth arcing up into the sky beyond the radius of the kerosene light. What was a moth doing at this time of year? He hadn't seen any for months. It may have been bred in the chicken coop. He put the hurricane lamp onto a rock and looked over the fields. Among the trees in the distance he saw what looked like more bugs. Lightning bugs within the trees by the river. But this was winter! He moved forward with the lamp.

The distance was further than he thought. Snow above the ankles of his untied boots. One hand in a pocket, the other holding a lamp. And a moon lost in the thickness of clouds so it did not shine a path for him towards the trees. All that gave direction was a blink of amber. Already he knew it could not be lightning bugs. The last of the summer's fireflies had died somewhere in the folds of one of his handkerchiefs. (Years later, Clara making love to him in a car, catching his semen in a handkerchief and flinging it out onto bushes on the side of the road. *Hey, lightning bug!* he had said, laughing, offering no explanation.)

He waded through the snow, past outcrops of granite, and into the trees where the snow was not as deep. The lights still blinked in front of him. There was laughter. Now he knew what it was. He crept on into the familiar woods as if walking into, testing the rooms of a haunted house. He knew who it was but he did not know what he would see. Then he was at the river. He put the lamp down beside the oak and walked in darkness towards the bank.

The ice shone with light. It seemed for a moment that he had stumbled on a coven, or one of those strange druidic rituals – illustrations of which he had pored over in his favourite history book. But even to the boy of eleven, deep in the woods after midnight, this was obviously benign. Something joyous. A gift. There were about ten men skating, part of a game. One chased the others and as soon as someone was touched he became the chaser. Each man held in one hand a sheaf of cattails and the tops of these were on fire. This is what lit the ice and had blinked through the trees.

They raced, swerved, fell and rolled on the ice to avoid each other but never let go of the rushes. When they collided sparks fell onto the ice and onto their dark clothes. This is what caused the howls of laughter – one of them stationary, struggling to shake off a fragment that had fallen inside his sleeve, yelling out for the others to stop.

Patrick was transfixed. Skating the river at night, each of them moving like a wedge into the blackness magically revealing the grey bushes of the shore, *his* shore, *his* river. A tree branch reached out, its hand frozen in the ice, and one of them skated under it, crouching – cattails held behind him like a flaming rooster tail.

The boy knew they were the loggers from the camp. He longed to hold their hands and skate the length of the creek slowing down through cut rock and under bridges and into town with these men, knowing they would have to return to those dark cabins by the mill.

It was not just the pleasure of skating. They could have done that during the day. This was against the night. The hard ice was so certain, they could leap into the air and crash down and it would hold them. Their lanterns replaced with new rushes which let them go further past boundaries, speed! romance! one man waltzing with his fire. . . .

To the boy growing into his twelfth year, having lived all his life on that farm where day was work and night was rest, nothing would be the same. But on this night he did not trust either himself or these strangers of another language enough to be able to step forward and join them. He turned back through the trees and fields carrying his own lamp. Breaking the crust with each step seemed graceless and slow.

So at this stage in his life his mind raced ahead of his body.

THE BRIDGE

A TRUCK CARRIES fire at five A.M. through central Toronto, along Dundas Street and up Parliament Street, moving north. Aboard the flatbed three men stare into passing darkness – their muscles relaxed in this last half-hour before work – as if they don't own the legs or the arms jostling against their bodies and the backboard of the Ford.

Written in yellow over the green door is DOMINION BRIDGE COMPANY. But for now all that is visible is the fire on the flatbed burning over the three-foot by three-foot metal dish, cooking the tar in a cauldron, leaving this odour on the streets for anyone who would step out into the early morning and swallow the air.

The truck rolls burly under the arching trees, pauses at certain intersections where more workers jump onto the flatbed, and soon there are eight men, the fire crackling, hot tar now and then spitting onto the back of a neck or an ear. Soon there are twenty, crowded and silent.

The light begins to come out of the earth. They see their hands, the textures on a coat, the trees they had known were there. At the top of Parliament Street the truck turns east, passes the Rosedale fill, and moves towards the half-built viaduct.

The men jump off. The unfinished road is full of ruts and the fire and the lights of the truck bounce, the suspension wheezing. The truck travels so slowly the men are walking faster, in the cold dawn air, even though it is summer.

Later they will remove coats and sweaters, then by eleven their shirts, bending over the black rivers of tar in just their trousers, boots, and caps. But now the thin layer of frost is everywhere, coating the machines and cables, brittle on the rain puddles they step through. The fast evaporation of darkness. As light emerges they see their breath, the clarity of the air being breathed out of them. The truck finally stops at the edge of the viaduct, and its lights are turned off.

The bridge goes up in a dream. It will link the east end with the centre of the city. It will carry traffic, water, and electricity across the Don Valley. It will carry trains that have not even been invented yet.

Night and day. Fall light. Snow light. They are always working – horses and wagons and men arriving for work on the Danforth side at the far end of the valley.

There are over 4,000 photographs from various angles of the bridge in its time-lapse evolution. The piers sink into bedrock fifty feet below the surface through clay and shale and quicksand – 45,000 cubic yards of earth are excavated. The network of scaffolding stretches up.

Men in a maze of wooden planks climb deep into the shattered light of blond wood. A man is an extension of hammer, drill, flame. Drill smoke in his hair. A cap falls into the valley, gloves are buried in stone dust.

Then the new men arrive, the "electricals," laying grids of wire across the five arches, carrying the exotic three-bowl lights, and on October 18, 1918 it is completed. Lounging in mid-air.

The bridge. The bridge. Christened "Prince Edward." The Bloor Street Viaduct.

During the political ceremonies a figure escaped by bicycle through the police barriers. The first member of the public. Not the expected show car containing officials, but this one anonymous and cycling like hell to the east end of the city. In the photographs he is a blur of intent. He wants the virginity of it, the luxury of such space. He circles twice, the string of onions that he carries on his shoulder splaying out, and continues.

But he was not the first. The previous midnight the workers had arrived and brushed away officials who guarded the bridge in preparation for the ceremonies the next day, moved with their own flickering lights – their candles for the bridge dead – like a wave of civilization, a net of summer insects over the valley.

And the cyclist too on his flight claimed the bridge in that blurred movement, alone and illegal. Thunderous applause greeted him at the far end.

On the west side of the bridge is Bloor Street, on the east side is Danforth Avenue. Originally cart roads, mud roads, planked in 1910, they are now being tarred. Bricks are banged into the earth and narrow creeks of sand are poured in between them. The tar is spread. *Bitumiers, bitumatori*, tarrers, get onto their knees and lean their weight over the wooden block irons, which arc and sweep. The smell of tar seeps through the porous body of their clothes. The black of it is permanent under the nails.

They can feel the bricks under their kneecaps as they crawl backwards towards the bridge, their bodies almost horizontal over the viscous black river, their heads drunk within the fumes.

Hey, Caravaggio!

The young man gets up off his knees and looks back into the sun. He walks to the foreman, lets go of the two wooden blocks he is holding so they hang by the leather thongs from his belt, bouncing against his knees as he walks. Each man carries the necessities of his trade with him. When Caravaggio quits a year later he will cut the thongs with a fish knife and fling the blocks into the half-dry tar. Now he walks back in a temper and gets down on his knees again. Another fight with the foreman.

All day they lean over tar, over the twenty yards of black river that has been spread since morning. It glistens and eases in sunlight. Schoolkids grab bits of tar and chew them, first cooling the pieces in their hands, then popping them into their mouths. It concentrates the saliva for spitting contests. The men plunk cans of beans into the blackness to heat them up for their lunch.

In winter, snow removes the scent of tar, the scent of pitched cut wood. The Don River floods below the unfinished bridge, ice banging at the feet of the recently built piers. On winter mornings men fan out nervous over the whiteness. Where does the earth end? There are flares along the edge of the bridge on winter nights – worst shift of all – where they hammer the nails in through snow. The bridge builders balance on a strut, the flares wavering behind them, aiming their hammers towards the noise of a nail they cannot see.

*   *   *

The last thing Rowland Harris, Commissioner of Public Works, would do in the evenings during its construction was have himself driven to the edge of the viaduct, to sit for a while. At midnight the half-built bridge over the valley seemed deserted – just lanterns tracing its outlines. But there was always a night shift of thirty or forty men. After a while Harris removed himself from the car, lit a cigar, and walked onto the bridge. He loved this viaduct. It was his first child as head of Public Works, much of it planned before he took over but he had bullied it through. It was Harris who envisioned that it could carry not just cars but trains on a lower trestle. It could also transport water from the east-end plants to the centre of the city. Water was Harris' great passion. He wanted giant water mains travelling across the valley as part of the viaduct.

He slipped past the barrier and walked towards the working men. Few of them spoke English but they knew who he was. Sometimes he was accompanied by Pomphrey, an architect, the strange one from England who was later to design for Commissioner Harris one of the city's grandest buildings – the water filtration plant in the east end.

For Harris the night allowed scope. Night removed the limitations of detail and concentrated on form. Harris would bring Pomphrey with him, past the barrier, onto the first stage of the bridge that ended sixty yards out in the air. The wind moved like something ancient against them. All men on the bridge had to buckle on halter ropes. Harris spoke of his plans to this five-foot-tall Englishman, struggling his way into Pomphrey's brain. Before the real city could be seen it had to be imagined, the way rumours and tall tales were a kind of charting.

One night they had driven there at eleven o'clock, crossed the barrier, and attached themselves once again to the rope harnesses. This allowed them to stand near the edge to study the progress of the piers and the steel arches. There was a fire on the bridge where the night workers congregated, flinging logs and other remnants onto it every so often, warming themselves before they walked back and climbed over the edge of the bridge into the night.

They were working on a wood-facing for the next pier so that concrete could be poured in. As they sawed and hammered, wind shook the light from the flares attached to the side of the abutment. Above them, on the deck of the bridge, builders were carrying huge Ingersoll-Rand air compressors and cables.

An April night in 1917. Harris and Pomphrey were on the bridge, in the dark wind. Pomphrey had turned west and was suddenly stilled. His hand reached out to touch Harris on the shoulder, a gesture he had never made before.

– Look!

Walking on the bridge were five nuns.

Past the Dominion Steel castings wind attacked the body directly. The nuns were walking past the first group of workers at the fire. The bus, Harris thought, must have dropped them off near Castle Frank and the nuns had, with some confusion at that hour, walked the wrong way in the darkness.

They had passed the black car under the trees and talking cheerfully stepped past the barrier into a landscape they did not know existed – onto a tentative carpet over the piers, among the night labourers. They saw the fire and the men. A few tried to wave them back. There was a mule attached to a wagon. The hiss and jump of machines made the ground under them lurch. A smell of creosote. One man was washing his face in a barrel of water.

The nuns were moving towards a thirty-yard point on the bridge when the wind began to scatter them. They were thrown against the cement mixers and steam shovels, careering from side to side, in danger of going over the edge.

Some of the men grabbed and enclosed them, pulling leather straps over their shoulders, but two were still loose. Harris and Pomphrey at the far end looked on helplessly as one nun was lifted up and flung against the compressors. She stood up shakily and then the wind jerked her sideways, scraping her along the concrete and right off the edge of the bridge. She disappeared into the night by the third abutment, into the long depth of air which held nothing, only sometimes a rivet or a dropped hammer during the day.

Then there was no longer any fear on the bridge. The worst, the incredible, had happened. A nun had fallen off the Prince Edward Viaduct before it was even finished. The men covered in wood shavings or granite dust held the women against them. And Commissioner Harris at the far end stared along the mad pathway. This was his first child and it had already become a murderer.

The man in mid-air under the central arch saw the shape fall towards him, in that second knowing his rope would not hold them both. He reached to catch the figure while his other hand grabbed the metal pipe edge above him to lessen the sudden jerk on the rope. The new weight ripped the arm that held the pipe out of its socket and he screamed, so whoever might have heard him up there would have thought the scream was from the falling figure. The halter thulked, jerking his chest up to his throat.

The right arm was all agony now – but his hand's timing had been immaculate, the grace of the habit, and he found himself a moment later holding the figure against him dearly.

He saw it was a black-garbed bird, a girl's white face. He saw this in the light that sprayed down inconstantly from a flare fifteen yards above them. They hung in the halter, pivoting over the valley, his broken arm loose on one side of him, holding the woman with the other. Her body was in shock, her huge eyes staring into the face of Nicholas Temelcoff.

Scream, please, Lady, he whispered, the pain terrible. He asked her to hold him by the shoulders, to take the weight off his one good arm. A sway in the wind. She could not speak though her eyes glared at him bright, just staring at him. *Scream, please.* But she could not.

During the night, the long chutes through which wet concrete slid were unused and hung loose so the open spouts wavered a few feet from the valley floor. The tops of these were about ten feet from him now. He knew this without seeing them, even though they fell outside the scope of light. If they attempted to slide the chute their weight would make it vertical and dangerous. They would have to go further – to reach the lower-deck level of the bridge where there were structures built for possible water mains.

We have to swing. She had her hands around his shoulders now, the wind assaulting them. The two strangers were in each other's arms, beginning to swing wilder, once more, past the lip of the chute which had tempted them, till they were almost at the lower level of the rafters. He had his one good arm free. Saving her now would be her responsibility.

She was in shock, her face bright when they reached the lower level, like a woman with a fever. She was in no shape to be witnessed, her veil loose, her cropped hair open to the long wind down the valley. Once they reached the catwalk she saved him from falling back into space. He was exhausted. She held him and walked with him like a lover along the unlit lower parapet towards the west end of the bridge.

Above them the others stood around the one fire, talking agitatedly. The women were still tethered to the men and not looking towards the stone edge where she had gone over, falling in darkness. The one with that small scar against her nose . . . she was always falling into windows, against chairs. She was always unlucky.

The Commissioner's chauffeur slept in his car as Temelcoff and the nun walked past, back on real earth away from the bridge. Before they reached Parliament Street they cut south through the cemetery. He seemed about to faint and she held him against a gravestone. She forced him to hold his arm rigid, his fist clenched. She put her hands underneath it like a stirrup and jerked upwards so he screamed out again, her whole body pushing up with all of her strength, groaning as if about to lift him and then holding him, clutching him tight. She had seen the sweat jump out of his face. *Get me a shot. Get me. . . .* She removed her veil and wrapped the arm tight against his side. *Parliament and Dundas . . . few more blocks.* So she went down Parliament Street with him. Where she was going she didn't know. On Eastern Avenue she knocked at the door he pointed to. All these abrupt requests – scream, swing, knock, get me. Then a man opened the door and let them into the Ohrida Lake Restaurant. *Thank you, Kosta. Go back to bed, I'll lock it.* And the man, the friend, walked back upstairs.

She stood in the middle of the restaurant in darkness. The chairs and tables were pushed back to the edge of the room. Temelcoff brought out a bottle of brandy from under the counter and picked up two small glasses in the fingers of the same hand. He guided her to a small table, then walked back and, with a switch behind the zinc counter, turned on a light near her table. There were crests on the wall.

She still hadn't said a word. He remembered she had not even screamed when she fell. That had been him.

*   *   *

Nicholas Temelcoff is famous on the bridge, a daredevil. He is given all the difficult jobs and he takes them. He descends into the air with no fear. He is a solitary. He assembles ropes, brushes the tackle and pulley at his waist, and falls off the bridge like a diver over the edge of a boat. The rope roars alongside him, slowing with the pressure of his half-gloved hands. He is burly on the ground and then falls with terrific speed, grace, using the wind to push himself into corners of abutments so he can check driven rivets, sheering valves, the drying of the concrete under bearing plates and padstones. He stands in the air banging the crown pin into the upper cord and then shepherds the lower cord's slip-joint into position. Even in archive photographs it is difficult to find him. Again and again you see vista before you and the eye must search along the wall of sky to the speck of burned paper across the valley that is him, an exclamation mark, somewhere in the distance between bridge and river. He floats at the three hinges of the crescent-shaped steel arches. These knit the bridge together. The moment of cubism.

He is happiest at daily chores – ferrying tools from pier down to trestle, or lumber that he pushes in the air before him as if swimming in a river. He is a spinner. He links everyone. He meets them as they cling – braced by wind against the metal they are rivetting or the wood sheeting they hammer into – but he has none of their fear. Always he carries his own tackle, hunched under his ropes and dragging the shining pitons behind him. He sits on a coiled seat of rope while he eats his lunch on the bridge. If he finishes early he cycles down Parliament Street to the Ohrida Lake Restaurant and sits in the darkness of the room as if he has had enough of light. Enough of space.

His work is so exceptional and time-saving he earns one dollar an hour while the other bridge workers receive forty cents. There is no jealousy towards him. No one dreams of doing half the things he does. For night work he is paid $1.25, swinging up into the rafters of a trestle holding a flare, free-falling like a dead star. He does not really need to see things, he has charted all that space, knows the pier footings, the width of the crosswalks in terms of seconds of movement – 281 feet and 6 inches make up the central span of the bridge. Two flanking spans of 240 feet, two end spans of 158 feet. He slips into openings on the lower deck, tackles himself up to bridge level. He knows the precise height he is over the river, how long his ropes are, how many seconds he can free-fall to the pulley. It does not matter if it is day or night, he could be blindfolded. Black space is time. After swinging for three seconds he puts his feet up to link with the concrete edge of the next pier. He knows his position in the air as if he is mercury slipping across a map.

*   *   *

A South River parrot hung in its cage by the doorway of the Ohrida Lake Restaurant, too curious and interested in the events of the night to allow itself to be blanketed. It watched the woman who stood dead centre in the room in darkness. The man turned on one light behind the counter. Nicholas Temelcoff came over to the bird for a moment's visit after getting the drinks. "Well, Alicia, my heart, how are you?" And walked away not waiting for the bird's reply, the fingers of his left hand delicately holding the glasses, his arm cradling the bottle.

He muttered as if continuing his conversation with the bird, in the large empty room. From noon till two it was full of men, eating and drinking. Kosta the owner and his waiter performing raucous shows for the crowd – the boss yelling insults at the waiter, chasing him past customers. Nicholas remembered the first time he had come there. The dark coats of men, the arguments of Europe.

He poured a brandy and pushed it over to her. "You don't have to drink this but you can if you wish. Or see it as a courtesy." He drank quickly and poured himself another. "Thank you," he said, touching his arm curiously as if it were the arm of a stranger.

She shook her head to communicate it was not all right, that it needed attention.

"Yes, but not now. Now I want to sit here." There was a silence between them. "Just to drink and talk quietly. . . . It is always night here. People step in out of sunlight and must move slow in the darkness."

He drank again. "Just for the pain." She smiled. "Now music." He stood up free of the table as he spoke and went behind the counter and turned the wireless on low. He spun the dial till there was bandstand. He sat down again opposite her. "Lot of pain. But I feel good." He leaned back in his chair, holding up his glass. "Alive." She picked up her glass and drank.

"Where did you get that scar?" He pointed his thumb to the side of her nose. She pulled back.

"Don't be shy . . . talk. You must talk." He wanted her to come out to him, even in anger, though he didn't want anger. Feeling such ease in the Ohrida Lake Restaurant, feeling the struts of the chair along his back, her veil tight on his arm. He just wanted her there near him, night all around them, where he could look after her, bring her out of the shock with some grace.

"I got about twenty scars," he said, "all over me. One on my ear here." He turned and leaned forward so the wall-light fell onto the side of his head. "See? Also this under my chin, that also broke my jaw. A coiling wire did that. Nearly kill me, broke my jaw. Lots more. My knees. . . ." He talked on. Hot tar burns on his arm. Nails in his calves. Drinking up, pouring her another shot, the woman's song on the radio. She heard the lyrics underneath Temelcoff's monologue as he talked and half mouthed the song and searched into her bright face. Like a woman with a fever.

This is the first time she has sat in a Macedonian bar, in any bar, with a drinking man. There is a faint glow from the varnished tables, the red checkered tablecloths of the day are folded and stacked. The alcove with its serving counter has an awning hanging over it. She realizes the darkness represents a Macedonian night where customers sit outside at their tables. Light can come only from the bar, the stars, the clock dressed in its orange and red electricity. So when customers step in at any time, what they are entering is an old courtyard of the Balkans. A violin. Olive trees. Permanent evening. Now the arbour-like wallpaper makes sense to her. Now the parrot has a language.

He talked on, slipping into phrases from the radio songs which is how he learned his words and pronunciations. He talked

355

about himself, tired, unaware his voice split now into two languages, the woman hearing everything he said and trying to
remember it all. He could see her eyes were alive, interpreting
the room. He noticed the almost-tap of her finger to the radio
music.

The blue eyes stayed on him as he moved, leaning his head
against the wall. He drank, his breath deep into the glass so the
fumes would hit his eyes and the sting of it keep him awake.
Then he looked back at her. How old was she? Her brown hair
so short, so new to the air. He wanted to coast his hand
through it.

"I love your hair," he said. "Thank you . . . for the help. For
taking the drink."

She leaned forward earnestly and looked at him, searching
out his face now. Words just on the far side of her skin, about to
fall out. Wanting to know his name which he had forgotten to
tell her. "I love your hair." His shoulder was against the wall
and he was trying to look up. Then his eyes were closed. So
deeply asleep he would be gone for hours. She could twist him
around like a puppet and he wouldn't waken.

She felt as if she were the only one alive in this building. In
such formal darkness. There was a terrible taste from that one
drink still on her tongue, so she walked behind the zinc counter,
turning on the tap to wash out her mouth. She moved the dial
of the radio around a bit but brought it back securely to the
same station. She was looking for that song he had half-sung
along with earlier, the voice of the singer strangely powerful
and lethargic. She saw herself in the mirror. A woman whose
hair was showing, caught illicit. She did what he had wanted to
do. She ran her hand over her hair briefly. Then turned from
her image.

Leaning forward, she laid her face on the cold zinc, the chill there even past midnight. Upon her cheek, her eyelid. She let her skull roll to cool her forehead. The zinc was an edge of another country. She put her ear against the grey ocean of it. Its memory of a day's glasses. The spill and the wiping cloth. Confessional. Tabula Rasa.

At the table she positioned the man comfortably so he would not fall on his arm. *What is your name?* she whispered. She bent down and kissed him, then began walking around the room. This orchard. Strangers kiss softly as moths, she thought.

*   *   *

In certain weather, when fog fills the valley, the men stay close to each other. They arrive for work and walk onto a path that disappears into whiteness. What country exists on the other side? They move in groups of three or four. Many have already died during the building of the bridge. But especially on mornings like this there is a prehistoric fear, a giant bird lifting one of the men into the air. . . .

Nicholas has removed his hat, stepped into his harness, and dropped himself off the edge, falling thirty feet down through fog. He hangs under the spine of the bridge. He can see nothing, just his hands and the yard of pulley-rope above him. Six in the morning and he's already lost to that community of men on the bridge who are also part of the fairy tale.

He is parallel to the lattice-work of hanging structures. Now he enters the cages of steel and wood like a diver entering a sunken vessel that could at any moment tip over into deeper fracture zones of the sea floor. Nicholas Temelcoff works as the guy derricks raise and lower the steel – assembling it further out towards the next pier. He directs the steel through the fog. He is a fragment at the end of the steel bone the derrick carries on the end of its sixty-foot boom. The steel and Nicholas are raised up to a temporary track and from there the 'travellers' handle it. On the west end of the viaduct a traveller is used to erect the entire 150-foot span. The travellers are twin derricks fitted with lattice-work booms that can lift twelve tons into any position, like a carrot off the nose of the most recently built section of the bridge.

Nicholas is not attached to the travellers, his rope and pulleys link up only with the permanent steel of a completed section of the bridge. Travellers have collapsed twice before this and fallen to the floor of the valley. He is not attaching himself to a falling structure. But he hangs beside it, in the blind whiteness, slipping down further within it until he can shepherd the new ribs of steel on to the end of the bridge. He bolts them in, having to free-fall in order to use all of his weight for the final turns of the giant wrench. He allows ten feet of loose rope on the pulley, attaches the wrench, then drops on to the two-foot handle, going down with it, and jars with the stiffening of the bolt, falling off into the air, and jars again when he reaches the end of the rope. He pulleys himself up and does it again. After ten minutes every bone feels broken – the air he stops in feels hard as concrete, his spine aching where the harness pulls him short.

He rises with the traveller from the lower level, calling out numbers to the driver above him through the fog, alongside the clattering of the woodwork he holds on to, the creaks and bends of the lattice drowning out his call of *one – two – three – four* which is the only language he uses. He was doing this once when a traveller collapsed at night – the whole structure – the rope shredding around him. He let go, swinging into the darkness, *anywhere* that might be free of the fifteen tons of falling timber which crashed onto the lower level and then tumbled down into the valley, rattling and banging in space like a trolley full of metal. And on the far end of the swing, he knew he had escaped the timber, but not necessarily the arm-thick wires that were now uncoiling free, snaking powerfully in every direction through the air. On his return swing he curled into a ball to avoid them, hearing the wires whip laterally as they completed the energy of the break. His predecessor had been killed in a similar accident, cut, the upper half of his body found an hour later, still hanging in the halter.

By eight A.M. the fog is burned up and the men have already been working for over two hours. A smell of tar descends to Nicholas as workers somewhere pour and begin to iron it level. He hangs waiting for the whistle that announces the next journey of the traveller. Below him is the Don River, the Grand Trunk, the CN and CP railway tracks, and Rosedale Valley Road. He can see the houses and work shacks, the beautiful wooden sheeting of the abutment which looks like a revival tent. Wind dries the sweat on him. He talks in English to himself.

*   *   *

She takes the first step out of the Ohrida Lake Restaurant into the blue corridor – the narrow blue lane of light that leads to the street. What she will become she becomes in that minute before she is outside, before she steps into the six-A.M. morning. The parrot Alicia regards her departure and then turns its attention back to the man asleep in the chair, one arm on the table, palm facing up as if awaiting donations, his head against the wall beside a crest. He is in darkness now, the open palm callused

359

and hard. Five years earlier or ten years into the future the woman would have smelled the flour in his hair, his body having slept next to the dough, curling around it so his heat would make it rise. But now it was the hardness of his hands, the sound of them she would remember like wood against glass.

*   *   *

Commissioner Harris never speaks to Nicholas Temelcoff but watches often as he hooks up and walks at the viaduct edge listening to the engineer Taylor's various instructions. He appears abstracted but Harris knows he listens carefully. Nicholas never catches anyone's eye, as if he must hear the orders nakedly without seeing a face around the words.

His eyes hook to objects. Wood, a railing, a rope clip. He eats his sandwiches without looking at them, watching instead a man attaching a pulley to the elevated railings or studying the expensive leather on the shoes of the architects. He drinks water from a corked green bottle and his eyes are focused a hundred feet away. He never realizes how often he is watched by others. He has no clue that his gestures are extreme. He has no portrait of himself. So he appears to Harris and the others as a boy: say, a fanatic about toy cars, some stage they all passed through years ago.

Nicholas strides the parapet looking sideways at the loops of rope and then, without pausing, steps into the clear air. Now there is for Harris nothing to see but the fizzing rope, a quick slither. Nicholas stops twenty feet down with a thud against his heart. Sometimes on the work deck they will hear him slowly begin to sing various songs, breaking down syllables and walking around them as if laying the clauses out like tackle on a pavement to be checked for worthiness, picking up one he fancies for a moment then replacing it with another. As with sight, because Nicholas does not listen to most conversations around him, he assumes no one hears him.

For Nicholas language is much more difficult than what he does in space. He loves his new language, the terrible barriers of it. " 'Does she love me? – Absolutely! Do I love her? – Positively!' " Nicholas sings out to the forty-foot pipe he ferries across the air towards the traveller. *He* knows Harris. He *knows* Harris by the time it takes him to walk the sixty-four feet six inches from sidewalk to sidewalk on the bridge and by his expensive tweed coat that cost more than the combined weeks' salaries of five bridge workers.

The event that will light the way for immigration in North America is the talking picture. The silent film brings nothing but entertainment – a pie in the face, a fop being dragged by a bear out of a department store – all events governed by fate and timing, not language and argument. The tramp never changes the opinion of the policeman. The truncheon swings, the tramp scuttles through a corner window and disturbs the fat lady's ablutions. These comedies are nightmares. The audience emits horrified laughter as Chaplin, blindfolded, rollerskates near the edge of the unbalconied mezzanine. No one shouts to warn him. He cannot talk or listen. North America is still without language, gestures and work and bloodlines are the only currency.

But it was a spell of language that brought Nicholas here, arriving in Canada without a passport in 1914, a great journey made in silence. Hanging under the bridge, he describes the adventure to himself, just as he was told a fairy tale of Upper America by those who returned to the Macedonian villages, those first travellers who were the judas goats to the west.

Daniel Stoyanoff had tempted them all. In North America everything was rich and dangerous. You went in as a sojourner and came back wealthy – Daniel buying a farm with the compensation he had received for losing an arm during an accident in a meat factory. Laughing about it! Banging his other hand down hard onto the table and wheezing with laughter, calling them all fools, sheep! As if his arm had been a dry cow he had fooled the Canadians with.

Nicholas had been stunned by the simplicity of the contract. He could see Stoyanoff's body livid on the killing floor – standing in two inches of cow blood, screaming like nothing as much as cattle, his arm gone, his balance gone. He had returned to the village of Oschima, his sleeve flapping like a scarf, and with cash for the land. He had looked for a wife with two arms and settled down.

In ten years Daniel Stoyanoff had bored everyone in the village with his tall tales and he couldn't wait for children to grow up and become articulate so he could thrill them with his sojourner's story of Upper America. What Daniel told them was that he had in fact lost both arms in the accident, but he happened to be rooming with a tailor who was out of work and who had been, luckily, on the killing floors of Schnaufer's that morning. Dedora the tailor had pulled gut out of a passing cat, stitched Daniel's right arm back on, and then turned for the other but a scrap dog had run off with it, one of those dogs that lounged by the doorway. Whenever you looked up from cutting and slicing the carcasses you would see them, whenever you left work at the end of the day in your blood-soaked overalls and boots they followed you, licking and chewing your cuffs.

Stoyanoff's story was told to all children of the region at a certain age and he became a hero to them. *Look*, he would say, stripping off his shirt in the Oschima high street, irritating the customers of Petroff's outdoor bar once more, *look at what a good tailor Dedora was – no hint of stitches.* He drew an imaginary line around his good shoulder and the kids brought their eyes up close, then went over to his other shoulder and saw the alternative, the grotesque stump.

Nicholas was twenty-five years old when war in the Balkans began. After his village was burned he left with three friends on horseback. They rode one day and a whole night and another day down to Trikala, carrying food and a sack of clothes. Then they jumped on a train that was bound for Athens. Nicholas had a fever, he was delirious, needing air in the thick smoky compartments, wanting to climb up onto the roof. In Greece they bribed the captain of a boat a napoleon each to carry them over to Trieste. By now they all had fevers. They slept in the basement of a deserted factory, doing nothing, just trying to keep warm. There had to be no hint of illness before trying to get into Switzerland. They were six or seven days in the factory basement, unaware of time. One almost died from the high fevers. They slept embracing each other to keep warm. They talked about Daniel Stoyanoff's America.

On the train the Swiss doctor examined everyone's eyes and let the four friends continue over the border. They were in France. In Le Havre they spoke to the captain of an old boat that carried animals. It was travelling to New Brunswick.

Two of Nicholas' friends died on the trip. An Italian showed him how to drink blood in the animal pens to keep strong. It was a French boat called *La Siciliana*. He still remembered the name, remembered landing in Saint John and everyone thinking how primitive it looked. How primitive Canada was. They had to walk half a mile to the station where they were to be examined. They took whatever they needed from the sacks of the two who had died and walked towards Canada.

Their boat had been so filthy they were covered with lice. The steerage passengers put down their baggage by the outdoor taps near the toilets. They stripped naked and stood in front of their partners as if looking into a mirror. They began to remove the lice from each other and washed the dirt off with cold water and a cloth, working down the body. It was late November. They put on their clothes and went into the Customs sheds.

Nicholas had no passport, he could not speak a word of English. He had ten napoleons, which he showed them to explain he wouldn't be dependent. They let him through. He was in Upper America.

He took a train for Toronto, where there were many from his village; he would not be among strangers. But there was no work. So he took a train north to Copper Cliff, near Sudbury, and worked there in a Macedonian bakery. He was paid seven dollars a month with food and sleeping quarters. After six months he went to Sault Ste. Marie. He still could hardly speak English and decided to go to school, working nights in another Macedonian bakery. If he did not learn the language he would be lost.

The school was free. The children in the class were ten years old and he was twenty-six. He used to get up at two in the morning and make dough and bake till 8:30. At nine he would go to school. The teachers were all young ladies and were very good people. During this time in the Sault he had translation dreams – because of his fast and obsessive studying of English. In the dreams trees changed not just their names but their looks and character. Men started answering in falsettos. Dogs spoke out fast to him as they passed him on the street.

When he returned to Toronto all he needed was a voice for all this language. Most immigrants learned their English from recorded songs or, until the talkies came, through mimicking actors on stage. It was a common habit to select one actor and follow him throughout his career, annoyed when he was given a small part, and seeing each of his plays as often as possible – sometimes as often as ten times during a run. Usually by the end of an east-end production at the Fox or Parrot Theatres the actors' speeches would be followed by growing echoes as Macedonians, Finns, and Greeks repeated the phrases after a half-second pause, trying to get the pronunciation right.

This infuriated the actors, especially when a line such as "Who put the stove in the living room, Kristin?" – which had originally brought the house down – was now spoken simultaneously by at least seventy people and so tended to lose its spontaneity. When the matinee idol Wayne Burnett dropped dead during a performance, a Sicilian butcher took over, knowing his lines and his blocking meticulously, and money did not have to be refunded.

Certain actors were popular because they spoke slowly. Lethargic ballads, and a kind of blues where the first line of a verse is repeated three times, were in great demand. Sojourners walked out of their accent into regional American voices. Nicholas, unfortunately, would later choose Fats Waller as his model and so his emphasis on usually unnoticed syllables and the throwaway lines made him seem high-strung or dangerously anti-social or too loving.

But during the time he worked on the bridge, he was seen as a recluse. He would begin sentences in his new language, mutter, and walk away. He became a vault of secrets and memories.

Privacy was the only weight he carried. None of his cohorts really knew him. This man, awkward in groups, would walk off and leave strange clues about himself, like a dog's footprints on the snowed roof of a garage.

*   *   *

Hagh! A doctor attending his arm, this is what woke him, brought him out of his dream. *Hah!* It was six hours since he had fallen asleep. Kosta was there. He saw that the veil and his shirt had been cut open by the doctor. Somehow, they said, he had managed to get his arm back into the socket.

He jerked his hand to the veil, looking at it closely.

She had stayed until Kosta came down in the early morning. She talked to him about the arm, to get a doctor, she had to leave. She spoke? Yes yes. What did she sound like? Hah? What more did Kosta know about her? He mentioned her black skirt. Before he left, Nicholas looked around the bar and found strips of the black habit she had cut away to make a skirt for the street.

When he walks into the fresh air outside the Ohrida Lake Restaurant, on the morning after the accident on the bridge, he sees the landscape as something altered, no longer so familiar that it is invisible to him. Nicholas Temelcoff walks now seeing Parliament Street from the point of view of the woman – who had looked through his belt-satchel while he slept, found his wide wire shears, and used them to cut away the black lengths of her habit. When he walks out of the Ohrida Lake Restaurant that morning it is her weather he grows aware of. He knows he will find her.

There are long courtships which are performed in absence. This one is built perhaps on his remark about her hair or her almost-silent question as he was falling off some tower or bridge into sleep. The verge of sleep was always terrifying to Nicholas so he would drink himself into it blunting out the seconds of pure fear when he could not use his arms, would lie there knowing he'd witness the half-second fall before sleep, the fear of it greater than anything he felt on the viaduct or any task he carried out for the Dominion Bridge Company.

As he fell, he remembers later, he felt a woman's arm reaching for him, curious about his name.

He is aware of her now, the twin. What holds them together is not the act which saved her life but those moments since. The lost song on the radio. His offhand and relaxed flattery to a nun with regard to her beauty. Then he had leaned his head back, closed his eyes for too long, and slept.

A week later he rejoins the flatbed truck that carries the tar and fire, jumps on with the other men, and is back working at the bridge. His arm healed, he swings from Pier D to Pier C, ignores the stories he hears of the nun who disappeared. He lies supine on the end of his tether looking up towards the struts of the bridge, pivoting slowly. He knows the panorama of the valley better than any engineer. Like a bird. Better than Edmund Burke, the bridge's architect, or Harris, better than the surveyors of 1912 when they worked blind through the bush. The panorama revolves with him and he hangs in this long silent courtship, her absence making him look everywhere.

In a year he will open up a bakery with the money he has saved. He releases the catch on the pulley and slides free of the bridge.

THE SEARCHER

PATRICK LEWIS arrived in the city of Toronto as if it were land after years at sea. Growing up in the country had governed his childhood: the small village of Bellrock, the highway of river down which the log drivers came, drinking, working raucous, and in the spring leaving the inhabitants shocked within the silence. Now, at twenty-one, he had been drawn out from that small town like a piece of metal and dropped under the vast arches of Union Station to begin his life once more. He owned nothing, had scarcely any money. There was a piece of feldspar in his pocket that his fingers had stumbled over during the train journey. He was an immigrant to the city.

What remained in Patrick from his childhood were letters frozen inside mailboxes after ice storms. What he remembered was loving only things to do with colour, hating the whiteness, stepping into the warm brown universe of barns, the breath and steam of cattle rolling out, the acrid shit and urine he could summon up even now in the heart of Toronto. The smell had paraded grandly over his first seduction in a hay bed, the angry girl slapping him when both were full and guilty. What he remembered was frozen laundry, carrying overalls like a body into the kitchen and seating them in a chair, hoping his father would see them before they melted and lolled over the table.

Then summer. Blackflies and mosquitoes. Leaping not into hay but into the black underwater colour of creek, walking naked to the farmhouse, chewing rhubarb, clothes under one arm. You bit the glossy skin of the raw rhubarb and ripped its fibres open and sucked the flavour out. You put the smallest pellet of raspberry onto your tongue and opened it delicately with your teeth. You stood in a field on a hot day obsessed with this precise taste.

Now, in the city, he was new even to himself, the past locked away. He saw his image in the glass of telephone booths. He ran his hands over the smooth pink marble pillars that reached up into the rotunda. This train station was a palace, its niches and caverns an intimate city. He could be shaved, eat a meal, or have his shoes coloured.

He saw a man with three suitcases, well-dressed, shouting out in another language. The man's eyes burned through everyone who at first received his scream personally. But the phrases were for angels in the air to assist him or for demons to leave him. Two days later Patrick returned to pick up his luggage from a locker. He saw the man again, still unable to move from his safe zone, in a different suit, as if one step away was the quicksand of the new world.

Patrick sat on a bench and watched the tides of movement, felt the reverberations of trade. He spoke out his name and it struggled up in a hollow echo and was lost in the high air of Union Station. No one turned. They were in the belly of a whale.

When Ambrose Small, the millionaire, disappeared in 1919, it was discovered that the police had his Bertillon record. Between 1889 and 1923 the Bertillon identification system was used to locate criminals and missing persons. Bertillon's method consisted of the measurement of certain parts of the body: the length of head, width of head, length of right ear, length of left foot, length of left middle finger, the length of left forearm. In homes and prisons and mortuaries all over North America limbs were measured and the results sent in to the Toronto police. During the fever of the case over 5,000 people claimed to be Ambrose Small. They claimed they had amnesia, were kidnapped in a brown sack, were disfigured, were hidden in geological holes in the Scarborough Bluffs, were stretched to longer than five foot six inches on racks, were overfed, had all their hair removed, had their memories wiped clean by certain foods, had their pigmentation altered, were turned into women, had the length of their right ear changed, were in the meantime hungry and penniless and would someone mail $500 to Nelson, B.C., or Wichita, Kansas, or Cornerbrook, Newfoundland.

A woman in Hamilton saw Ambrose with his throat cut. She woke one morning to feel blood on the pillow, looked up and saw someone was sawing her neck, and she said I am Ambrose Small. Then she woke up again. Another had a vision that she was unlocking the safe at the Grand Opera House and saw a curled-up skeleton inside resting on documents.

The press leapt upon every possibility.

MYSTERY MAN OF NORTH RESEMBLES SMALL
— *Star, May 27, 1921*
Remains may be exhumed if further clues come to light.

SKELETON FOUND IN WHITBY FIELD
— *Telegram, June 2, 1921*
"The possibility that it might be Ambrose Small occurred to me when we were digging it up," Acting Chief Thomas reflected this evening.

IOWA DETECTIVE IS CERTAIN HE HAS FOUND A.J. SMALL
— *Mail, August 16, 1921*
John Brophy, Head of Brophy Detective Agency, Iowa, who was ousted from his job as Assistant Chief of Police, claims to have a man under guard whom he has identified as A.J. Small. Brophy said he would produce Small when the Canadian authorities are ready to pay the reward offered.

"The man is Small," he said.

The man was recovering from a pistol wound in the neck, concussion of the brain and minor injuries. Both his legs had been cut off near the knees.

"I will tell you what Small told me after he had identified his own picture," he said. " 'All I can remember is that there was a blow and then darkness, then terrible suffering. From then on I remembered nothing until I was brought here. I think I was in Omaha, that's all.' "

Between 1910 and 1919 Ambrose Small had been the jackal of Toronto's business world. He was a manipulator of deals and property, working his way up from nothing into the world of theatre management. He bought Toronto's Grand Opera House when he was twenty-eight years old, and then proceeded to buy theatres all over the province – in St. Catharines, Kingston, Arkona, Petrolia, Peterborough, and Paris, Ontario, until he held the whole web of theatre traffic in his outstretched arms. He built the Grand in London, Ontario – the largest theatre in North America, save for Shea's Hippodrome. He owned ninety-six theatres. He became a gambler at the track, obsessed with greyhounds.

He married Theresa Kormann, and in so doing alienated his sisters. His wife was a prohibitionist and Small offered her the theatre for one night a week and she put on temperance shows and nobody came. *"Pass by the open doorway, ignore the foul saloon,"* the chorus sang to a mostly empty auditorium. On other nights, performances of *Ben-Hur* and *Naughty Miss Louise* packed the theatre. In the Glen Road house, Small held appalling parties. Showgirls, live peacocks, staggered out drunk in the morning hours and strolled aimlessly home along the Rosedale streets – the chauffeurs of the rich following at a tactful distance in their car.

In Paris, Ontario, he met an actress named Clara Dickens and she became his lover. She was twenty-one years old and Small was thirty-five and he charmed her with his variousness. He was a spinner. He was bare-knuckle capitalism. He was a hawk who hovered over the whole province, swooping down for the kill, buying up every field of wealth, and eating the profit in mid-air. He was a jackal. This is what the press called him and he laughed at them, spun a thread around his critics and bought them up. Either he owned people or they were his enemies. No compatriots. No prisoners. In the tenth century, he liked to say, the price of a greyhound or a hawk was the same as that for a man.

Each morning he rose and walked to his offices at the Grand Theatre on Adelaide Street. He got there at least an hour before any of his staff and plotted out the day. This was the time he loved most, choreographing his schemes, theorizing on bids and counter-bids and interest rates and the breaking point of his adversaries. He pulled out an imported avocado pear, sliced it into thin green moons, and sat at his roll-top desk eating it and thinking. By the time his staff arrived he had worked out all possible scenarios at his empty desk. He went down to the barbershop, lay back, and was shaved and manicured. His day was over. The machine of Ambrose Small began to tick across the city.

With his lover Clara Dickens he was gregarious, generous, charming. Seeing him once or twice a week she knew the best of Ambrose. She steered him away from his peacock parties. They went on excursions. He bought hotels, he bought houses under different names all over Ontario. "I'm a thief," he'd say. "All thieves must plan their escape routes." The names of the towns, his pseudonyms, slipped memorized into his brain, unrecorded anywhere else. He bought or consumed, it seemed to Clara, anything he alighted on.

On December 16, 1919, Ambrose Small failed to keep an appointment. A million dollars had been taken from his bank account. He had either been murdered or was missing. His body, alive or dead, was never found.

Most criminal investigations in the early part of the century were dignified and leisurely. Villains took their time, they took trains and ships. In 1910, Dr. Crippen's arrest on board a liner, through the use of a radio-phone (while he was reading *The Four Just Men*), was thought by the public to be in bad taste. But there was something about the Ambrose Small case that created a feeling of open season. It was an opportunity for complaint about the state of the world; Small's blatant capitalism had clarified the gulf between the rich and the starving.

For the first year after Small's disappearance the public watched the police try to solve the case. But when they failed, and when the family put up an $80,000 reward for the millionaire's whereabouts, the public shouldered itself into the case. Now everyone looked for him. By 1921, one could be hired by a company at $4 a week as a 'searcher' and these individuals roamed the city and the smaller towns dragging suspicious strangers into police stations and having their measurements taken under the Bertillon process. The searchers resembled the press gangs of earlier centuries, and there were many rival organizations at work, investing in the project as if it were an oil field or a gold mine.

In 1924, after working for a year at various jobs in Toronto, Patrick Lewis became a searcher. The organizations were still active. It did not matter that five years had passed. No body had been found to fit Small's Bertillon chart and hordes of the otherwise unemployed were being hired. In these hard times any hope of a 'gusher' or 'strike' was worth pursuing. The search had turned the millionaire's body into a rare coin, a piece of financial property.

What held most interest for Patrick was the collection of letters the police had handed over to the family. Gradually he came into contact with Small's two sisters, who until then had found no one to take the letters seriously. Cranks, mediums, blackmail threats, the claims of kidnappers – the police and Small's wife had scorned them all. Patrick was befriended by the sisters at their house on Isabella Street. Clara Dickens knew him best, they told him. She was the rare lover. Talk to Briffa, said the sisters, he also thought she was the perfect woman for Ambrose – not Theresa, the wife, the *saint*.

Patrick took the train to Paris, Ontario, and met the radio actress Clara Dickens. She stood in the hall beside her mother and said she would not speak about Ambrose Small. She claimed not to have seen him since he disappeared. He stood there watching her. She asked him to leave.

In the books he read, women were rescued from runaway horses, from frozen pond accidents. Clara Dickens stood on the edge of the world of wealth. When she spoke to him she had been bending to one side as she attached an earring, gazing into the hall mirror, dismissing him, their eyes catching in the reflection. He was dazzled by her – her long white arms, the faint hair on the back of her neck – as if she without turning had fired a gun over her shoulder and mortally wounded him. The 'rare lover,' the 'perfect woman.'

And what else was she, apart from being the lover of Ambrose Small? Dressed up, about to go out, she had looked like a damsel fly, the sequins and gauze up to her neck. But there was something about the way she stood there, not turning around to talk to him properly.

When he went back the next morning she opened the door, her sleeves rolled up, those arms covered with flour up to her elbows.

– I thought you were rich, he said.

– Why? Do you want me to hire you to find my beloved?

All that evening and late into the morning hours Patrick tried to seduce Clara Dickens and then the next day when he was exhausted she seduced him. He was reading through the old news clippings about Ambrose in the Paris library when Clara arrived. He was almost asleep over the 1919 files, his cheek awkward on his shoulder as if someone had come up to him in the silence of the reading room and broken his neck. She strolled into the library dressed in white and stood in front of the bookshelves.

– I'll drive you back to the Arlington Hotel.

Her voice wakened him. She turned a chair around so she could straddle it and she leaned forward, her elbows against its back. In her white dress she seemed the focus of all sunlight in the library. There was laughter and then tenseness on her face. Her long arm reached forward and picked up a clipping.

– You think I am the line to him, don't you? You think that he must have left his shadow on me.

He couldn't talk back against her beauty. He noticed a fragment of water under her eyelid, a sun tear she was unaware of.

– Come. I'll drive you back to the hotel.

At that hour he did not think of seduction. He was exhausted by all their conversations the previous night on her porch overlooking Broadway Street. They had been outrageous and flamboyant in each other's company, their arguments like duets. He normally took months to approach someone, and at the slightest rejection he would turn and never go back. But he argued just so they could remain together on that porch deep in moonlight, half-laughing at the other's ploys. She wouldn't let him kiss her or hold her standing up – didn't want all of their bodies touching, that possibility.

They had walked in rain beside the Grand River towards her car. A gift from Ambrose, no doubt, he thought to himself. He was so tired there was no sophistication or cunning in him that night. And she herself did not know how to deal with this sudden obsession for her. She had driven him slowly back to the Arlington Hotel and they sat in the car.

– Tomorrow the library for me, he said.
– I could come and join you.

She clicked her tongue and jerked her head to the side suggestively.

It was two in the morning. She sat half-facing him, her feet already out of their shoes, one knee pointed towards him by the gear-shift. She let him kiss her goodnight and he sat there for a moment gazing at her face patterned by streetlight.

He got out and closed the door too energetically and realized after he had taken three steps how that had sounded. He turned back.

– That wasn't a slam.
– I know.

She was sitting there very alone, still, looking towards the seat he had left, her head down.

– Goodnight.
– Goodnight, Patrick.

Now they stepped from the news library into bright sunlight and they got into her car, Patrick carrying his cardboard box of notes. Both of them were so tired they hardly spoke during the drive back to the hotel.

His room when they got there was full of bright daylight and traffic noises came through the open window. They slept almost immediately, holding each other's hands.

When he woke, her eyes were studying him. Only her dark neck and face were visible. He felt awkward, having slept in his clothes.

  – Hello.

  – Sing to me, she murmured.

  – What?

  – I want it formal. Can you sing?

She smiled and he moved across the bed to her softness.

After they had made love he brought his pillow as close as he could for comfortable focus and gazed at her. When he woke she was gone, there was no answer on her telephone. He came back to the bed and inhaled whatever perfume there was left on the pillow.

* * *

  – Patrick, is that you?

  – Yes, Clara.

  – Doesn't sound like you.

  – I was asleep.

  – I'm taking you somewhere. Pick up some booze.

And a corkscrew. I've got the food. We should be away a few days.

It was a winding road they drove on towards Paris Plains, past gorges and tobacco fields.

— We're going to my friend's farmhouse.

— Ambrose?

— No, her name is Alice. I'll tell you about her later.

— You've got all the time in the damn world now.

— Later.

They entered a small farmhouse which had a woodstove in the kitchen. Bird feathers had been prised under the edges of wallpaper, here and there. In the front room there was a bed in an alcove, windows on three sides of it. A mat on the floor. There was hardly any furniture. It looked to him like the quarters of a monk. The friend was not to arrive for a couple of days, Clara said.

Later that night they lay on the bed by the three windows, barely dressed. He liked to sleep separate, in his own world, but with her he kept waking, reaching to hold her flesh against him. During the night Clara turned slowly like something on the floor of the ocean. She would put more and more clothes on in the darkness. She was always cold at night, in this room of the sea.

— You awake?

— What time is it? she said.

— Still night.

— Ahh.

— I love you. Were you ever in love? Apart from Ambrose.

— Yeah.

He was put off by her casual admission.

— I fell in love with a guy named Stump Jones when I was sixteen.

— Stump!

– There was a problem with the name.
– I'll say.
– Goodnight, Patrick, I'm sleepy.
– Hey!

He got up and strolled around the farmhouse happier and more at ease than he had ever been. She was already back in deep sleep, snoring, wearing one of his shirts to keep warm. A smile on her face. Clara the smirker. He wanted to get hold of Stump Jones and beat the hell out of him. Sixteen! Where had he been at sixteen? She had been Small's lover, Stump's lover, and who else? He found himself at this hour in the spell of her body, within the complex architecture of her past.

He had been looking through the window for over ten minutes when he suddenly focused on a shadow on the glass and saw it was a tree frog. He lit the oil lamp and held it up to the creature. A *pseudacris triseriata*. Hello friend, he breathed towards the pale-green speckled body hanging against the pane.

– Clara . . .
– What is it?
– Ambrose.

Love was like childhood for him. It opened him up, he was silly and relaxed.

– What!

She was wide awake, watching him as if he were crazy.

– Come here, I want you to see this.

She looked at the window and then back at him, refusing to speak.

– He wants you with all your clothes off.
– It's three in the morning, Patrick, you're supposed to

be asleep. You're supposed to be searching for my beloved. (*Beloved!* He grinned.) Do you want to make love, is that it?

— It's a tree frog!

— A tree frog in the moonlight is not rare.

— Yes it is, they only come out during the day. He wants to consider your thorax, your abdomen.

— Is this some kind of Bolshevik gesture?

She unbuttoned the shirt, stood between him and the glass.

— Tomorrow night he'll probably bring his pals to see you. Some places call them bell frogs. When they get excited they make a sound like a bell. Sometimes they bark like dogs.

She leaned forward and put her mouth to the green belly against the glass and kissed it.

— Hello Ambrose, she whispered, how are you doing?

Patrick put his arms around her and held her breasts.

— Marry me, willya . . .

He started barking.

— One of these days, soon, I'll go.

— To join Ambrose.

— Yes . . . I know he's alive.

— I have a fear I won't see you again.

— You talk on, Patrick, but you have no remorse.

— A strange word. It suggests a turning around on yourself.

— Don't speak. Here . . .

He met Ambrose in a dream. At the door he said, "There is this grey figure attached to my body, Patrick. I want you to cut it off me." They were old friends. All Patrick had was a penknife. He unfolded the blade and made Ambrose move into the hall, underneath the one light near the iron elevators. It was easier to see what it was now. A grey peacock had been sewn onto his friend. Patrick began to cut it away.

Ambrose was quiet. There appeared to be no pain at all. Patrick got down to the ankles and with a final saw from the knife the surplus figure curled off. It lay there like excess undercarpeting that had not been cleared away. They walked back to Small's door, shook hands, and parted. As he was falling through the final buildings of his dream he heard the news of Small's murder – he had been found vertically sliced in two.

– What?
– I said, were you dreaming?
– I don't know. Why?
– You were twitching.
– Hmmm. What kind of twitching?
– You know, like a dog asleep in front of the fire.
– Maybe I was chasing a rabbit.

They were sitting on the floor leaning into the corner of the room, her mouth on his nipple, her hand moving his cock slowly. An intricate science, his whole body imprisoned there, a ship in a bottle. I'm going to come. Come in my mouth. Moving forward, his fingers pulling back her hair like torn silk, he ejaculated, disappearing into her. She crooked her finger, motioning, and he bent down and put his mouth on hers. He took it, the white character, and they passed it back and forth between them till it no longer existed, till they didn't know who had him like a lost planet somewhere in the body.

The next day they drove along the country roads in her Packard. He watched her as she spoke of the Wheeler Needle Works where her father had worked, the Medusa factory by the railway.

– This is the tour of my teenage life, Patrick. I'll show you where I almost got seduced.
– The crucial years.
– Yes.

He loved the eroticism of her history, the knowledge of where she sat in schoolrooms, her favourite brand of pencil at the age of nine. Details flooded his heart. Clara said once, "When I know a man well socially, the only way I'll ever get to know him better will be to sleep with him." Seduction was the natural progression of curiosity. And during these days he found he had become interested only in her, her childhood, her radio work, this landscape in which she had grown up. He no longer wanted Small, he wanted to exorcise Small from Clara's mind.

It was raining and they couldn't get out of the car. She rolled down the window.

– This is where I used to bury my lunch.

Taking his pocket handkerchief, she wet a corner with her tongue.

— You've got mud on you, she said, rubbing his forehead.

All these gestures removed place, country, everything. He felt he had to come back to the world.

— Tell me something about Ambrose quickly.
— Whenever he lied his voice became quiet and reasonable.
— What else.
— We used to fuck on the *Cayuga*.
— The day ferry? Jesus, on the *Cayuga*?

He was drawing out her history with Small, a splinter from a lady's palm. He was constantly appalled.

— Would it be forgivable to say I stayed with him because he gave me a piano?
— What are you telling me?
— I loved the piano. It was something to get lost in. My exit, my privacy. He had his money, gambling, he had his winning elsewhere. I had my radio work and my piano. Everyone has to scratch on walls somewhere or they go crazy. And you?
— I don't know.
— There was a time when I could have slept with his friend Briffa, for instance. Around him the air was always fraught with possibilities.
— I like fraught air.
— Briffa was lovely. European courtesy, a suggestion of brutality, happily married. I liked him because he was shaved down and focused. He decorated theatres. He had his vision, and that of course is a great aphrodisiac. The only man I met who had a vision. Ambrose

didn't. But he drew people like Briffa and others around him. Nobody else would touch them, let alone give them jobs. It was a battle – Small and his friends against the rest. Ambrose was laying siege, attacking all those remnants of wealthy families who really were the end of the line.

   – And you were the pianist.

   – Yes, the pianist, the musical interlude, the romance in the afternoon.

   – He was the first to bugger me.

Patrick lay shocked and still beside her in the afternoon sunlight. When he spoke of his own past he was not calm like her. He flashed over previous relationships, often in bad humour. He would disclose the truth of his past only if interrogated with a specific question. He defended himself for most of the time with a habit of vagueness.

There was a wall in him that no one reached. Not even Clara, though she assumed it had deformed him. A tiny stone swallowed years back that had grown with him and which he carried around because he could not shed it. His motive for hiding it had probably extinguished itself years earlier. . . . Patrick and his small unimportant stone. It had entered him at the wrong time in his life. Then it had been a flint of terror. He could have easily turned aside at the age of seven or twenty, and just spat it out and kept on walking, and forgotten it by the next street corner.

So we are built.

   – Who are your friends, Patrick?

– You. Only you.

– Alice comes tomorrow.

– We should go then.

– No, we can stay. You'll like her. But sometime after that I'll leave you.

– For Ambrose.

– Yes, for Ambrose. And you must never follow me.

– It takes me a long time to forgive.

– Don't worry, Patrick. Things fill in. People are replaced.

He wondered if at first she had been something he wanted to steal, not because she was Clara but because she belonged to the enemy. But now there was her character. This daughter of the foreman at Wheeler Needle Works, who seemed to have entered him like a spirit, bullying his private nature. She had been the lover of Ambrose Small, had been caught in the slow discreet wheel of the rich. And she would have learned those subtle rules that came alongside their gifts.

She started laughing, the hair on her temples still wet after their lovemaking. He sensed suddenly the sweat on himself as well. As he held her, he still didn't know who she was.

After midnight Clara strolls behind her friend Alice, removes the shawl from her shoulders, and ties it on as a headband. Patrick watches Clara intently – the bones, the planes of lamplight on her face, hair no longer in the way. Follow me, she could say in her shawl headband, and he would be one of the Gadarene swine.

– Did I tell you, Clara laughs, how I helped my father shave dogs? A true story. My father loved to hunt. He had four redbone hounds, with no names – they disappeared so often we used numbers. During the summer, hunters steal dogs and my father was always worried about theft. So we'd drive to the worst barber in Paris and ask him to clip the dogs. He was always insulted by this, though he had not much other business.

I'd sit in the barber chair and hold the dog in my lap while it got clipped, and then we drove back with naked dogs. At home my dad got out his cow razor. He'd shave the midriffs to the skin, then we'd hose them and leave them to dry in the sun. After lunch my father wrote out DICKENS 1, DICKENS 2, and DICKENS 3 with tree paint in neat letters on their sides. I was allowed to paint the name on the last dog. We had to hold them to the ground until the paint dried properly. I wrote DICKENS 4.

Those were favourite times. All day we'd talk about things I was not sure of. About plants, what wine tasted like. He put me right on how to have babies. I thought I had to take a watermelon seed, put it between two pieces of bread and drink lots of water. I thought this was how my parents talked when they were alone. We'd chat to the dogs too who were nonplussed, looking thin and naked. Sometimes it seemed to me I'd just had four babies. Great times. Then my father died of a stroke when I was fifteen. Dammit.

– Yeah, says Patrick, my father too. . . . My father was a wizard, he could blow logs right out of the water.

– What happened?

– He got killed setting charges in a feldspar mine. The company had tried to go too deep and the section above him collapsed. There wasn't an explosion. The shelf just slid down with him into the cave and drowned him. He was buried in feldspar. I didn't even know what it was. They use it in everything – chinaware, tiles, pottery, inlaid table tops, even in artificial teeth. I lost him there.

– Here's to holy fathers, Alice says, holding up her glass.

Conversation dips again into childhood but the friend Alice plucks only details from the present to celebrate. She reveals no past, remains sourceless, like those statues of men with wrapped heads who symbolize undiscovered rivers.

All night as they talk the sky and the fields outside seem potent with summer storm. The night kitchen with these two actresses is overwhelming. Clara and Alice slip into tongues, impersonate people, and keep each other talking long into the night. Patrick is suddenly an audience. They imitate the way men smoke. They discuss how women laugh – from the raucous to the sullen to the mercenary. He is in a room full of diverse laughter, looking back and forth from Clara's vividness and erotic movement, even when she stretches, to Alice's paleness and suppressed energy. "My pale friend," Clara had called her.

At three in the morning there is thunder in the distance. Patrick cannot keep his eyes open. He says goodnight, and abandons himself to the sofa, closing the door to the kitchen.

The two women continue talking and laughing, a glance of sheet lightning miles away. After an hour or so they say to each other, "Let's get him."

In the darkness of the farmhouse Clara and Alice approach his bed. They carry candles and a large roll of paper, whispering to each other. They uncover the face of Patrick hidden in the green blanket. This is enough. The candles are placed on a straightback chair. They cut the paper with draper's scissors and pin the four corners of it to the floor. They begin to draw hard and quickly, as if copying down a blueprint in a foreign country. It seems as illicit as that. Approaching a sleeping man to see what he will reveal of himself in his portrait at this time of the night.

He sleeps, and during the next while they work together on the same sheet which sometimes tears with the force of the crayon. They have done this often to each other, these spirit paintings, the head leaking purple or yellow – auras of jealousy and desire. Given the vagueness of his covered body, they draw upon all they know or can guess about him. They kneel, their heads bright beside the candlelight, crayoning against the texture of the floor. Anger, honesty, stumble out. One travels along a descant of insight and the other follows, completes the phrase, making the gesture safe.

A cave mural. The yellow light flickers upon his face against the sofa cushion, upon the two women sweating during this close night, their heads down as if pulling something out of a river. One leans back to stretch while the other explores the portrait. "Are we witches?" Alice asks.

Clara begins to laugh. She moans like a spirit looking for the keyhole out of the room. She places her hands on the frail walls, then her mouth explodes with noise and she tugs Alice out into the Ontario night. They crash down the wood steps, Clara's growls unnaming things, their bodies rolling among the low moon flowers and grass and then leaping up as the rain breaks free of the locked heat clouds, running into the thunder of a dark field, through the stomach-high beans and corn, the damp rustle of it against their skirts and outstretched arms – the house fever slipping away from them.

The rain comes through their thin cotton clothes against their muscles. Alice sweeps back her wet hair. A sudden flinging of sheet lightning and Clara sees Alice subliminal in movement almost rising up into the air, shirt removed, so her body can meet the rain, the rest of her ascent lost to darkness till the next brief flutter of light when they hold a birch tree in their clasped hands, lean back and swing within the rain.

They crawl delirious together in the blackness. There is no moon. There is the moon flower in its small power of accuracy, like a compass pointing to where the moon is, so they can bay towards its absence.

*   *   *

He moves quietly through the house in the early morning. At the top of the stairs he looks through a small round window into the fields. This is a fragile farmhouse. He has felt the winds shake it during the night. Now there is a strange peace, grass and trees seen through the white light of morning, the two women asleep. Yesterday they were up at dawn flinging rhubarb across the room at each other – as he discovered, waking to riotous laughter. He found them in the midst of battle, Alice bent over in laughter, in tears, and Clara suddenly sheepish when she saw him enter the kitchen.

Now there is no noise but the creak of his moving. In the bedroom he finds them asleep in each other's arms, unaware of daylight filling the room. He touches the elbow of Alice Gull and her flesh shifts away. He puts his hand into her palm and she grips it unconsciously, not fully awake.

> – Hi.
> – I have to go soon, he says. A train.
> – Ummm. We left you a present from last night.
> – Yes?
> – She'll explain it later.

She stretches carefully without disturbing Clara.

> – Throw me a shirt, I'll have breakfast with you.

In the kitchen Patrick cuts open a grapefruit and hands her half. Alice shakes her head. She remains sitting on the stool in the long pink shirt and watches him move, efficient in her kitchen. He slides through company, she notices, as anonymously as possible. She points to certain drawers silently when he asks for spoons or a spatula.

Patrick is not a breakfast talker and in fifteen minutes he is ready to leave. She holds his arm at the door. He kisses her accidentally too close to the eye.

— Give her a kiss for me.

— I will.

— Tell her I'll see her tonight at the hotel.

— Okay.

She closes the door firmly and watches him through the window on his walk to the train station, striding from one frame of glass to another.

She climbs back into bed with Clara, puts her arm around her to accept the warmth she has lost by rising. Welcomes the sleepy haven of Monday morning.

His mind remains against them, like an impress of his hand on their sleeping flesh, the cold train window at his cheek. Hungry for Clara, he thinks about Alice as if he has not focused on her before, as if Alice being touched by Clara has grown magically, fully formed.

*   *   *

In the Arlington Hotel that night he studies the large drawing Clara has tacked to the door. He has come off well, Clara tells him, the soul is pliable. He does not believe her. Unless his soul expands during sleep, unless sleep somehow attaches the disparate elements of his character. Perhaps the portrait will teach him. He loves the closeness between the two women and he enjoys their gift of his supposedly guardless nature.

— What did you think of her?

— I liked her.

— She's a great actress.

— On the radio?

— No, on the stage.

— Better than you, is she?

— By a hundred miles.

— Yes, I liked her.

Later he will think of the seconds when he was almost asleep and they entered the dark room with candles. The approach of magicians. He feels more community remembering this than anything in his life. Patrick and the two women. A study for the New World. Judith and Holofernes. St. Jerome and the Lion. Patrick and the Two Women. He loves the tableau, even though being asleep he had not witnessed the ceremony.

Sometimes when he is alone Patrick will blindfold himself and move around a room, slowly at first, then faster until he is immaculate and magical in it. He will parade, turn suddenly away from lampshades, duck under hanging plants, even run across the room and leap in his darkness over small tables.

All night long Patrick and Clara have talked, the name of Ambrose like a drip of water in their conversation. All night they have talked about her plan to join her 'beloved,' the sound of his name like a poison, like the word *nicotine*. She will leave tomorrow. She will not tell him where Small is. She demands that he not try to follow her after they drive to Toronto to put her on the train. Patrick feels he knows nothing of most of Clara's life. He keeps finding and losing parts of her, as if opening a drawer to discover another mask.

They sit half-dressed on the bed on this last morning. All night long they have talked and he has felt inarticulate against the power of his unseen enemy, unable to persuade Clara out of this journey towards Ambrose. He offers to perform his trick for her, draws her long silk shawl from the sleeve of her coat, doubles it, and ties it around his eyes.

He positions Clara on the bed and tells her not to move. Then he takes off into the room – at first using his hands for security, then ignoring them, just throwing his body within an inch of the window, swooping his head down parallel to shelves while he rushes across the room in straight lines, in curves, as if he has the mechanism of a bat in his human blood. He leaps across the bed delighted at her shriek. He is magnificent. He is perfect, she thinks.

He mutters to her as he moves – "Watch this tray" – as he flings it up and catches it. "And this eggshell on the floor which I'll crush like the bones of Stump Jones. You are so beautiful, Clara, I'll never go blind. I want to go to sleep gazing at your face each night. I couldn't be satisfied with just touching you, smelling you." He throws an apple into her lap, rips the date off the calendar. "I practised some nights when you were asleep." He leans forward and bites the apple, chewing and talking.

She refuses all this and moves off the bed, positioning herself on the northeast corner of the rug. She puts her palms against her ears to stop hearing his endearments and stands there with her elbows sticking out. He is moving, almost frantic, now yelling his love. She can still hear him, and presses her palms tighter against the sides of her head, and closes her eyes. She feels the floor shudder under her, feels she is surrounded, contained by his whirling. Suddenly she is hit hard and her left hand jars against her skull, knocking her over.

She gets to her knees, dazed, and looks around. Patrick is grabbing a part of the sheet towards his face. He is snuffling, blood begins to come out of his nose onto the sheet. The blindfold is around his neck like a collar. He looks up at her and, as if he can't see her, turns back to the sheet as he continues to bleed.

– You moved. I told you not to. You moved.

She still cannot stand up from the pain and the dizziness. She knows if she tries to stand she will fall over again. So she sits where she is. Patrick is bent over watching the sheet in his hands.

So much for the human element, he thinks.

All his life Patrick Lewis has lived beside novels and their clear stories. Authors accompanying their heroes clarified motives. World events raised characters from destitution. The books would conclude with all wills rectified and all romances solvent. Even the spurned lover accepted the fact that the conflict had ended.

After Clara leaves him, Patrick cleans his room on Queen Street obsessively. Soap crystals fizz in a pail, the mop slices the week's dust. Then he sits in the only dry corner where he has previously placed cigarettes and smokes the Roxy, dropping ash into the bucket beside him. The room smells like a clean butcher shop. The furniture – a table, a chair, and an iguana cage – is piled on the bed at the street end of the room.

Sometimes he leaves a book in this corner. He has already smelled the pages, touched the print's indentations. Now he can devour it like a loaf of bread with his bare hands. He wipes cigarette ash off his arm and opens *Wild Geese*. *"It was not openly spoken of, but the family was waiting for Caleb Gare. Even Lind Archer, the new school teacher, who had come late that afternoon all the way from Yellow Post with the Indian mail carrier and must therefore be hungry, was waiting."* Clara wiping his forehead with her handkerchief. *"The rocker seemed to say, 'Caleb! Caleb! Caleb!' It amused the Teacher, rather wanly."* Her ear listening to the skin that covered Patrick's heart.

He feeds the iguana, holding the vetch an inch from the neutral mouth. Only the eyelid sliding down changes its expression. An animal born of another planet. He strokes the jaw with the flower. Through the window he sees men appear in the blue Toronto sky, inching into the air, scaffolding it. Pieces of Clara float around him.

A kiss at Union Station, her mouth half-open.

> – I'm sorry to ask you but I can't take it across the country. Will you keep him?
> – What is this, a door prize?
> – Don't talk like that, Patrick.
> – Let it free, dammit.
> – It's blind!

Stumbling back from argument.

> – Feed it clover and vetch, lots of water. Rattle the cage before you put food in. Just to let him know.

So he had watched Clara climb, prim, silver-buckled, into the train. He walked home with the cage banging against his knee, threw in a cabbage, and left the animal alone for a week. It heard his tirades, the broken cups and glasses. The iguana knew Clara Dickens, knowledge of her was there within its medieval body. Patrick believed in archaic words like *befall* and *doomed*. The doom of Patrick Lewis. The doom of Ambrose Small. The words suggested spells and visions, a choreography of fate. A long time ago he had been told never to follow her. If Patrick was a hero he could come down on Small like an arrow. He could lead an iguana on a silver leash to its mistress.

Dear Clara

All these strange half-lit lives. Rosedale like an aquarium at night. Underwater trees. You in a long black dress walking without shoes in Ambrose's long garden while his wife slept upstairs. Howling up to disturb her night. The soft rich.

Ambrose had class because he had you. That's what they all knew – those half-formed people who were born with money and who did nothing except keep it like a thermometer up their ass. The mean rich. The soft rich. I know why you went with Ambrose. He was the harbour rat. An immigrant rat. He had to win or he lost everything. The others just had to get their oldest son into Upper Canada College. Crop rotation. The only one who could slide over the wall, skip along the broken glass, was Small. But I don't want Small, I want you. . . .

Dear Clara

All night the tense and bitter conversations of lovers after they exit from the Greenwood bar across the street from my room. I lie by the window for summer air, and late-night couples assuming privacy seduce or accuse or fight. *No I didn't. I'm sorry. Goddamn you!* Whispered. The slap, the blow of scorned love, the nails of the other in their rake across his eyes. This battle for territory, Clara, ownership and want, the fast breath of a fuck, human or cat – supernatural moans, moon talk – her hands over the face making him less anonymous, the back of her coat against brick. *You were telling him something, what were you telling him? Damn you! What! Nothing!*

I keep waking to sudden intimacy. Once I heard a strange humming below and looked out. A man with a carpet draped over his shoulder accompanied by a red dog. It was the neighbourhood thief, Caravaggio, returning from work. He passed calmly under me, absorbed in the eating of Sicilian ice cream. . . .

I woke to your voice in danger. You were whispering. I thought at first it was dialogue from the street but it was you and I froze in the darkness – a possible dream I did not wish to let slip. I know your hesitations, your cracking voice when you are lying or getting drunk. These are familiar to me. Clara? I said into the darkness, it's okay, it's okay. I was standing on the mattress at the foot of the bed. I could have touched the ceiling with both hands. But you didn't listen. I was aware of wind coming in off the street. A male voice laughed in your company. I turned and saw the lit cream-yellow of the radio dial. It was Mystery Hour, a replay from two or three years back. I had slept through hours of broadcasting and woke only to the pitch of your breaking voice. You had a bit part. In the plot you had fallen on bad times.

At Union Station I refused to leave you. Your face angry against the Bedford limestone, *Damn you, Patrick, leave me alone!* Your hair crashes against it as you gesture and break free of me.

At Gate 5 you stop, pause in the steam, putting your hands up in surrender like a cowboy. A truce. No we did not walk up those steps, our fingers locked like cogs. You were escaping the claustrophobia an obsessed lover brings. We placed our arms on each other's shoulders, panting. Your face poured its look out.

Dear Clara

I came up to you and asked for a dance. The man with you punched me in the face. I asked you once more and he punched me in the face. I wiped off the blood below my eye. Five minutes later I came back to your table and his men attacked me, leaving me in a back alley. In this dream I hadn't seen you for a long time and I loved you in your dress. It was a big celebration of some sort, you were with honourable company. I would be looking at your face and a hand would hit me. I would fall to the floor. I'd be lying there looking at your dress, then dragged away. I finally came back and asked you to dance. Two things happened. For a brief while we were dancing. I wanted to hold you close but I did not want to get blood on you and you said, "It's all right, Patrick," and then I was watching your face as they began forcing me back to the alley. The dream ended with me plotting with the Chinese to break up the party.

*   *   *

He opened the door to her and stepped back quickly, appalled. He had not expected her.

He walked into the empty rooms, gesturing towards the broken things he was trying to assemble, broken glass and crockery, things he had flung long ago, after Clara had gone.

– What are those things?
– Glass, a crossword puzzle . . . a story.

Alice grinned at him. How much did she know about him and Clara anyway?

– I'm trying to get my life in order, he said.
– Well, this should begin it.

She moved around the room, touching nothing, as if everything in the sparse living room were potent and part of his cure.

— How long has she been gone? A year and a half?
Two years?

— Longer. Not long enough.

He spoke in bursts. Sentences needed additions, parentheses,
to clarify not the information but his state.

— Give me a coffee, Patrick.

There was more than five feet between them. When she
moved closer towards a news clipping attached to the wall, he
automatically moved further back. He felt dangerous. Alice
seemed older, confident. She removed her coat and laid it on the
ground by the door. He followed her into the kitchen, pumped
water into the saucepan for coffee, and lit the gas. There were
no chairs so she sat on the counter opposite, watching him at
the stove. She was safe there.

— You look tired, she said.

— Oh, I'm okay. Physically I'm fine, just my mind. I'm
lucky, whatever state I'm in my body takes care of itself.

It was his longest speech for months.

— I'm the reverse. That's the only way I can tell if I'm
in bad shape mentally, through my body.

— Well, you're an actress, right?

— That's right.

His eyes were on everything but her, a bad sign. She slid off
the counter and approached him, then stopped, inches away.
His eyes caught hers, moved away, and then settled safely on
her cheek.

— The next move, Patrick.

His first smile for months. He leaned forward and clung to

her to stop her vanishing. She was smaller than he imagined. She wasn't thin, or very small, but he had thought her body against him would be a different size. He could see the red in her hair by the temples, the lines under her eyes.

The water in the saucepan was boiling and they did not move. They stood together feeling each other's spines, each other's hair at the back of the neck. Relax, she said, and he wanted to collapse against her, be carried by her into foreign countries, into the ocean, into bed, anywhere. He had been alone too long. This was a time when returning from work he would fall nightly into a cave of dreams, so later he was not sure it happened. It had been sudden, nothing was played out to conclusion, nothing solved by their time together, but it somehow kept him alive. She had come that day, he thought later, not for passion, but to save him, to veer him to some reality. If anyone knew where Clara was, she did.

He had almost walked past Alice the previous week, outside the Parrot Theatre. He had not seen her since the farmhouse near Paris Plains, two years earlier, and he had hardly recognized her. But she had yelled his name.

> – Were you at the play?
> – No . . .

He shrugged distractedly. His face and eyes were wild, were seeing nothing on the street around him. His clothes old, unironed, the collar bent up.

> – What are you doing now? she asked.

He moved himself away from her extended arm.

> – I'm working at a lumber yard.
> – Come and see the play some night. Meet me afterwards.

– Yes, all right.

The 'yes' was so he could get away. He had wanted to shake her to pieces, blame her for Clara. It seemed it was all a game of theatre the two of them had performed against him. A woman's education, removing his cleverness, even his revenge. He had turned and walked away from her.

Now, taking Alice's smallest finger, he walked with her from the kitchen.

> – How long have you lived here?
> – Almost a year.
> – There's just a bed!
> – There's an iguana.
> – Oh *you've* got him.

In bed her nature, her transparency, had startled him. As did her sudden animal growl onto his shoulder when she lay on top of him. They lay there in the blank room.

> – I think her mother knows where she is, Patrick.
> – Possibly.
> – You should look for her.
> – She told me not to.
> – You must remove her shadow from you.
> – I know that.
> – Then when we meet again we can talk . . . we can
> say hello.

She said that so strangely he would later recall it differently – clothed in sarcasm or tentative love or sadness.

She had lost an earring when she got up. She said it didn't matter, that it was artificial.

*   *   *

He went to see Clara's mother in Paris and had a late dinner with her.

– When she married she eloped. But that didn't last long.

– She *married* Stump Jones?

– And divorced him. Anyway, too many people laughed at his name. It was a terrible thing to live with and he would not change it. She was only eighteen. He said he'd gotten used to it.

– What was he like?

– Stump was good-looking and bad-tempered. It was the snickering over hotel registers that got to her. Patrick Lewis, now, that's a *brick* of a name. She told me a good deal about you.

– What did she say?

– That you were probably a romantic Bolshevik from southern Ontario.

– Well, I'm an eastern Ontario boy. Go on.

– She said she seduced you.

– She said *that* . . . she said things like *that* to you?

– Yes.

– Did she ever keep in touch with Stump?

– I don't think so.

– Do you have a photograph of them?

Mrs. Dickens got up from the sofa and went into the kitchen. He thought she was angry, felt him rude, so he followed her and started apologizing.

– Forget her, Patrick, it's been over two years.

He laughed.

She pulled open the cupboard drawer and handed him the honeymoon photograph. Both of them against some damn rocks. Stump looked okay, but it was her face he kept gazing at. So young, her hair almost blonde then, not dark as it was now. A fuller face, innocent.

– It's a foolish face, he said, not quite believing it was the same person.

– Yes, said her mother, she was foolish then.

– Where is she?

– I don't like him.

– Nobody does. Do you know where she is?

– In a place Small knows you will never look . . . in a place he knows you will never go back to.

– What do you mean?

But he knew then. Knew exactly where they were. He had been the searcher who had gazed across maps and seen every name except the one which was so well-known it had remained, like his childhood, invisible to him.

*   *   *

Patrick stares at the thin layer of moonlight on the wall. His body feels like the shadow of someone in chains. He had awakened once to Clara whispering at the foot of his bed in this Paris hotel room. Soaking wet. Two in the morning. She'd slid the buttons through the damp holes of her dress . . . and another time crawled from their bed to warm her hands on the radiator. . . . He undreams himself, remembers she has left him.

Gets out of bed and walks to the wall beside the radiator against which she had leaned.

He is standing in their old room at the Arlington Hotel. Without turning on any light he bends down and puts his face close to the wall at stomach level. Here they had pushed in frenzy, sexual madness. He finds the faint impression of her backbone on the white paint.

Ambrose Small holds a wooden match above his head, its glare falling onto the shoulders of his nightshirt. Four in the morning. Above him a silk bag holds naphtha. He has heard noises. His other hand turns a brass handle. Now the flame and gas combine and his room breaks open in yellow light. Patrick Lewis is sitting in an armchair, overcoat on, looking straight at him.

Small draws up a chair. A mutual excitement, as if each were looking into a mirror.

    – Where do you want me to begin, says Small, with my childhood?

Patrick smiles.

    – I don't want to talk about you, Small. I want Clara. Something about her cast a spell on me. . . . I don't know what it is.
    – It's her unfinished nature, Ambrose says quietly.
    – Perhaps.
    – Who else knows I am here?
    – No one. I came just to talk to her.
    – I'll wake Clara. Go outside, she'll come out and listen to you.

Patrick steps outside into the dark night and sits in one of the two chairs on the grass. He is among blue trees, he can smell gum on the branches. He can hear the river. He knows this place from his childhood, the large house belonging to the Rathbun Timber Company, which he had passed every day during the log drives. A last remnant from that era. He walks to the window and looks in. There is no longer light. Ambrose must have carried the lamp back into the bedroom of the house.

Water from the eaves dribbles onto Patrick's coat, some on his neck, and he steps back, stretching in the darkness. But there had been no rain. He notices a metal smell. He moves his eyes above the ledge of the window and simultaneously knows it has nothing to do with rain. He smells and feels kerosene pour across his shoulders, hears the rasp of the match that will kill him in the hand of Small who crouches on the roof. Patrick sees it fall like a knighthood towards his shoulders.

He is running along the rock path to the river before he knows for certain he is on fire. His hand pulls the knife out of his pocket and uses it to slice open the coat as he runs. He stops and begins to laugh. He is all right. Then he sees light in the trees around him and knows he is a hunchback of fire, and he runs – past the barrel for burning garbage, past the boat on the sand – and falls stomach down in the shallows, splashing forward. The air caught in his coat is a bubble on fire burning above the water. He turns and falls onto his back.

He remains in the water, only his head visible, scared to allow his shoulders into the air. There is no pain except in his hands, which still hold on to the knife. He sticks it into the river bottom. Patrick can feel the cuts in his palm. He can feel the itch on his chest from slashing open the coat.

He looks past his hand just in time. Ambrose is standing on the beach. The bottle with the burning-cloth neck is travelling in the air and the explosion when it hits the water makes the river around him jump like a basket of fish, makes the night silver. Patrick's left eye goes linen white, and he knows he is possibly blind there. He reaches for the knife and stumbles out, wading free of the water. Ambrose hasn't moved. He doesn't move as Patrick steps up to him and cuts him at the shoulder.

Then Patrick is running towards the old hotel in the village of Bellrock, a mile away. He does not trust himself to use shortcuts over the fields so he stays with the road, running past the house he was born in, over the bridge he had fished off, and up the stairs into the hotel room.

When Patrick woke, he could still not see properly out of one eye. His wet clothes were bunched on a chair in front of the small grate. Now and then he would get up, wrap the thin quilt around his chest, and sit by the window looking down at the river. The same river, downstream from Small's house, Depot Creek, scarred where the loggers tore open the banks to build dams. Some kids were fishing knee-deep by the dock. He sat at the window feeling the leak of air through the glass. His hands stiff on his lap seemed to be someone else's hands that he was looking at in a picture. He heard Clara's voice on the other side of the door.

He saw his ghost in the mirror. He pushed back the bolt with his shoulder, the quilt like a cape over him.

– Turn the handle, I can't do that.

As she came in, he moved his hands out of the way, the paws of a boxer. It hurt to put them down at his side.

   – Oh god it *is* you.
   – Hello, Clara.

She stood there, her coat open, her hands in her pockets. She was taking in what he looked like. His face was wet and he realized his damaged eye was crying, he was unable to control it. If you can't see you can't control anything, he thought. Patrick had imagined her so often when she had not been wearing these clothes. He lifted his left arm up to wipe his face with the quilt but when his arm got to the level of his shoulder it began to shake. She came forward and wiped his cheek with her open hand, then put the wet hand of salt to her mouth.

   – I can't see out of this eye.

Her hand came up to his face again, her fingers feeling his skin, the flesh on his cheek.

   – Can you feel that?
   – Yes.

Her fingers moved into his scalp. He didn't know where to put his hands. He couldn't get them out of the way.

   – What's wrong?
   – My hands.
   – Put them around me, we *have* touched before.
   – I don't want you to think . . .

He grinned and his face ached. They stood then like that in the room. His hands on either side of the rough material of her coat, her fingers gently parting his hair to feel his scalp.

   – There's blood here. What the hell were you two doing?

She moved out of his hold and shrugged off her coat.

– I know a doctor in town, but I'll clean you up first.

Patrick stood at the window looking out. She came up behind him.

– I've imagined us meeting all over the world, Patrick, but I never thought we'd meet here. By this river you told me about.

She put her head against him and they were still, as if asleep. Her finger traced a delicate line down along his shoulder, parallel to a cut.

– It would be terrible if we met under perfect conditions. Don't you think?

With a bowl of hot water beside her, she worked the dried blood out of his hair. He was tired and fought to stay awake. She squeezed the cloth dry and started washing his cuts, the one on his chest, his shoulder, and then finally his hands, getting him to gradually move his stiff fingers.

– Do you have your shaving stuff? Yes, you must.

She touched the menthol pencil to three cuts in front of his ear, then suggested that she shave him. She rinsed the razor and sat in front of him, straddling the chair.

– How are you, Patrick?

He gave his nervous laugh that she loved.

– I'm on the verge as usual.
– Don't lose that.

He looked directly into her eyes, aiming himself at her. The first time he had looked at her continually. There wasn't any pain in his face, she noticed, just thirst.

– Talk to me, Clara.
– All these small scars . . .

She wiped the razor on the quilt. He looked older. More brittle. This was the way to know somebody's face, she thought. She should have shaved him before. She should have understood his breakable quality sooner. He was a creature of habit, he belonged with the last century. She wanted to paint his face, to follow the lines of his cheek and eyebrow with colours. Make another spirit painting of him. He was less neutral now, his skin like the texture of a cave that would transform anything painted on it. She lathered his face, wanting to sculpt him. With her finger she wrote DICKENS 5 on his forehead. "I don't want you lost, Patrick. I can't have you but I don't want you to get lost."

She stepped bowlegged off the chair and stretched her body to break the cramp, moving backwards until she was leaning against the wallpaper. Then she walked to the window. She saw him gazing straight ahead towards the wallpaper, as if she had left her body there. Flowers, vines, now and then an English pheasant in the foliage, now and then a rip caused by a drunk logger in other times trying to get out of the room, unable to find the door. He sat looking at that landscape in front of him.

– Do you know this area had a Small sighting? It made the Toronto papers and I knew it was no coincidence. He had to be living in the town I came from because *you* were with him. He grilled you the way I did. Isn't that right?

— He wanted to know where you came from. I didn't tell him much. He wasn't interested in you, Patrick. He's a rich man who escaped from a rich shoe. He protects himself. He will never believe it was me you came after.

He turned his head and watched her face on the pillow looking up at the ceiling.

— In a way I knew I'd be injured when I saw you again. I had dreams about coming up to you at dances and being beaten back.

She leaned over and touched his chest.

— The doctor put on a good dressing.
— Does Small know you're here with me?
— Probably, but don't talk about him, Patrick. I'll go back in the morning.

When she looked at his face a short while later he was asleep. The medication had made him drowsy all evening. She kept watching him a long time. Around three in the morning she felt his body against her. They touched, both moving careful of his wounds, all over each other as if meeting in a dream. Later she made her way to the bathroom and came back in a silhouette. He was comfortable and tired.

— Goodnight, Clara.
— Goodnight, Patrick Lewis. My friend.

He slept gripping her hand.

She dressed in the darkness and left without waking him. The sun came up over Goose Island, hitting the tin roof of Mr. Moir's house as she walked home, past the Grants and the Meeks. She saw young George Grant with his brother Russell coming back with the cows and they spoke for a few minutes. She continued to the bend in the road and down the curling path to the house they lived in and would probably move from now. She felt somehow deliriously happy between the two points of this journey.

When she reached the house she didn't go in but went down to the beach and sat facing the water, leaning against the red boat. It was cold but she had her coat on and she was thinking. Not knowing what was happening now at the hotel, that with the light Patrick had awakened to find the sheets thick with blood which had escaped from his dressings, from their moving together in the darkness, discovering even the print of her hand perfect on the wallpaper, a print of blood on the English flowers of his bedroom where she had leaned to balance herself in their lovemaking as she crouched over him. The dressings hung off him like a limp white rib while Ambrose came down from the house and saw her sitting there thinking, looking at Patrick's river.

2

PALACE OF PURIFICATION

IN THE TUNNEL under Lake Ontario two men shake hands on an incline of mud. Beside them a pickaxe and a lamp, their dirt-streaked faces pivoting to look towards the camera. For a moment, while the film receives the image, everything is still, the other tunnel workers silent. Then Arthur Goss, the city photographer, packs up his tripod and glass plates, unhooks the cord of lights that creates a vista of open tunnel behind the two men, walks with his equipment the fifty yards to the ladder, and climbs out into sunlight.

Work continues. The grunt into hard clay. The wet slap. Men burning rock and shattering it wherever they come across it. Filling hundreds of barrels with liquid mud and hauling them out of the tunnel. In the east end of the city a tunnel is being built out under the lake in order to lay intake pipes for the new waterworks.

It is 1930. The cut of the shovel into clay is all Patrick sees digging into the brown slippery darkness. He feels the whole continent in front of him. They dig underneath one of the largest lakes in North America beside a hissing lamp, racing with the speed of their shadows. Each blow against the shale wall jars up from the palms into the shoulders as if the body is hit. Exhaustion overpowers Patrick and the other tunnellers within twenty minutes, the arms itching, the chest dry. Then an hour more, then another four hours till lunch, when they have thirty minutes to eat.

During the eight-hour shifts no one speaks. Patrick is as silent as the Italians and Greeks towards the *bronco* foremen. For eight hours a day the air around them rolls in its dirty light. From somewhere else in the tunnel there is the permanent drone of pumps attempting to suck out the water, which is constantly at their heels. All morning they slip in the wet clay unable to stand properly, pissing where they work, eating where someone else left shit.

As the muckers move forward with their picks and shovels, the gunnite crew sprays a mixture of concrete and sand onto the walls, which would otherwise crumble after a few hours of exposure to the air. And if they are digging incorrectly – just one degree up, burrowing too close to the weight of Lake Ontario during this mad scheme by Commissioner Harris to collect lake water 3,300 yards out in the lake? They have all imagined the water heaving in, shouldering them aside in a fast death.

Whenever the tunnellers reach large walls of rock or shale beds the foreman clears the tunnel and the transportation mules are herded back. Then Patrick separates himself from the others. He removes his belt that has the buckle, pats his wet clothes for any other sign of metal, and hoists the box of dynamite onto his shoulder. With a lamp he walks towards the far reaches of the tunnel alone. There is no sound here – no wind, no noise of work. He hears only the slosh of his feet tromping through water, his own breathing in the darkness.

At the end of the tunnel he holds the lamp up against the dark wall, trying to imagine the structure of the rock in front of him, the shape, its possible fissures. He puts the lamp down and augers out holes for the sticks of dynamite. Only at these times are his eyes close to what he digs into all day. The burn of the lamp spills against the wet earth as he works. Once it revealed the pale history of a fossil, a cone-shaped cephalopod, which he sheared free and dropped into his pocket.

Although he dynamites for the foreman, most of the time Patrick works with the muckers in the manual digging. He is paid extra for each of the charges laid. Nobody else wants the claustrophobic uncertainty of this work, but for Patrick this part is the only ease in this terrible place where he feels banished from the world. He carries out the old skill he learned from his father – although then it had been in sunlight, in rivers, logs tumbling over themselves slowly in the air.

He sidewinds the powder fuse, which will burn at two minutes to the yard, and ignites it. He picks up the lamp and begins his walk back to the others. There is no hurry, there is no other light in the tunnel but this one lamp and as he moves his shadow shifts like a giant alongside him. When he reaches the others at the shaft he hears with them the crumple of noise as the shale displaces and the rock splinters into shards and flints in the far darkness under the lake.

As the day progresses heat rises in the tunnel. The men remove their shirts and hammer them into the hard walls with spikes. Patrick can recognize other tunnellers on the way home by the ragged hole in the back of their shirts. It is a code among them, like the path of a familiar thick bullet in the left shoulder blade. At the end of the day they climb from the tunnel into the desert of construction which had been Victoria Park Forest, where the waterworks is now being built. They see each other's bodies steaming in the air.

Patrick embraces the last of the light on the walk home. In

the dry air the clay hardens on clothing, whitens his arms and hair. He takes a knife and cuts free the mud between his boots and trouser cuffs, brushes the blade over the laces to loosen them. In his Wyatt Avenue room he drops all his clothes in a corner, feeds the iguana, and crawls into bed. He picks the clothes up again at six in the morning hard as armour and bangs them against the wall of the fire escape till they crack apart and soften, the dust in the air around him. At the Thompson Grill he eats breakfast in ten minutes. He reads no paper, just watches the hands of the waitress break open the eggs. As he goes underground the humidity will fall back into his clothes quick as rain.

Carrying three lanterns, the crew of nine men walks towards the end of the tunnel. Already they can smell each other and the sweat from the previous days, the lamp wick raised to burn out odour. They can hear the mules and pit-horses who live down here, transporting the dug earth and mud barrels to the ladder. When these creatures were lowered down the shaft by rope they had brayed madly, thinking they were being buried alive. Patrick and the others walk silently, remembering the teeth of the animals distinct, that screaming, the feet bound so they wouldn't slash out and break themselves, lowered forty feet down and remaining there until they died or the tunnel reached the selected mark under the lake. And when would that be? The brain of the mule no more and no less knowledgeable than the body of a man who dug into a clay wall in front of him.

Above ground, like the blossoming of a tree, the excavations and construction were also being orchestrated. The giant centrifugal pumps, more valuable than life, were trolleyed into place with their shell-shaped impellers that in Commissioner Harris' dream would fan the water up towards the settling basins. Cranes lowered 800 tons of steel sheet piling rolled in Sault Ste. Marie. Trucks were driving in the bricks from Cooksville.

From across the province the subcontractors brought in their products and talents to build a palace for water. Richie Cut Stone Company, Raymond Concrete, Heather & Little Roofing and Sheet Metal, ornamental iron from Architectural Bronze and Iron Works, steel sashes from Canadian Metal Window and Steel Works, elevators from Otis-Fenson and Turnbull, glazing from Hobbs Glass, plasterers from Strauss & Scott, overhead doors from the Richard Wilcox Canadian Company. The Bavington Brothers sent painters, Bennett and Wright were responsible for heat and ventilation, the linoleum came from T. Eaton Company, the mastic flooring from Vulcan Asphalt. Mazes of electricity were laid down by Canadian Comstock, Alexander Murray composed the floor design. The tiling and terrazzo were by Italian Mosaic and Tile Company.

Harris had dreamed the marble walls, the copper-banded roofs. He pulled down Victoria Park Forest and the essential temple swept up in its place, built on the slope towards the lake. The architect Pomphrey modelled its entrance on a Byzantine city gate, and the inside of the building would be an image of the ideal city. The brass railings curved up three flights like an immaculate fiction. The subtle splay on the tower gave it an Egyptian feel. Harris could *smell* the place before it was there, knew every image of it as well as his arms – west wing, east wing. The Depression and the public outcry would slow it all down, but in spite of that half of it would be completed within a year. "The form of a city changes faster than the heart of a mortal," Harris liked to remind his critics, quoting Baudelaire.

He was providing jobs as he had in the building of the Bloor Street Viaduct, the St. Clair Reservoir, the men hired daily for grading, clearing bush, removing stumps, and rip-rapping the sides of streams. The Commissioner would slide these facts out, bounce them off his arms like oranges to journalists.

But Harris was building it for himself. For a stray dream he'd always had about water, water they should have taken across the Bloor Street Viaduct as he proposed. No one else was interested in water at this time. Harris imagined a palace for it. He wanted the best ornamental iron. He wanted a brass elevator to lead from the service building to the filter building where you could step out across rose-coloured marble. The neo-Byzantine style allowed him to blend in all the technical elements. The friezes depicted stylized impellers. He wanted herringbone tiles imported from Siena, art deco clocks and pump signals, unfloored high windows which would look over filter pools four feet deep, languid, reflective as medieval water gardens.

But first he needed to finish the spear of tunnel a mile out under the lake and organize the human digging and the human-and-mule dragging of pipes all the way out there for the intake of water. This was the other tentacle of his dream. The one that reached out and clung to him in a nightmare where faces peered out, working in that permanent rain of condensation.

He had sent Goss and his photographers down but he had not entered the tunnels himself. He was a man who understood the continuity of the city, the daily consumptions of water, the speed of raw water through a filter bed, the journeys of chlorine and sulphur-dioxide to the island filtration plant, the 119 inspections by tugboats each year of the various sewer outfalls, and the approximate number of valves and caissons of the East Toronto pumping stations, and the two miles a year of water-main construction – from the St. Clair Reservoir to the high-level pumping station – and the construction of the John Street surge tank. . . .

This was choreography in 1930.

In those photographs moisture in the tunnel appears white. There is a foreman's white shirt, there is white lye daubed onto rock to be dynamited. And all else is labour and darkness. Ash-grey faces. An unfinished world. The men work in the equivalent of the fallout of a candle. They are in the foresection of the cortex, in the small world of Rowland Harris' dream as he lies in bed on Neville Park Boulevard.

Such a strange dream for him. The silence of men coming out of a hole each within an envelope of steam. Horses under Lake Ontario. Swallowing the water one-and-a-quarter miles away, bringing it back into his body, and spitting it out clean.

*   *   *

Patrick ate most of his meals at the Thompson Grill on River Street where the waitress, through years of habit, had reduced to a minimum the action of pouring coffee or flipping an egg. He could spot the oil burns on her wrists, the permanent grimace in her eye from the smoke.

If she looked at those who ate here it occurred when they were not aware of it. She seemed self-sufficient, something underwater in the false yellow light of the narrow room against the street, the flawed glass creating shadows in the air. There was something transient about her though she had been there for years. Most of the chewers at the Thompson Grill had that quality.

Patrick would sit at an uncleared section so he could watch

the fingers of her left hand pluck up the glasses and cups while the other hand, the muscles in intricate movement under the skin, swabbed the counter clean. It was several months before he became aware of the tattoo high on her arm, seeing it through a tear in the seam where the cotton had loosened.

He came to believe she had the powers of a goddess who could condemn or bless. She would be able to transform the one she touched, the one she gripped at the wrist with her tough hand, the muscles stiffening up towards the blue-black of the half-revealed creature that pivoted on the bone of her shoulder. His eyes wanted to glimpse nothing else.

He pinned the note, saying *Waterworks – Sunday 8 p.m.* to the wall above his bed in case he forgot, though it had been his only invitation in two years. "The cheese stands alone," he'd sing to himself, while buying groceries along Eastern Avenue. Patrick loved that song. He found himself muttering "The farmer takes the dog . . . the farmer takes the dog" among the Macedonians, as if perfecting a password. The southeastern section of the city where he now lived was made up mostly of immigrants and he walked everywhere not hearing any language he knew, deliriously anonymous. The people on the street, the Macedonians and Bulgarians, were his only mirror. He worked in the tunnels with them.

He had discovered the Macedonian word for iguana, *gooshter*, and finally used it to explain his requests each evening at the fruit stall for clover and vetch. It was a breakthrough. The woman gazed at him, corrected his pronunciation, and yelled it to the next stall. She came around the crates and outlined the shape of a lizard. *Gooshter?* Four women and a couple of men then circled him trying desperately to leap over the code of languages between them. His obsession with vetch had puzzled them. He had gone at one point into the centre of the city, bought some, and returned to the Macedonians to show them what he needed. The following week, a store owner had waved it to him as he came down Eastern Avenue. Vetch was *fee-ee*. But now they were onto serious things. A living creature, a *gooshter*, had been translated. He was surrounded. They were trying to discover how many he had. Was raising them one of his professions? They knew where he lived, of course, had seen his yellow light looking down on Wyatt Avenue, knew he was alone, knew down to the very can of peaches what he ate in a week. Peaches on Friday. They had sent someone to find Emil, who spoke the best English, and when the boy arrived he said, "Peaches on Friday, right?"

Patrick felt ashamed they could discover so little about him. He had reduced himself almost to nothing. He would walk home at dusk after working in the lake tunnel. His radio was on past midnight. He did nothing else that he could think of. They approved of his Finnish suit. *Po modata eleganten!* which meant stylish! stylish! He was handed a Macedonian cake. And suddenly Patrick, surrounded by friendship, concern, was smiling, feeling the tears on his face falling towards his stern Macedonian-style moustache. Elena, the great Elena who had sold him vetch for over a year, unpinned the white scarf around her neck and passed it to him. He looked up and saw the men and women who could not know *why* he wept now among these strangers who in the past had seemed to him like dark blinds on his street, their street, for he was their alien.

And then he had to remember new names. Suddenly formal, beginning with Elena. The women shook his hand, the men embraced and kissed him, and each time he said Patrick.

Patrick. Patrick. Knowing he must now remember every single person. And now, because it was noon, the King Street Russian Mission Brass Band fifty yards down the road, they invited him to lunch which was set up on tables beside the stalls and crates. He was guest of honour. Elena on one side of him, Emil on the other, and a table of new friends.

He was brought a plate of cabbage rolls – *sarmi*, Elena said, and suddenly the awful sulphurous odour he had smelled for the last year since moving was explained. Emil was describing the technique of soaking cabbage leaves in a solution of salt and water and a bit of vinegar and leaving it there for days. Patrick ate everything that was put in front of him. During coffee, Kosta, the owner of the Ohrida Lake Restaurant, sent along a question to Emil. Emil asked two or three others first to see if this question was apt. Then he turned to Patrick. "What else can you do?" The table was silent. Elena put her hand on his and sent a qualifier via Emil. "It does not matter if you don't do anything." The others down the table nodded.

– I used to be a searcher. I can work dynamite.

Emil's translation created an even greater silence. Patrick could hear every note of the Russian Mission Band down the street. Then Kosta jumped up and yelled something at Patrick. His face looked at him with anger, full of passion. Emil turned to Patrick now, having to yell above the sudden din at the table. "He says 'Me too, me too.'" Kosta grabbed a round loaf of bread, leapt free of the bench, and booted it down the road in the direction of the Russian Mission Band.

Later that afternoon when Patrick was showing the iguana to the street, the man Kosta said, "The waterworks at eight, Sunday night. A gathering." Then he drifted away, not allowing Patrick to reply or question the invitation.

An hour after dusk disappeared into the earth the people came in silence, in small and large families, up the slope towards the half-built waterworks. Emerging from darkness, mothlike, walking towards the thin rectangle of the building's southern doorway. The movement was quickly over, the wave of bodies had seemed a shadow of a cloud over the slope.

Inside the building they moved in noise and light. It was an illegal gathering of various nationalities and the noise of machines camouflaged their activity from whoever might have been passing along Queen Street a hundred yards away. Many languages were being spoken, and Patrick followed the crowd to the seats that were set up around a temporary stage. He saw Kosta, who was busy greeting and shepherding people, and he watched him until Kosta caught his eye. Patrick waved and Kosta raised his hand and continued with what he was doing. Patrick felt utterly alone in this laughing crowd that traded information back and forth, held children on their laps.

The four-piece band was playing by the stage. It was a party and a political meeting, all of them trespassing, waiting now for speeches and entertainment. Patrick found a seat and took a sip from his flask. Almost immediately the electric lights were turned off, leaving only the glow from oil lamps on the edge of the platform.

The puppets arrived on stage in a mob, their wooden bones clattering. The semicircle of oil lamps cast yellow onto this section of the pumping station – onto the generators, the first few rows of the audience, the mosaic tiles, and brass banisters. Patrick looked up and saw the grid above them on the upper level, hardly visible, where the puppeteers must have been lying in darkness.

The forty puppets moved into the light, their paws gesturing at the air. The males had moustaches and beards, the females had been given rouged faces. There was one life-sized puppet. This giant in their midst was the central character in the story, its face brightly coloured: green-shadowed eyes and a racoon ring of yellow around them so they were like targets. All of the puppets looked stunned. Feet tested air before each exaggerated step was taken on this dangerous new country of the stage. Their costumes were a blend of several nations. It was five minutes into the dance before Patrick realized that the large puppet was human. And this was only because the dancer moved out of his puppet movements and began to twirl in gestures impossible for wood.

The large figure began to distinguish itself from the others. It became a hero not by size but by gesture and the detail of character. Perhaps it was an exceptional puppet of cloth as opposed to an exceptional human being. Behind the curled moustache it was perturbed and nervous – ambitious, scared, at times greedy. It varied its emotions from fear to desire. The other puppets included a prune-faced rich woman, a policeman, the sly friend, the family matriarch. The hero linked them all. There was no noise, no drum-beat or song. Just the clattering of their feet, just the wooden hands touching each other gently the way fingernails touch glass. The puppets ranged all over the stage or huddled together as a chorus, warning the hero of his ambition, gesturing him down with laws. The human puppet, alien and naive and gregarious, upset everything. The face, in spite of the moustache, was dark and young. He wore a Finnish shirt and Serbian pants.

A plot grew. Laughing like a fool he was brought before the authorities, unable to speak their language. He stood there assaulted by insults. His face was frozen. The others began to pummel him but not a word emerged – just a damaged gaze in the context of those flailing arms. He fell to the floor pleading with gestures. The scene was endless. Patrick wanted to rip the painted face off. The caricature of a culture. His eyes could not move away from that face.

The audience around him was silent. The only sounds on stage were grunts of authority. They were all waiting for the large puppet to speak, but it could say nothing. The thick eyebrows, the big nose, the curled moustache – all of which parodied them – became haunting. When the figure wheeled now the sweat on the pink brocade shirt made it blood-red along the spine and shoulders. It stamped a foot to try and bring out a language. The other puppets shifted like bamboo to the side of the stage. The figure knelt, one hand banging down on the wooden floor as if pleading for help – a terrible loudness entering the silent performance.

The audience began to clap in unison with the banging hand, the high hall of the waterworks echoing. Patrick was unable to move, his eyes locked upon the crouched figure, the manic hand. If it was not stopped it would burst. That was absurd. He wanted the hall to be quiet, the figure's terror stopped. He could see the yellow-ringed eyes, the shirt bloody from the darkness of sweat, the mask of the painted face looking up like a dog. Patrick stood up and stumbled over feet until he reached the aisle. He wanted to be out of here, out of this building. He was covered in the heartbeat of applause which started to come faster. Each footstep as he moved released the terrible noise. He was among members of the band, the silent band which sat there waiting for the next act when they would be required to play. He saw the huge instruments on their laps, which in their curls and convolutions looked like frozen organs of the body. He climbed up, slipping at first because he still couldn't remove his eyes from the face and the banging white hand. He stepped over a lamp. Then he was up there on stage, and as soon as he approached the exhausted figure he saw up close that the performer was much smaller, that it was a woman.

He knelt and held her by the shoulders, his arm on her damp back. He leaned forward, caught the hand still trying to smash down again like a machine locked in habit, a swimmer unable to stop. He swerved the palm away from the floor and brought it slowly down to her thigh. Then he looked up, through the halo of light into the sudden silence.

There was a crowd standing on the upper level as well. Hundreds more than he had thought. He looked back at the woman, the costume made of false silk, a cheap glittering material from the streets, drenched in sweat. This close he could recognize nothing of the figure he had seen perform. It seemed washed out, exhausted statuary. One tear of sweat cut a path through the thick makeup. Now the eyes, hidden in the circles of paint, focused on him, then reacted with shock. She bent forward. He felt his hand slide against the sweat of her cheek. He had forgotten where he was. She pulled herself up, her arm on his shoulder. She walked downstage slowly towards the kerosene lights, spreading her hands wide and then clapping them. A slow beat. There. There. There.

Then, with her arms out, the crowd cheering, she raised her swollen hand and now everyone was standing yelling at her.

She brought her fingers to her lips and the audience became quiet. She threw the name of the next performer into their midst like a bell, and a man walked into the light carrying an umbrella. The crowd was immediately with him. Patrick began to move backwards to the makeshift curtain. He looked down embarrassed and when he looked up again she had left the stage.

Backstage he would be an outsider. He recalled the touch of that hand on his shoulder as she pulled herself up. And the voice he had recognized. He tried to remember the washed-out face, its features under the makeup. Behind the curtain there were just a few performers in half-light – one kerosene lamp on the floor. How should he enter a room where a giant takes off its head? Where a dwarf stands up to full height. The Macedonian juggler he had watched perform half an hour earlier with absolute abandon was packing the thirty hard oranges neatly into his suitcase. No sofas, or arches of light, just performers cleaning up. A man putting on his socks. Someone reading *The Racing News*. At the far end of the hall he saw an Indian walking a puppet towards a corridor, as if escorting someone frail. Patrick went after him. The man turned right along the Venturi corridor and disappeared behind another curtain. Here among the strangely shaped pipes and meters the air was humid. A great cheer went up from the audience. As the man came out Patrick caught his arm and asked him where the puppet dancer was. The Indian jerked his head towards the curtain and handed him a flashlight.

He walked into pitch darkness. When he turned on the flashlight he saw swaying feet. He moved the light up the brocade robe – a king hung up there, the strings and wood handle attached to a pipe. Three or four ceiling pipes held all of the puppets in mid-air. He swung the amber beam from side to side, and everywhere he turned, the light picked out faces and arms that no longer looked like puppets but relaxed humans, a shadow conference. It was a king's court, silent – a custom of the East. Whenever the royal gong struck, the court of the Moghul prince Akbar remained frozen at whatever they were doing. It was the whim of a monarch during which time he moved among his retainers and subjects to study their dress and activity. Movement meant execution. He walked into kitchens, armouries, bedrooms where lovers would lie frozen on the verge of touching, walked past dining-tables where the court sat hungry or bored looking at the cooling food, stepped into the quarters of falconers where only the birds moved and fussed on their perches.

So Patrick moved in this darkness, the eye of the flashlight swallowing the colours, the room turning under his gaze like a jewel. What had been theatrical seemed locked within metamorphosis. He wanted to put his hand up and unbutton a blouse, remove a shoe. He moved quickly towards a figure but it was only a queen draped over a chair, sitting the way a queen would sit. He heard the cheers from the hall once more.

Patrick switched off the light and stood there. His eyes remembering scarlet, the puff of a blue sleeve, the flat brown feet pathetic as a peacock's under such grand costuming. A broken ochre hand. A *splash*. He turned to face the sound.

He moved forward, one hand in front of him to hold away the costumed bodies, lifting his feet up high so he would not trip in the darkness. He thought, I am moving like a puppet. He touched an arm in the darkness not fully realizing it was human. A hand came from somewhere and held his wrist. "Hello, Patrick." He turned on the flashlight. She was waiting for the light, like a good actress, ready to be revealed.

"No one is allowed here while I wash. I knew it had to be you. . . ." She was wearing a singlet and had been washing herself from a bowl, her hands now squeezing out a cloth in the basin and wiping her face, streaks of flesh across the paint. One line of colour remained that seemed to show her frowning. Behind her a puppet slowly pivoted. He could smell the candle she must have blown out as soon as she heard him enter. "You can help with the paint on my neck."

Patrick did not speak. The light moved down her arm to the bowl, illuminated her hand which wet the cloth, squeezed it, and moved forward to give it to him. She saw his right hand reach to take it from her. His hand began to wipe her neck. He removed the brown paint, turned her around and slowly wiped the vermilion frown-mark by her mouth, the light close on her face.

He rinsed out the cloth again and holding her forehead steady wiped the targets off her eyes, cloth over one finger for precision, the blue left iris wavering at the closeness . . . so that it was not Alice Gull but something more intimate – an eye muscle having to trust a fingertip to remove that quarter-inch of bright yellow around her sight.

They were now many hours into the night. In her room on Verral Avenue. He had just seen the sleeping child.

    – I wasn't married, she said. Her father is dead. He was like a *comitidjiis*. A *chetnik*. Do you know what that means?

He shook his head continuing to look out the window into the rain. He felt there was space in her small rooms only when he looked out.

    – Open it, Patrick. If it's raining the cat will want to come in. They are national guerrillas. Political activists. Freedom-fighters in Bulgaria and Turkey and Serbia. They were tortured, then some of them came here. They have a very high level of justice.

She smiled, then continued.

    – They are very difficult to live with.
    – I think I have a passive sense of justice.
    – I've noticed. Like water, you can be easily harnessed, Patrick. That's dangerous.
    – I don't think so. I don't believe the language of politics, but I'll protect the friends I have. It's all I can handle.

She sat on the mattress looking up at him, the cat purring in her lap as she dried it with a towel.

    — That's not enough, Patrick. We're in a thunderstorm.

    — Is that a line from one of your tracts?

    — No, it's a metaphor. You reach people through metaphor. It's what I reached you with earlier tonight in the performance.

    — You appealed to my sense of compassion.

    — Compassion forgives too much. You could forgive the worst man. You forgive him and nothing changes.

    — You can teach him, make him aware . . .

    — Why leave the power in his hands?

There was no reply from him. He turned away from her, back to the open window and the rain.

    — You believe in solitude, Patrick, in retreat. You can afford to be romantic because you are self-sufficient.

    — Yes, I've got about ten bucks to my name.

    — I'm not talking about money. Working in the tunnels is terrible, I know that. But you have a choice, what of the others who don't?

    — Such as.

    — Such as this kid. Such as three-quarters of the population of Upper America. They can't afford your choices, your *languor.*

    — They could succeed. Look at —

    — Come on, Patrick, of course some make it. They do it by becoming just like the ones they want to overtake. Like Ambrose. Look at what he became before he disappeared. He was *predatory.* He let nothing cling to him, not even Clara. I always liked you because you knew that. Because you hated that in him.

— I hated him because I wanted what he had.

— I don't think so. You don't want power. You were born to be a younger brother.

She stood up now and began pacing. She needed to move her arms, be more forceful.

— Anyway, we're not interested in Ambrose anymore. To hell with him, he's damned.

The power of the girl's father was still in her. Patrick couldn't tell how much of a role it was. She spoke slowly now.

— There is more compassion in my desire for truth than in your 'image' of compassion. You must name the enemy.

— And if he is your friend?

— *I'm* your friend. Hana there sleeping is your friend. The people tonight in the audience were your friends. They're compassionate too. Listen, they are terrible sentimentalists. They love your damn iguana. They'll cry all through their sister's wedding. They'll cry when their sister says she has had her first kiss. But they must turn and kill the animals in the slaughter-houses. And the smell of the tanning factories goes into their noses and lungs and stays there for life. They never get the smell off their bodies. Do you know the smell? You can bet the rich don't know it. It brutalizes. It's like sleeping with the enemy. It clung to Hana's father. They get skin burns from the galvanizing process. Arthritis, rheumatism. *That's* the truth.

— So what do you do?

— You name the enemy and destroy their power. Start

with their luxuries – their select clubs, their summer mansions.

Alice stopped pacing, put a hand up to the low slope of the ceiling and pushed against it.

– The grand cause, Patrick.

He knows he will never forget a word or a gesture of hers tonight, in this doll-house of a room. He sits on the bed looking up at the avid spirit of her.

– Someone always comes out of the audience to stop me, Patrick. This time it was you. My old pal.
– I don't think you will convert me.
– Yes. I can.
– If it was valuable to some cause for me to kill someone would you want me to do it?

She picked up the cat again.

– Would the girl's father have done that?
– I don't think I'm big enough to put someone in a position where they have to hurt another.

It had stopped raining. They climbed out onto the fire escape, Alice carrying the sleeping girl, the air free and light after the storm. She was smiling at the girl. He felt he was looking at another person.

– Hana is nine years old. Already too smart. Not enough a child, and that's sad.
– You've got a lot more time with her.
– No. I feel she's loaned to me. We're veiled in flesh. That's all.

They looked out over the low houses of Queen Street, the metal of the fire escape wet around them, cool, a shock to their arms on this summer night. The rain had released the smells from the street and lifted them up. He lay back like the child, a raindrop now and then touching his shirt like a heartbeat.

— *I don't know*, she whispered, near him.

He reached to where she was and she put her hand against him. The sky looked mapped, gridded by the fire escape. Above and below them a few neighbours came out onto the frail structures, laughing with relief at the cooler air. They would wave now and then, formally, to Alice and her companion. He was suddenly aware that he had a role.

A bottle of fruit whiskey on the end of a long piece of twine swung from side to side in front of them. Alice caught it and pulled it in. "To impatience," she said. She drank, offered him some, and then holding the rope let the bottle down to another level. In this way it moved among the others.

To the south they could see the lights of the Victory Flour Mills. The Macedonians, who disliked the raindrops on their hair, asked their wives to pass them their hats through the window, and felt more secure. They saw Alice's man who worked in the tunnels. They sat among their families, looking towards the lake. The vista was Upper America, a New World. Landscape changed nothing but it brought rest, altered character as gradually as water on a stone. Patrick lay back again beside Alice and the girl Hana.

— You should sit up, she said after a while. You will see something beautiful.

A rectangle of light went on below them. Then another. The night-shift workers were starting to get up. They could be seen in grey trousers and undershirts, washing at their kitchen sinks. The neighbourhood was soon speckled with light while the rest of the city lay in sleep. Soon they could hear doors closing on the street below them. Figures filed out, Macedonians and Greeks, heading for the killing floors and railway yards and bakeries.

– They don't want your revolution, Patrick said to Alice.
– No. They won't be involved. Just you. You're a mongrel, like me. Not like my daughter here. But like me.
– So what do you want?
– Nothing but thunder.

* * *

Alice and Hana were still on the fire escape, curled up together, when he left. He closed the door on them quiet as a thief.

He would have to go back to his room, take his clothes out into the alley and beat the hardened mud out of them, then walk to work. It was about five A.M., his head and body buzzing, overloaded with false energy. Later, he knew, he would be unable to lift his arms above his head, would stagger under the weight of a pickaxe. But for now the dawn in him, the sun, wakened his blood.

He remembered Clara in the Paris hotel talking about how Alice had been after the child's father had died. "Hana wasn't born yet. But Cato died and I think she went into madness, into something very alone. He was killed up north when she was pregnant."

In the Thompson Grill, the counter radio was already playing songs about the heart, songs about women who let their men go as casually as a river through their fingers. The waitress with the tattoo gave him his coffee. The music this morning threw him across eras. He was eighteen again and he fell into a girl's arms, drunk and full of awe during his first formal dance, painted moonlight on the ceiling, the floating lights through the scrims that bathed the couples translating them. He had stepped up cocky and drunk onto the sprung floor and was suddenly close enough to see the girl's lost eyes, undisguised by the colours, and he too was lost. A chameleon among the minds of women.

– *What did you think of my friend?*
– *I liked her.*
– *She's a great actress.*
– *Better than you, is she?*
– *By a hundred miles, Patrick.*
– *Yes, I liked her.*

His mind skates across old conversations. The past drifts into the air like an oasis and he watches himself within it. The girl's eyes that night when he was eighteen were like tunnels into kindness and lust and determination which he loved as much as her white stomach and her ochre face. He saw something there he would never fully reach – the way Clara dissolved and suddenly disappeared from him, or the way Alice came to him it seemed in a series of masks or painted faces, both of these women like the sea through a foreground of men.

These were days that really belonged to the moon.

He was restless and full of Alice Gull. When the tunnel at the waterworks was completed, Patrick got a job at Wickett and Craig's tannery. His flesh tightened in this new dry world, his damp stiffness fell away.

All day he thought of her as he cut skins in the Cypress Street leather factory. Jobs were still scarce and it was only through Alice's friends that he was hired. Patrick's shoulder nudged the bolster that released rolls of leather onto the floor and he waded into the brown skins with the pilot knife, slicing the hides in straight lines. When his line was finished he would stand breathing in the cold air till someone else came off the cutter's alley. He was no longer aware of the smell from the dyers' yards. Only if it rained would the odour assault his body.

He was one of three pilot men. Their knives weaved with the stride of their arms and they worked barefoot as if walking up a muddy river, slicing it up into tributaries. It was a skill that insisted on every part of the body's balance. Alice would smell the leather on him, even after he had bathed in the courtyards when work was over, the brief pelt of water and steam on the row of them standing on the cobblestones. They were allowed only ten seconds of water. The men who dyed the leather got longer but the smell on them was terrible and it never left.

Dye work took place in the courtyards next to the ware-house. Circular pools had been cut into the stone – into which the men leapt waist-deep within the reds and ochres and greens, leapt in embracing the skins of recently slaughtered animals. In the round wells four-foot in diameter they heaved and stomped, ensuring the dye went solidly into the pores of the skin that had been part of a live animal the previous day. And the men stepped out in colours up to their necks, pulling wet hides out after them so it appeared they had removed the skin from their own bodies. They had leapt into different colours as if into dif-ferent countries.

What the dyers wanted, standing there together, the repre-sentatives from separate nations, was a cigarette. To stand dur-ing the five-minute break dressed in green talking to a man in yellow, and *smoke*. To take in the fresh energy of smoke and swallow it deep into their lungs, roll it around and breathe it up so it would remove with luck the acrid texture already deep within them, stuck within every corner of their flesh. A ciga-rette, a star beam through their flesh, would have been enough to purify them.

That is how Patrick would remember them later. Their bodies standing there tired, only the heads white. If he were an artist he would have painted them but that was false celebra-tion. What did it mean in the end to look aesthetically plum-aged on this October day in the east end of the city five hundred yards from Front Street? What would the painting tell? That they were twenty to thirty-five years old, were Macedonians mostly, though there were a few Poles and Lithuanians. That on average they had three or four sentences of English, that they had never read the *Mail and Empire* or *Saturday Night*. That during the day they ate standing up. That they had con-sumed the most evil smell in history, they were consuming it now, flesh death, which lies in the vacuum between flesh and skin, and even if they never stepped into this pit again – a year from now they would burp up that odour. That they would die of consumption and at present they did not know it. That in winter this picturesque yard of colour was even more beautiful, the thin layer of snowfall between the steaming wells. Below-zero weather and the almost naked men descend into the vats at the same whistle and cover themselves later with burlap as they stand waiting.

The only virtue to winter was the removal of smell. They did not want a cigarette then, they could hardly breathe. Their mouths sent forth plumes. They stood there, the steam coming through the burlap. And when they stopped steaming they knew they were too cold and had to go in. But during October, as Patrick watched them during his break from the hide-room, they desired a cigarette. And they could never smoke – the acid of the solutions they had stepped into and out of so strong that they would have ignited if a flame touched them.

A green man on fire.

They were the dyers. They were paid one dollar a day. Nobody could last in that job more than six months and only the desperate took it. There were other jobs such as water boys and hide-room labourers. In the open cloisters were the sausage and fertilizer makers. Here the men stood, ankle-deep in salt, filling casings, squeezing out shit and waste from animal intestines. In the further halls were the killing-floors where you moved among the bellowing cattle stunning them towards death with sledge hammers, the dead eyes still flickering while their skins were removed. There was never enough ventilation, and the coarse salt, like the acids in the dyeing section, left the men invisibly with tuberculosis and arthritis and rheumatism. All of these professions arrived in morning darkness and worked till six in the evening, the labour agent giving them all English names. Charlie Johnson, Nick Parker. They remembered the strange foreign syllables like a number.

For the dyers the one moment of superiority came in the showers at the end of the day. They stood under the hot pipes, not noticeably changing for two or three minutes – as if, like an actress unable to return to the real world from a role, they would be forever contained in that livid colour, only their brains free of it. And then the blue suddenly dropped off, the colour disrobed itself from the body, fell in one piece to their ankles, and they stepped out, in the erotica of being made free.

What remained in the dyers' skin was the odour that no woman in bed would ever lean towards. Alice lay beside Patrick's exhausted body, her tongue on his neck, recognizing the taste of him, knowing the dyers' wives would never taste or smell their husbands again in such a way; even if they removed all pigment and coarse salt crystal, the men would smell still of the angel they wrestled with in the well, in the pit. Incarnadine.

"I'll tell you about the rich," Alice would say. "The rich are always laughing. They keep saying the same things on their boats and lawns: *Isn't this grand! We're having a good time!* And whenever the rich get drunk and maudlin about humanity you have to listen for hours. But they keep you in the tunnels and stockyards. They do not toil or spin. Remember that . . . understand what they will always refuse to let go of. There are a hundred fences and lawns between the rich and you. You've got to know these things, Patrick, before you ever go near them – the way a dog before battling with cows rolls in the shit of the enemy."

In Kosta's house he relaxes as Alice speaks with her friends, slipping out of English and into Finnish or Macedonian. She knows she can be unconcerned with his lack of language, that he is happy. She converses with full energy in this theatre of the dinner table, her face vivid; a scar, a mole will exaggerate when not disguised by the content of conversation. He in fact pleasures in his own descant interpretations of what is being said. He catches only the names of streets, the name of Police Chief Draper, who has imposed laws against public meetings by foreigners. So if they speak this way in public, in *any* language other than English, they will be jailed. A rule of the city. The *broncos* will have them arrested as many already have been in various rallies in High Park or in the Shapiro Drug Store clash with the Mounties in the previous year.

He watches each of her friends and he gazes at the small memory painting of Europe on the wall – the spare landscape, the village imposed on it. He is immensely comfortable in this room. He remembers his father once passing the foreign loggers on First Lake Road and saying, *"They don't know where they are."* And now, in this neighbourhood intricate with history and ceremony, Patrick smiles to himself at the irony of reversals. Before the meal, Kosta's wife had come up to him, pointed to one of the pictures and named her village, then she had pressed the side of her stomach with both hands sensually to make clear to Patrick that she would be serving liver.

If only it were possible that in the instance something was written down – idea or emotion or musical phrase – it became known to others of the era. The rejected *Carmen* of 1875 turning so many into lovers of opera. And Verdi in the pouring rain believing he was being turned into a frog – even this emotion realized by his contemporaries.

Patrick listens now as Alice reads to him from the letters of

Joseph Conrad – an extract which she has copied. She has already asked him who he likes to read and he has mentioned Conrad. "Yes, but," she says rising as the child cries, "have you read his *letters*?" In the other room she comforts the girl Hana out of a nightmare.

"Wait," she continues, "I've got something to show you." Very excited now, as if she fears he will get up and leave before she can present this gift. She too likes Conrad. She likes his theatrical style. There are some novelists whose work actors love but who could not write a simple scene for the stage. They write the scenes actors dream, and Conrad was that for Alice.

> – Listen: "An idle and selfish class loves to see mischief being made, even if it is made at its own expense."
> – *Ha*, he laughs.
> – He's complaining about Tory views on Spanish liberal insurgents of the 1830s, based in London. "Of course I do not defend political crimes. It is repulsive to me by tradition, by sentiment, and even by reflection. But some of these men struggled for an idea, openly, in the light of day, and sacrificed to it all that to most men makes life worth living. Moreover a sweeping assertion is always wrong, since men are infinitely varied; and harsh words are useless because they cannot combat ideas. And the ideas (that live) should be combatted, not the men who die."

It was a letter Conrad had written to a newspaper. So Patrick listened to his contemporary.

— How can I convert you? she would ask in the darkness of the bedroom.

— The trouble with ideology, Alice, is that it hates the private. You must make it human.

— These are my favourite lines. I'll whisper them. "I have taught you that the sky in all its zones is mortal. . . . Let me now re-emphasize the extreme looseness of the structure of all objects."

In the darkness he can see just the faint aura of her hair.

— Say it again.

*   *   *

On Saturday afternoons the dye washers and cutters, men from the killing beds, the sausage makers, the electrocuters – all of them from this abattoir and tannery on Cypress Street – were free. After bathing under the pipes they walked up Bathurst Street to Queen, the thirty or so of them knowing little more than each other's false names or true countries. *Hey Italy!* They were in pairs or trios, each in their own language as the dyers had been in their own colours. After a beer they would continue up Bathurst to the Oak Leaf Steam Baths. Paying their quarters they were each handed a towel, a sheet, a padlock, and a canvas bag. They stripped, packed their clothes and salaries into the bag, locked it, and strung the keys around their necks. There was a sense of relaxation among all of them. *Hey Canada!* A wave to Patrick. It was Saturday.

In the whitewashed rooms they sat naked within the steam, brushing a scab, considering a scar on the shoulder. Someone he had never spoken to caught his eye and both of them were so tired they could not turn away their gaze, just watched the other bluntly. He knew nothing about the men around him except how they moved and laughed – on this side of language. He himself had kept his true name and voice from the bosses at the leather yard, never spoke to them or answered them. A chain was pulled that forced wet steam into the room so that their bodies were separated by whiteness coming up through the gridded floors, tattoos and hard muscles fading into unborn photographs. They shifted, stood up, someone began to sing.

The wet heat focused the exhaustion and under the cold shower the last of the tension fell to his feet. For the last hour they lay on the green bunks, a radio on the windowsill transmitting the Saturday afternoon opera, with a sign above it in three languages insisting that no one change the station.

He lay there, not wanting translation, letting the emotion of the music fall onto him. Soon this arm would become the arm Alice kissed. They were all being released from the week's work and began to allow themselves ease, the clarified world of passion. The music of *La Bohème*, the death of Mimi, hovering over their unprotected bodies, the keys hanging from the cords around their necks.

*   *   *

Then it was her hand in the doorway touching his heart, against his ribs, aware through her fingers of his weariness. In the small room where he could take three steps and touch the window. There was Patrick and Alice and Hana. If it was warm they would eat on the fire escape. Or if Alice was working he and Hana walked over to the Balkan Café where they sat on wire chairs and were served by long-aproned waiters. They ordered *bop* and *manja,* Hana telling him in her clear, exact voice what the names meant. *Bop* was beans. *Manja* was stew. As he watched Hana, her face drifted into Alice's and back again as if two glass negatives merged, then moved apart. It was not so much the features as the mannerisms of Alice that he witnessed in her daughter.

He was at ease with the precise Hana and the way she seriously articulated herself among strangers. That voice knew what it wanted and knew what it was allowed. He wanted to pick Hana up and embrace her on the street but felt shy, though in games or in a crowded streetcar her arm lay across him as if needing his warmth and closeness. As he did hers.

But his relationship with Alice had a horizon. She refused to speak of the past. Even her stories about Hana's father, though intricate, gave nothing away of herself. She was never self-centred in her mythologies. She would turn any compliment away. Her habit of sitting pale and naked at the breakfast table, cutting up whatever fruit they had into three portions, or sitting down with fried eggs made him once whisper to her that she was beautiful. "I'm terrific over eggs," she shot back, her mouth full. She did not get dressed. She planned to go back to bed as soon as Patrick left for the tannery and Hana left for school. Alice worked in the evenings.

His relationship with Hana was clearer. There would always be something careful about her. As if she had been badly scalded and so would approach all water tentatively for fear it was boiling. With her there would be brief conflicts, a discussion, and then everything was settled. She would not be bossed and she was self-sufficient. She didn't expect forgiveness.

They sat at the round tables at the Balkan Café eating a large meal and with ice creams strolled over at ten to the Parrot Theatre to pick up Alice. They had all the time in the world,

Hana translating the information she received on the street, speaking to a butcher who walked beside them for a hundred yards carrying a pig's head. Patrick watched the gestures towards him. They knew who he was now. A hat raised off a head in slow motion, a woman's nod to his left shoulder.

He lived – in his job and during these evening walks – in a silence, with noise and conversation all around him. To be understood, his reactions had to exaggerate themselves. The family idiot. A stroke victim. "Paderick," the shopkeepers would call him as he handed them money and a list of foods Hana had written out in Macedonian, accepting whatever they gave him. He felt himself expand into an innocent. Every true thing he learned about character he learned at this time in his life. Once, when they were at the Teck Cinema watching a Chaplin film he found himself laughing out loud, joining the others in their laughter. And he caught someone's eye, the body bending forward to look at him, who had the same realization – that this mutual laughter was conversation.

He was always comfortable in someone else's landscape, enjoyed being taught the customs of a place. Patrick wanted the city Hana had constructed for herself – the places she brought together and held as if on the delicate thread of her curiosity: Hoo's Trading Company where Alice bought herbs for fever, gaslit diners whose aquarium windows leaned against the street. They watched the water-nymph follies at Sunnyside Park, watched the Italian gymnasts at the Elm Street gym, heard the chanting of English lessons to large groups at Central Neighbourhood House – one pure English voice claiming *My name is Ernest*, and then a barrage of male voices claiming their names were Ernest.

But Hana's favourite place of spells was the Geranium Bakery, and one Saturday afternoon she took him there to meet her friend Nicholas. She guided Patrick among the other workers and sacks of flour and rollers towards Nicholas Temelcoff, who turned towards her and stretched his arms out wide. It was a joke, he was covered in flour and did not really expect to be embraced. He shook Patrick's hand and began to show them around the bakery, Hana scooping bits of raw dough with her finger and eating them. Temelcoff was meticulously dressed in jacket and tie but wore no apron so that the flour dust continued to settle on him as he moved through the bakery. He pulled chains that hung from the ceiling to start rollers moving on the upper level. He brought a small doll out of his pocket and handed it to Hana – and this time she embraced him, her head on his chest. The two men had said no more than four polite sentences to each other by the time Patrick left with the girl.

One night Hana pulled out a valise from under the bed and showed him some mementoes. There was a photograph of her as a baby – with her first nickname, Piko, scrawled in pencil on it. Three other photographs: a group of men working on the Bloor Street Viaduct, a photograph of Alice in a play at the Finnish Labour Temple, three men standing in snow in a lumber camp. A sumac bracelet. A rosary. These objects spread out on the bed replaced her father's absence.

So he discovered Cato through the daughter. The girl had been told everything about him, told of his charm, his cruelty, his selfishness, his heroism, the way he had met and seduced Alice. "You didn't know Cato, did you?" "No." "Well he was supposed to be very passionate, very cruel." "Don't talk like that, Hana, you're ten years old, and he's your father." "Oh, I love him, even if I never met him. That's just the truth."

She was totally unlike Patrick, always practical. When he returned from the steambaths on the first Saturday she had inquired about the price and he saw her trying to work out if it was worth it. "I would have paid anything," he muttered, and he saw she could not understand or accept such extravagance in him. She thought him foolish. In the same way, her portrait of her father lacked any sentimentality.

– Who were those people in the bridge picture, Hana?
– Oh she must have known them.

*　　*　　*

Alice was in sunlight on the grass slope leading down from the waterworks, looking out onto the lake, her hand keeping the sun out of her eyes. "I had to learn I couldn't trust him. Not that he ever wanted me to. You must realize that Cato was not his real name, it was his war name. And who knows who he was with or what he was doing on a Wednesday or a Friday. He was self-made. He worked hard, he spoke out. On Thursdays he came shimmering along on his bike, dropped his tackle in the hall as if he were a hurried fisherman, and said, *Let's go!*"

– How long did you stay together?
– Till he died. We were always breaking up. He thought his life was too complicated. We spent half our time worrying with each other about this. And then on Wednesday nights I would dream out the next afternoon on our bicycles along that stretch of road, in April flood or summer dust. You could blindfold me now, Patrick, and I would be able to take you there, fifty yards off the road, across a creek – lots of mud here, turn right – this is where we always got our feet wet, some gum off a low

pine on my hair as I'd leap the creek. Shoulder-high cattails and ferns, then into the longhouse of cedars. Spring crows in the cedar branches! Needles on the earth half a foot deep! When we made love there he would bury something, a small bottle, a pencil, a handkerchief, a sock. He left something everywhere we made love. Such sexual archaeology. There was a piece of wood that looked like the roof of a doghouse. When we got lost we'd always have to look for that – when snow changed the shape of trees or fall made skeletons of everything, or in summer when everything was overgrown chaos. We would go there all through the year, every season, and winter was strangely easier than summer with its bugs and deer flies. We could make hollows in the snow, we were protected from wind by the trees. It is important to be close to the surface of the earth.

He began to like it, I think, us not being lovers indoors. Still, we always fought. I told him once if he ever broke up with me and said we were 'crazy' and that we had to stop, I would knife him.

– You told me that too.

– I feel charmed, Patrick, that I knew him as well as I know you.

– I feel jealous. No. I don't feel jealous.

– Because he's dead? You listen to me so calmly, all this intimacy. . . .

– Hana showed me the pictures. Who were the men on the bridge?

– That's the past, Patrick, leave it alone. Anyway, you should get Hana to talk to you about Cato and the socks. That's her favourite story.

"They were in the woods and came into a field to get away from the bugs. It was summer. Lots of bugs, my mom said. So they took off their clothes and went for a swim in the river. When they came back, there were all these young bulls where their clothes were. About five of them in a circle around the clothes. Only they were not interested in the clothes except for his socks! They were sniffing them up in the air and tossing them back and forth. It really embarrassed Cato. My mom told me he didn't want to talk about it to others. I just love that – all those serious bulls throwing his socks back and forth. Mom thinks they were very excited."

Patrick had the photograph from Hana's suitcase in his pocket. In books he had read, even those romances he swallowed during childhood, Patrick never believed that characters lived only on the page. They altered when the author's eye was somewhere else. Outside the plot there was a great darkness, but there would of course be daylight elsewhere on earth. Each character had his own time zone, his own lamp, otherwise they were just men from nowhere.

He was in the Riverdale Library looking for any reference to the building of the Bloor Street Viaduct. He collected the newspapers and journals he needed and went and sat in the Boys and Girls Room with its high rafters and leaded windows that let in oceans of light. He revelled in this room, the tiny desks, the smell of books. It was how he imagined the dining hall of a submarine would look.

He read the descriptions of the bridge's opening on October 18, 1918. One newspaper had a picture of a cyclist racing across. He worked backwards. It had taken only two years to build. It had taken years before that to agree on how it was to be done, Commissioner Harris' determination forcing it through. He looked at the various photographs: the shells of wood structures into which concrete was poured, and then the wood removed like hardened bandages to reveal the piers. He read up on everything – survey arguments, the scandals, the deaths of workers fleetingly mentioned, the story of the young nun who had fallen off the bridge, the body never found. He read about the flooding Don River underneath, ice dangers, the decision to use night crews and the night deaths that followed. There was an article on daredevils. He heard the library bell. He turned the page to the photograph of them and he pulled out the picture he had and laid it next to the one in the newspaper. Third from the left, the newspaper said, was Nicholas Temelcoff.

Leaving the library, Patrick crossed Broadview Avenue and began walking east. He paused, suddenly stilled, wanting to go back, but the library was closed now and it would be pointless. They would not print the photograph of a nun. A dead or a missing nun.

He took a step forward. Now he was walking slowly, approaching a street-band, and the click of his footsteps unconsciously adapted themselves to the music that began to surround him. The cornet and saxophone and drum chased each other across solos and then suddenly, as Patrick drew alongside them, fell together and rose within a chorus.

He saw himself gazing at so many stories – knowing of Alice's lover Cato and Hana's wanderings in the baker's world. He walked on beyond the sound of the street musicians, aware once again of the silence between his individual steps, knowing now he could add music by simply providing the thread of a hum. He saw the interactions, saw how each one of them was carried by the strength of something more than themselves.

If Alice had been a nun . . .

The street-band had depicted perfect company, with an ending full of embraces after the solos had made everyone stronger, more delineated. His own life was no longer a single story but part of a mural, which was a falling together of accomplices. Patrick saw a wondrous night web – all of these fragments of a human order, something ungoverned by the family he was born into or the headlines of the day. A nun on a bridge, a daredevil who was unable to sleep without drink, a boy watching a fire from his bed at night, an actress who ran away with a millionaire – the detritus and chaos of the age was realigned.

*   *   *

The articles and illustrations he found in the Riverdale Library depicted every detail about the soil, the wood, the weight of concrete, everything but information on those who actually built the bridge. There were no photographers like Lewis Hine, who in the United States was photographing child labour everywhere – trapper boys in coal mines, seven-year-old doffer girls in New England mills. *To locate the evils and find the hidden purity.* Official histories and news stories were always soft as rhetoric, like that of a politician making a speech after a bridge is built, a man who does not even cut the grass on his own lawn. Hine's photographs betray official history and put together another family. The man with the pneumatic drill on the Empire State Building in the fog of stone dust, a tenement couple, breaker boys in the mines. His photographs are rooms one can step into – cavernous buildings where a man turns a wrench the size of his body, or caves of iron where the white faces give the young children working there the terrible look of ghosts. But Patrick would never see the great photographs of Hine, as he would never read the letters of Joseph Conrad.

Official histories, news stories surround us daily, but the events of art reach us too late, travel languorously like messages in a bottle.

Only the best art can order the chaotic tumble of events. Only the best can realign chaos to suggest both the chaos and order it will become.

Within two years of 1066, work began on the Bayeux Tapestry, Constantin the African brought Greek medicine to the western world. The chaos and tumble of events. The first sentence of every novel should be: "Trust me, this will take time but there is order here, very faint, very human." Meander if you want to get to town.

*   *   *

I have taught you that the sky in all its zones is mortal.

Her favourite sentence hovers next to Patrick as he wakens. By dawn he is on the livid floor of the tannery with the curved pilot knife. All day long as he cuts into the leather his mind moves over the few details she has given him about her life. Even in the farmhouse at Paris Plains there had been a silence about her youth, even with Cato she gave out only his war name. If Alice Gull had been a nun? A rosary, a sumac bracelet . . .

At six in the evening he returns from work and her open palms press into his ribs. He lifts Alice into his arms and Hana jumps onto her mother's back. So they move, cumbersome, through the small room, falling onto the bed. The game is that Hana has to try and push them off, putting her feet against the wall and her shoulders against them. Then they are on the floor and Hana falls on top. Then he and Hana try to lift Alice back onto the bed.

He is always surprised at Alice's body. She seems physically frail, as if a jostle will break her, but she is agile, a dancer as much as an actress moving fluidly through rooms. She thinks the twentieth century's greatest invention is the jitterbug. She can almost forgive capitalism for that. She is in love with Fats Waller. Patrick has seen her sit at the piano in the Balkan Café and sing

> *"Needed no star*
> *Wanted no moon*
> *Always thought it too dumb . . .*
> *Then all at once*
> *Up jumped you*
> *With love."*

Clara, she would say later, was the classical one, *she* could play the piano like a queen stepping across mud. I play the way I think. And heartbreaking romance is all I want in music.

But Alice's tenderest speech to him, as she sat on his belly looking down, concerned her missing of Clara. "I love Clara," she said to him, the lover of Clara. "I miss her. She made me sane for all those years. That was important for what I am now."

She could move like . . . she could sing as low as . . . Why is it that I am now trying to uncover every facet of Alice's nature for myself?

He wants everything of Alice to be with him here in this

room as if she is not dead. As if he can be given that gift, to relive those days when Alice was with him and Hana, which in literature is the real gift. He turns the page backwards. Once more there is the image of them struggling and tickling Alice until she releases her grip on her shirt and it comes off with a flourish, and Hana jumps up, waving it like a rebel's flag in the small green-painted room. All these fragments of memory . . . so we can retreat from the grand story and stumble accidentally upon a luxury, one of those underground pools where we can sit still. Those moments, those few pages in a book we go back and forth over.

*   *   *

Nicholas Temelcoff's fingers sink into a ball of dough and pull it apart, then they reassemble it and fling it down onto the table. He looks up and sees Patrick enter the Geranium Bakery, awkwardly look around, and then approach him. Patrick pulls out the photograph and places it in front of Temelcoff.

Behind them the pulleys and rollers move hundreds of loaves into the ovens, pause, then continue out. Temelcoff in his grey clothes talks with Patrick about the bridge and the nun – reminded of the exact date which his memory had lost – and pleasure and wonder fill him. He stands in the centre of the bakery thinking, throwing a small ball of dough up and catching it, unaware of this gesture for so long that Patrick, a yard from him, cannot reach him. Temelcoff is somewhere else, the eyes magnified behind the spectacles, the ball of dough falling surely back into the hand, the arm that caught her in the air and pulled her back into life. *"Talk, you must talk,"* and so mockingly she took a parrot's name. *Alicia.*

Nicholas Temelcoff never looks back. He will drive the bakery van over the bridge with his wife and children and only casually mention his work there. He is a citizen here, in the present, successful with his own bakery. His bread and rolls and cakes and pastries reach the multitudes in the city. He is a man who is comfortable among ovens, the smell of things rising, the metamorphosis of food. But he pauses now, reminded about the details of the incident on the bridge.

He stands exactly where Patrick left him, thinking, as those would who believe that to continue a good dream you must lie down the next night in exactly the same position you awakened in, where the body parted from its images. Nicholas is aware of himself standing there within the pleasure of recall. It is something new to him. This is what history means. He came to this country like a torch on fire and he swallowed air as he walked forward and he gave out light. Energy poured through him. That was all he had time for in those years. Language, customs, family, salaries. Patrick's gift, that arrow into the past, shows him the wealth in himself, how he has been sewn into history. Now he will begin to tell stories. He is a tentative man, even with his family. That night in bed shyly he tells his wife the story of the nun.

Cato would always arrive late, Alice remembers, his bicycle clanging to the pavement outside her window. She would climb onto the handlebars and they'd weave down to the lake laid out like crinoline. They'd lie against the railway embankment a few yards from Lake Ontario. The branches in winter were encased in ice and she would lean her head back, exposing her white neck, and take twig and icicle in her mouth and snap it off with the pressure of her tongue.

But at other times she was glad she didn't live with him permanently, to be pulled continually by his planet. If you were close to Cato you had to be a representative of his world, his friends, his plans for the week. Strangers, old lovers, ambled up to him on the street and embraced him and *they* had to join the group. It was impossible to go two blocks on a bicycle with him without running into someone who needed help to find a friend or move a cabinet. "Just *one day*, Cato," she'd say. "Even *four hours*!"

And so he became the man who was Thursday to her. They disappeared into the ravines, the woods north of the city, or her favourite place – against the thick stones of the railway embankment, the willow bending over clothed in ice, loving each other along with the sound of the spring breakup. Kissing each other with stones in their mouths. The freeze still over the March lake, she would lie on her stomach, his hand under her, the shudder of the passing train, the Apalachicola boxcars, reaching through his palm to her breast.

So Thursday jumped out of the week like a fold-out bed. But there were no beds for them ever. By the time Hana was born he was dead.

Patrick laid his head on her stomach, watching the secret lift of her skin at each heartbeat. Talking on the nights they could afford to stay up late. "He was born up north, you know, quite near where he died." Her hand brushed against his chest. "His father moved here from Finland as a logger. Here his family no longer had to bow to priests or dignitaries and they were soon involved in the unions. Cato was born here. His father skated three miles for the doctor the night he was born. He skated across the lake holding up cattails on fire."

Patrick stopped her hand moving.

– So they were *Finns*.
– What?
– Finns. When I was a kid . . .

Now in his thirties he finally had a name for that group of men he witnessed as a child.

She looked at Patrick, who was smiling as if a riddle old and tiresome had been solved, a burr plucked from his brain. In the green room the moon showed her face clearly. A moon returning from when he was eleven. He loved the power of coincidence, the pleasure of strangeness. *Hello Finland!*

– Come into me.

And who was she? And where was she from? His hands on her shoulders, his arms straight, so their upper torsos were

469

separate, their faces apart. The brain and eyes interpreting pleasure in the other, these textures that brushed and gripped. He
pivoted on her hands against his belly, moving deeper, moving
back, and was still. Not a movement of the eye. He knew now
he was the sum of all he had been in his life since he was that
boy in the snow woods, her hands collapsing to hold him
against her harder. Fingernail at his spine. His cheek against
her turquoise eye.

He lay in bed looking at the light of the moon in the bones of
the fire escape. The light of the electric clock advertising Cabinet Cigars. Out there the beautiful grey of the Victory Flour
Mills at midnight, its clean curves over the lake. Any decade
you wished.

– God I love your face . . .

She has delivered him out of nothing. This woman who
jumps onto him laughing in mid-air and growls at his neck and
pulls him like a wheel over her.

How can she who had torn his heart open at the waterworks
with her art lie now like a human in his arms? Or stand catatonic in front of bananas on Eastern Avenue deciding which
bunch to buy? Does this make her more magical? As if a fabulous heron in flight has fallen dead at his feet and he sees the
further wonder of its meticulous construction. How did someone conceive of putting this structure of bones and feathers
together, deciding on the weight of beak and skull, and give it
the ability to fly?

His love of the theatre was that of an amateur. He picked up
gossip, mementoes, handbills. He loved technique, to walk
backstage and see Ophelia with her mad face half rubbed off.
This was humanity in theatre, the scar – the old actor famous

for playing whimsical judges, who rode the Queen streetcar east of the city and ate his dinner alone before joining his sleeping wife. Patrick liked that. He wanted to be fooled by the person he felt could not fool him, who stopped three yards past the side curtain and became somebody else.

But with Alice, after the episode at the waterworks and in other performances, he can never conceive how she leaps from her true self to her other true self. It is a flight he knows nothing about. He cannot put the two people together. Did the actor – holding her on stage, reciting wondrous language, holding his painted face inches away from her painted face, kissing her ear in drawing-room comedies – know the person she had stepped from to be there?

In the midst of his love for Alice, in the midst of lovemaking even, he watches her face waiting for her to be translated into this war bride or that queen or shopgirl, half expecting metamorphosis as they kiss. Annunciation. The eye would go first, and as he draws back he will be in another country, another century, his arms around a stranger.

There had been an earring missing beside the bed or at the sink in the kitchen. He had watched her move around the room half-naked, dressing, bending down to a pile of clothes in his room without furniture, a long time ago, saying *Can't find my earring, does it matter?* As if another woman would find it. Alice departing with one ear undressed. *If we meet again we can say hello, we can say goodbye.*

Dear Alice –

The only heat in this bunkhouse is from a small drum stove. In the evenings air is thick from the damp clothes in the rafters above the fire and from tobacco smoke. To avoid suffocating, the men in the upper bunks push out the moss chinking between logs.

Patrick reads slowly, knowing he will be given the letter only once, on this summer night under the one lightbulb of the room, far from winter weather. Hana sits on the bed and watches him. For what? He thinks as he reads what his face should express to the letter-writer's daughter. He holds the grade-school notebook which the words fill. She has removed it from the suitcase and presented it to him. *Dear Alice,* scrawled, the handwriting large and hurried but the information detailed as if Cato were trying to hold everything he saw, at the lumber camp near Onion Lake, during his final days.

I write at a table hammered permanently into the floor. The log bunks are nailed into the walls. Fires die out at night and men wake with hair frozen to damp icicles on the wall. "In the bleak mid-winter – Frosty wind made moan – Earth stood hard as iron – Water like a stone." That was the first hymn I learned in

English, written by someone in an English village.
And it describes this place better than anything else.

Patrick sees Cato writing by tallow light . . . sealing the letter, passing the package to someone leaving the camp the next morning. When Alice opens the package five weeks later she pulls the exercise book to her face and smells whatever she can of him, for he has been dead a month. She smells the candlewax, she imagines the odour of the hut, the cold pencil he has sharpened before beginning to write his unsigned letters about camp conditions and strike conditions. Cato sits dead centre, at the food table, the pipe smoke moves live and grey around him. His hair smells of it, it has entered deep into his shirt and sweater, it hangs against his stubbled beard.

None of the camp bosses knows who he is or of his connection to the planned strike. But they soon discover this. He slips out of the lumber camp on foot and goes into open snow country. The nearest town is Port Arthur, over a hundred and twenty miles away, and he aims himself towards it.

Four men on horseback attempt to capture Cato over the next week. But Cato knows snow country; he was born into it. He can, it seems, disappear under the surface of it. He avoids the familiar route, sleeps in trees, even risks crawling on all fours over thin-iced lakes – hearing the surface crack and groan under him. Now and then he sees flares belonging to his hunters. At each camp he writes into a notebook, jams it into a tin, and buries the tin deep under the snow or ties it onto a high branch. Meanwhile his package of letters is travelling, passed from hand to hand before it nestles in a bag next to a rolled-up swede saw on a logger's back on the final leg of the journey.

While he is cutting a hole in the ice at Onion Lake, Cato sees the men. They ride out of the trees and execute him. They find no messages or identification on him. They try burning the body but he will not ignite. There have been union men before him and there will be union men after him. The man with the swede saw posts his bundle of letters in Algoma unaware that the sender is dead, shot to death, buried in the ice of a shallow river.

> *They lose two days a month because of wet weather. Travelling eats up $10 a season; mitts $6; shoes and stockings $25; working clothes $35. Being forced to buy their supplies in camps means 30 per cent tagged onto city prices . . .*

Patrick reads, aware that the smell of smoke is no longer on the porous paper. The words on the page form a rune – flint-hard and unemotional in the midst of the inferno of Cato's situation.

And who is he to touch the lover of this man, to eat meals with his daughter, to stand dazed under a lightbulb and read his last letter?

He remains standing alone in the room Hana has now left. She had seen him hypnotized, as if the letter stared back at him. He realizes what he is doing, that he has become a searcher again with this family. As if he had leaned forward to the woman he had just met in Paris Plains and said, Who is your lover? Tell me the most painful thing that has happened to you. For he has over the years learned the answers. He holds now the last ten minutes of Cato's language. In his mind he sees Alice pick up the package which death has made impossible – after the murder, the discovery of the body in ice, his burial, and the acquittal of the bosses at the inquiry.

Patrick has clung like moss to strangers, to the nooks and fissures of their situations. He has always been alien, the third person in the picture. He is the one born in this country who knows nothing of the place. The Finns of his childhood used the river, even knew it by night, the men of burning rushes delirious in the darkness. This he had never done. He was a watcher, a corrector. He could no more have skated along the darkness of a river than been the hero of one of these stories. Alice had once described a play to him in which several actresses shared the role of the heroine. After half an hour the powerful matriarch removed her large coat from which animal pelts dangled and she passed it, along with her strength, to one of the minor characters. In this way even a silent daughter could put on the cloak and be able to break through her chrysalis into language. Each person had their moment when they assumed the skins of wild animals, when they took responsibility for the story.

Clara and Ambrose and Alice and Temelcoff and Cato – this cluster made up a drama without him. And he himself was nothing but a prism that refracted their lives. He searched out things, he collected things. He was an abashed man, an inheritance from his father. Born in Abashed, Ontario. What did the word mean? Something that suggested there was a terrible horizon in him beyond which he couldn't leap. Something hollow, so when alone, when not aligned with another – whether it was Ambrose or Clara or Alice – he could hear the rattle within that suggested a space between him and community. A gap of love.

He had lived in this country all of his life. But it was only now that he learned of the union battles up north where Cato was murdered some time in the winter of 1921, and found under the ice of a shallow creek near Onion Lake a week after he had written his last letter. The facts of the story had surrounded Hana since birth, it was a part of her. And all of his life Patrick had been oblivious to it, a searcher gazing into the darkness of his own country, a blind man dressing the heroine.

Every Sunday they still congregated at the waterworks. They walked over grills under which foam rushed, they opened doorways to waterfalls. The building, now three-quarters finished, spread ceremonial over the rise just south of Queen Street, looking onto the lake. Because of its structure the main pumping station could be filled with lamps and no light would be betrayed to the outside world. The sound of pumps churning drowned out the noise of their meetings.

On Sundays, as darkness fell, the various groups walked up to the building from the lakeshore where they would not be seen. There was food, entertainment, political speeches. A man who mimicked the King of England stepped forward with a monologue summarizing the news of the past week. Numerous communities and nationalities spoke and performed in their own languages. When they finished, the halls were cleaned up, the floors swept.

Patrick and Alice walked home along Queen Street. The girl was asleep in Patrick's arms, so at some point, tired from her weight, they would sit on a bench and lay Hana out, her head on Alice's lap. He loved this part of the city, the evening streets an extension of his limbs.

— I want to look after Hana.
— You already do.
— More formally. If that will help.

— She knows you love her.

A July night. On what summer night was it that she spoke of Clara and how she missed her? All these incidents and emotions to cover and the story like a tired child tugging us on, not letting us converse with ease, sleeping on our shoulder so it is difficult to embrace the person we love. He loved Alice. He leaned against her and he could feel her hair still wet from the sweat of the performance.

    — You will catch a cold.
    — Ah yes.

*   *   *

Now he aches for her smallness, her intricacy — he needs a second glance whenever he thinks of her. In the middle of a field she removes her blouse. Sightings of her breasts. *Trompe l'oeil.* An artist has picked up a pencil and made a fine crosshatched shadow and so they come into existence. He sits and watches her sniffing the wind across a field. The woman he looked through when in love with Clara. Clara's eclipse. The phrase like a flower or event named during the last century.

During Cato's funeral, while Alice held the infant Hana, there was an eclipse. The mourners stood still while the Finnish Brass Band played Chopin's "Funeral March" into the oncoming darkness and throughout the seventeen minutes of total eclipse. The music a lifeline from one moment of light to another.

Now he aches for her, for those days that belonged to the moon. They would sit side by side in a Chinese restaurant, empty but for the two of them. Wanting to face each other but wanting to hold each other and having to decide on one pleasure. The intricate choices of desire.

I don't think I'm big enough to put someone in a position where they will hurt another. That's what you said, Alice, that made me love you most. Made me trust you. No one else would have worried about that, could have said it and made me believe it, that first night in your room. Every bird and insect froze into the element of air at that moment when the sentence slid up, palpable, out of your mouth. You unaware you were expressing a tenderness, thinking you were being critical of yourself.

And another gesture of yours at a dance. I was dancing with someone else and could see you, dying to dance, and stepping up to a man and delicately tapping him on his shoulder, a shy yet determined expression on your face.

They sit in a field. They sit in the red and yellow and gold decor of the restaurant, empty in the late afternoon but for them. Hunger and desire spiriting him across the city, onto trolley after trolley, in order to reach her arm, her neck, this Chinese restaurant, that Macedonian café, this field he is now in the centre of with her. There are country houses on the periphery so they have walked to its centre, the distant point, to be alone.

He will turn while walking and see the fragility of her breasts – the result of a pencil's shading.

She drops into his arms, held out stern as a school desk. He walks then, he dances with the wheat in his hands. When he was twelve he turned the pages always towards illustration and saw the heroes carry the women across British Columbian streams, across the foot of waterfalls. And now her hand above her eyes shielding out the sun. Her shirt on her lap. He has come across a love story. This is only a love story. He does not wish for plot and all its consequences. Let me stay in this field with Alice Gull. . . .

REMORSE

HE HAD ALWAYS wanted to know her when she was old. Patrick sits in her green room, in front of leaves and berries in the old river bottle – a bouquet of weeds collected by Alice the day before her death. Sumac and valley grasses that she picked under the viaduct. When night comes he lights the kerosene lamp, which throws a shadow of this still-life against the wall so it flickers dark and alive.

Let me now re-emphasize the extreme looseness of the structure of things. Whispered to him once.

He undresses and climbs into the bed, where there is the smell of her, where he is unable to sleep. He stays in her room, he escorts her last flowers through death and afterlife, after whatever spirit in them has evaporated out of their brownness. He knows he doesn't have long before he loses the exact memory of her face. His mind moves closer to the skin at the side of her nose where the scar lies. She was always too conscious of it, a line she assumed unbalanced her face. How can he evoke her without this fine line?

He had wanted to know her when she was old. At lunches she would argue her ideas against him, holding up her glass, "To impatience! To the evolving human!" while he was intent on her shoulder, romantic towards the dazzle of her hair. Her grin was always there when he spoke of growing old with her – as if she had made some other pact, as if there was another arrow of alliance. He couldn't wait to know her when, in years to come, they would be solvent, sexually calmer, less like wildlife. There was always, he thought, this pleasure ahead of him, an ace of joy up his sleeve so he could say you can do anything to me, take everything away, put me in prison, but I will know Alice Gull when we are old. Even if we cannot be lovers I will come each afternoon, come as if courting, and over lunch we will share our thoughts, laughing, so this talk will be love.

He had wanted that. And what had she wanted?

> — I was happiest when I was pregnant. When I *bloomed*.
>
> — I don't understand why you like me.
>
> — I feel good about myself since I met you. Since the days with Clara, when you could see nothing else but her and I was watching you. I wasn't jealous. I wasn't in love with you. I was learning wonderful things then, with Clara. You and I will never enter certain rooms together, Patrick. A woman needs a woman to laugh with, over some things. Clara and I felt like a planet! But there was a time after that when I went under. And you gave me an energy. A confidence.

Now there is a moat around her he will never cross again. He will not even cup his hands to drink its waters. As if, having travelled all that distance to enter the castle in order to learn its wisdom for the grand cause, he now turns and walks away.

*   *   *

Patrick steps out of the Verral Avenue rooms. He enters Union Station and, once he is travelling, the landscape slurs into darkness. He focuses thirty yards past the train window until his mind locks, thinking of nothing, not even the death of Alice. By his feet is a black cardboard suitcase. He can think now only of objects. Something alive, just one small grey bird on a branch, will break his heart.

The night train travelling north to Huntsville contains a regatta crowd – men in straw boaters and silk scarves jubilant around him. They weave towards the sleeping cars, passing Patrick, who stands in the corridor, their drunk bodies brushing against him. He gazes through his reflection, hypnotized by the manic parade of sky and rock and tree and moon. No resolution or pause. *Alice*. . . . He breathes out a dead name. Only a dead name is permanent.

Rectangles of light sweep along the earth. He walks to the end of the corridor, opens the door, and stands in the no man's land between carriages, holding onto the stiff accordion-like walls, within the violent rattle of the train.

Alice had an idea, a cause in her eye about wealth and power, forever and ever. And at the end as she turned round to him on the street hearing her name yelled, surprised at Patrick being near, there was nothing completed or attained. And he could think of nothing but the eyes looking for him above the terrible wound suddenly appearing as she turned.

They arrive in Huntsville at three in the morning. Patrick watches a porter travel the corridor of sleeping berths, tagging the shoes left out to be cleaned, and return a few minutes later with a sack into which he throws them all. The passengers will not be awakened until seven.

The stewards sit on the steps of the train polishing shoes.

They speak quietly, smoking cigarettes. Patrick sees them in the yellow spray of the station lamp. He strolls to the end of the platform where there is darkness. Bush. He feels transparent, minuscule. Civilization now, on this August night, is two men cleaning shoes as they sit on the steps of a train. He looks at them from the darkness. He has walked through the pools of light hanging over this platform and light has not attached itself to him. Walking through rain would have left him wet. But light, or a man polishing one tan shoe at four A.M., is only an idea. And this will not convert Patrick, whose loss creates venom. At times like this he could put his hand under the wheel of a train to spite the driver. He could pick up a porcupine and thrash it against the fence not caring how many quills were flung into his hands and neck in retaliation.

At eight A.M. the passengers walk from the train, sleepy, dazed by their own movement, to the dock belonging to the Huntsville and Lake-of-Bays Navigation Company. Patrick carries his fragile suitcase and boards *The Algonquin* steamer.

Most of the regatta crowd will be guests at either Bigwin Inn or the Muskoka Hotel. Patrick watches the scenery as the boat passes the thick-treed islands. Now and then there is a clearing of lawn imposed on the landscape. The setting seems strangely spartan to attract so many wealthy people, to be the playground of the rich. He finds a deck-chair and sleeps, and even in sleep his hand clutches the suitcase. He wakes to every hoot of the whistle as the boat winds its way through North Portage. When they pass Bigwin Island, they are greeted by the Anglo-Canadian Band playing on the rock promontory – tubas, trumpets, violins, and various other instruments. Patrick waves along with the others. He will not be coming back this way. He might as well wave now.

In the Garden of the Blind, on Page Island, a stone cherub holds out a hand from which water leaps up into the air. A tree full of birds spreads itself high over the southern area of the lawn. There is a falling of sounds – bird-calls like drops of water – onto the blind woman sitting there. Seeds float down onto the gravel borders, a sound path for those walking without sight. On one of the benches, under the tree, Patrick sits reading the newspaper.

If he closes his eyes, these noises will overpower him, in the way he imagines the cherub accepts that water which leaps from his palm into air and then falls back onto his face. He watches a bird dart. The woman on his right hears the rustle of his newspaper and realizes he is alien here.

He is one island over from last night's fire, hiding now in this garden, unseen among the blind, till nightfall.

He had loosened the cap on the paraffin can and enclosed it gurgling within his black cardboard suitcase. Then he began his walk along the mezzanine of the empty Muskoka Hotel. He had waited until the guests and staff were outside on the lawns, busy with the regatta dinner. He leaned over the banister to look at the stuffed animal-heads below him, the liquid leaking down, then walked on, the suitcase innocent in his right hand, down the stairs to the lobby. The smell was evident now. *Fire!*

he yelled. He lit a match, dropped it, and the fire ran upstairs and round and round the circular mezzanine. His arm was on fire. He plunged the sleeve of his jacket into an aquarium. The suitcase at the foot of the stairs exploded. He moved alone through the lobby of the Muskoka Hotel, the deerheads above him on fire.

He walked from the fire towards the water. As he made his way to the rowboat, he checked the explosive hidden under the dock. Everyone on the blue evening lawn looked at the flames, dumbfounded. Some men saw him unhook the boat and pointed. Patrick stood in the boat and waved. They waved back uncertainly, then started to run towards the dock casually, in case Patrick turned out to be a friend, then jumped onto the dock and began running towards him.

He lit the fuse, which raced towards the two men and started to row away from the dock. The fuse, like a nervy kid, buzzed and ran under the men's feet. They stopped and turned. Now they realized what it was. The older man leaped into the water and the other, his hands on his hips, paused as the blue fizzing ran into the small explosion that separated the dock from the shore.

What he begins to witness now, in the Garden of the Blind, is not sound but smell – the plants chosen with care so visitors can move from fragrance to fragrance with precise antennae. To his left he can smell mock orange. He leans over the raised bed – three feet higher than the path – and sniffs deeply.

Patrick hears footsteps and a hand touches his back. The blind woman who heard the rustle of newspapers now attaches herself to him.

– You can see, she says.

— Yes.

She smiles.

— You have a loud nose.

Her name is Elizabeth, and she offers to show him the garden. She mentions that her sister is better at identifying flowers and herbs because she does not drink. "I drink like a porpoise but only from the afternoon on. Tragic love affair in my thirties." They walk together and Patrick watches how her relaxed body drifts in this world, moving surely towards the basil and broadleaf sorrel. She lowers her hand in passing to brush the soft silk of the foliage called Rabbit's Grass. Her garden is a ballroom and she introduces him to the intimacies of dill and caraway, those shy sisters; she advises him to bend down and bruise certain leaves which are too subtle for him to appreciate when untouched.

"To focus your nasal powers you must forget about sounds. The bird sounds here are lovely but sometimes I come here drunk or with a hangover and the noise is awful. Then I want to pour medicinal fluids into my handkerchief, climb into the branches, and chloroform them." In the centre of the garden just north of the water-splashed cherub is another tree where there are no birds. "You must be looking at the camphor . . . birds recognize death better than us. Plants have complex genealogies. To a bird a succulent fruit must first be judged by its bloodlines. You may like cashew nuts or mango, or find sumac beautiful, but a bird knows that these are all, strangely, part of the poison-ivy family."

She leads him towards the imported exotics — fruitless persimmon, and the *pimpernella*, which is anise. She is curious about him but he will not say very much though he is courteous and he likes her. He will have to stay here till night and then try to swim from the island out to a boat. Along the beds on the east side of the garden there is tarragon and lavender and cardamom. She puts her hands up bluntly to his face and searches him. She finds a welt by his ear.

— Put perumel on this. A balm.
— I am wanted by the police.
— For?
— For wilful destruction of property.

She laughs.

— Don't resent your life.

They are a frieze, a statue in this garden, a woman with her soft palms covering a tall man's face, blinding him.

When she moves her hands away from his eyes she feels the gasp on his face which is not shock or disgust but something else.

— What is it?

Her green eye echoes somewhere within him. *Aetias Luna* — and its Canadian name, *papillon lune*. Lunar moth. Moon moth. Her other eye is simply not there, the old loose flesh of the eyelid covering nothing. But this eye is forest green, moth green, darting all over as if to catch his gaze, moving with delight over his shoulders, alighting on his ear, his nose. He had loved the lunar moth, its flare of the lower wing like a signature, a papyrus textured object whose small furred body he used to see pulsing on a branch or rock within his lantern light. The woman shifts the watery green mirror of her eye attempting to reflect everything around her.

– What is it?

Patrick allows her to guide him back to the bench. They sit and she grips his hand, not letting go of him. He feels she receives all of his qualities, in this still garden, raucous with noise. The blue veins are narrow and clear in the tight skin of her hands. He is unable to talk, even if all he said would be hidden within her blindness. Alice Gull, he could say, who once pushed her hands up against the slope of a ceiling and spoke of a grand cause, who leapt like a live puppet into his arms, who died later on a bloody pavement, ruined in his arms.

No one else enters the garden as they sit there. Beside the wooden seat is mint pepper, rosemary. In the flower-bed to the right of where they sit is *artemesia advacumculas*, whose human name she says she doesn't know. The muscles in her hand finally loosen and he turns to look at her face. She is now resting, leaning back, gently asleep. He moves his hand from her grip and leaves her.

Now he is part of the evening water, the reflection of dock lights rolling off him. Six stars and a moon. The news of the fire has left the Muskokas in an uproar and Patrick struggles to get free of the current off Page Island in order to swim towards that boat. It has crept across the blackness of the lake at a snail's pace and is now about 500 yards off shore. A night cruise with dancing – he can hear music as he swims, voices and tambourine falling like muffled glass into the water. A half-moon, a few stars, a loop of dock lights.

Somewhere in his past he has dreamed such a moment: a criminal swimming in darkness to a lighted ship. He feels removed from any context of the world, wanting to sleep at this moment, wanting to swim back into the current he has just escaped, return to the Garden of the Blind, and sleep. But he is magnetized to the nameless steamer.

A deadhead touches him in the ribs, comes up under him, and Patrick hears himself shout out in the shriek of an animal. The dreams he had of swimming to a ship involved tropic winds and crocodiles. He splashes out to discover what touched him, but it is gone. "It was a deadhead," he says to himself, talking out loud now, determined, the fear suddenly an energy in him. Brushed by this deadhead he is fully alive, feral, exhilarated. He remembers his departure from the world, stepping out onto the *porte-cochère* of the Muskoka Hotel, flames behind him. Now he will be a member of the night. He sees his visage never emerging out of shadows. Unhistorical.

He swims on, smelling traces of hickory smoke from the campfires on the island. He is delirious with hunger. Music from the boat. *"Beware of frozen ponds, peroxide blondes, stocks and bonds. . . ."* the singer's voice over the muffle of orchestra. And what will they do as they see him climb up a rope into their company, lake weed draped over his shoulder, the blood from the log's glance on his ribs?

He is alongside the boat, in the shadow of the moon, looking up. *The Cherokee.* The panel windows from the stateroom and lounge throw out light that falls on the water. Higher up is the open deck, the dancing couples, the band. He pulls himself up on the vertical strips of rubber that protect the sides of the steamer when it docks. He smells food on deck, climbs fast, and goes headfirst through a window and lands on a table. He is in the kitchens.

A cook turns at the crash to see Patrick on his back surrounded by double-diamond glass. Patrick puts a finger to his lips, keeping it there till the man nods and moves to close the door. Patrick gets down off the table, glass all around him. On deck the pause in conversation is replaced by louder laughter, cheers for the dropped tray or whatever they thought caused the noise. The cook walks over with a broom and sweeps while Patrick stands there removing his wet clothes. There is a cut near his ribs and on his thigh. Then the cook mimes going to sleep and is gone like a ghost out of the room. Patrick walks to the switch and dims out the kitchen light.

It must be around midnight. The noise on deck is ceaseless with the orchestra weaving its way through suspicious love, tentative love. The frail music filters down into this large kitchen which he seems to own. He knows he will be caught, probably imprisoned, but for now he thrills to this brief freedom.

He squeezes out the clothes, turns on the large ovens, spreads his shirt and trousers flat, and slides them in with a baker's paddle. Then he looks for food. There are some cooked potatoes. He pulls out a slab of raw meat from the fridge and crouches behind the counter. He eats only the potato demurely. He cuts the meat into strips with a sharp knife and eats it, licking the juice that dribbles down his arm. Now and then he gets up to drink from the taps and to keep an eye on his clothes cooking at low heat in the oven.

3

CARAVAGGIO

THERE WAS A blue tin jail roof. They were painting the Kingston Penitentiary roof blue up to the sky so that after a while the three men working on it became uncertain of clear boundaries. As if they could climb up further, beyond the tin, into that ocean above the roof.

By noon, after four hours, they felt they could walk on the blue air. The prisoners Buck and Lewis and Caravaggio knew this was a trick, a humiliation of the senses. Why an intentional blue roof? They could not move without thinking twice where a surface stopped. There were times when Patrick Lewis, government paintbrush in hand, froze. Taking a seemingly innocent step he would fall through the air and die. They were fifty yards from the ground. The paint pails were joined by rope – one on each slope – so two men could move across the long roof symmetrically. They sat on the crest of the roof during their breaks eating sandwiches, not coming down all day. They leaned the heels of their hands into the wet paint as they worked. They would scratch their noses and realize they became partly invisible. If they painted long enough they would be eradicated, blue birds in a blue sky. Patrick Lewis understood this, painting a bug that would not move away alive onto the blue metal.

Demarcation, said the prisoner named Caravaggio. *That is all we need to remember.*

And that was how he escaped – a long double belt strapped

under his shoulders attaching him to the cupola so he could hang with his arms free, splayed out, while Buck and Patrick painted him, covering his hands and boots and hair with blue. They daubed his clothes and then, laying a strip of handkerchief over his eyes, painted his face blue, so he was gone – to the guards who looked up and saw nothing there.

When the search had died down, and the lights-out whistle had gone off, Caravaggio still remained as he was, unable to see what he knew would be a sliver of new moon that gave off little light. A thief's moon. He could hear Lake Ontario in this new silence after the wind died. The flutter of sailboats. A clatter of owl claw on the tin roof. He began to move in his cocoon of dry paint – at first unable to break free of the stiffness which encased him, feeling his clothes crack as he bent his arm to remove the handkerchief. He saw nothing but the night. He unhooked the belt. Uncoiling the rope hidden around the cupola, he let himself down off the roof.

He ran through the township of Bath with the white rectangle over his eyes, looking for a hardware store he could break into. He was an exotic creature who had to escape from his blue skin before daylight. But there was not one hardware or paint shop. He broke into a clothing store and in the darkness stripped and dressed in whatever would fit him from the racks. In the rooms above the store he could hear jazz on the radio, the music a compass for him. His hands felt a mirror but he would not turn on the light. He took gloves. He jumped onto a slow milk-train and climbed onto the roof. It was raining. He removed his belt, tied himself on safely, and slept.

In Trenton he untied himself and rolled off down the embankment just as the train began to move again. He was still blue, unable to see what he looked like. He undressed and laid his clothes out on the grass so he could see them in the daylight in a human shape. He knew nothing about the town of Trenton except that it was three hours from Toronto by train. He slept again. In the late afternoon, walking in the woods that skirted the industrial section, he saw REDICK'S SASH AND DOOR FACTORY. He groomed himself as well as he could and stepped out of the trees – a green sweater, black trousers, blue boots, and a blue head.

There was a kid sitting on a pile of lumber behind the store who saw him the moment he stepped into the clearing. The boy didn't move at all, just regarded him as he walked, trying to look casual, the long twenty-five yards to the store. Caravaggio crouched in front of the boy.

> – What's your name?
> – Alfred.
> – Will you go in there, Al, and see if you can find me some turpentine?
> – Are you from the movie company?
> – The movie? He nodded.

The kid ran off and returned a few minutes later, still alone. That was good.

> – Your dad own this place?
> – No, I just like it here. All the doors propped outside, where they don't belong – things where they shouldn't be.

While the boy spoke Caravaggio tore off the tail of his shirt.

> – There is another place in town where you can see outboard motors and car engines hanging off branches.
> – Yeah? Al, can you help me get this off my face and hair?

– Sure.

They sat in the late afternoon sunlight by the doors, the boy dipping the shirt-tail into the tin and wiping the colour off Caravaggio's face. The two of them talked quietly about the other place where the engines hung from the trees. When Caravaggio unbuttoned his shirt the boy saw the terrible scars across his neck and gasped. It looked to him as if some giant bird had left claw marks from trying to lift off the man's head. Caravaggio told him to forget the movie, he was not an actor, he was from prison. "I'm Caravaggio – the painter," he laughed. The boy promised never to say anything.

They decided that his hair should be cut off, so the boy went back into the store and came back giggling and shrugging with some rose shears. Soon Caravaggio looked almost bald, certainly unrecognizable. When the owner of Redick's Door Factory was busy, Caravaggio used the bathroom, soaping and washing the turpentine off his face. He saw his neck for the first time in a mirror, scarred from the prison attack three months earlier.

In the yard the boy wrote out his name on a piece of paper. From his pocket he took out an old maple-syrup spile with the year 1882 on it, and he wrapped the paper around it. When the man came back, cleaned up, the boy handed it to him. The man said, "I don't have anything to give you now." The kid grinned, very happy. "I know," he said. "Remember my name."

He was running, his boots disappearing into grey bush. Away from Lake Ontario, travelling north where he knew he could find some unopened cottage to stay quietly for a few days. Landscape for Caravaggio was never calm. A tree bending with difficulty, a flower thrashed by wind, a cloud turning black, a cone falling – everything moved anguished at separate speeds. When he ran he saw it all. The eye splintering into fifteen sentries, watching every approach.

He ran with the Trent canal system on his right, passing the red lock buildings and their concrete platforms over the water. Every few miles he would stop and watch the glassy waters turn chaotic on the other side of the sluice gate, then he was off again. In two days he was as far north as Bobcaygeon. He slept that night among the lumber at the Boyd Sawmill and one evening later he was racing down a road. It was dusk. He had slept out three nights now. The last of the blue paint at his wrist.

The first cottages showed too many signs of life, the canoes already hauled out. He retreated back up their driveways. He came to a cottage with a glassed-in porch and green shutters, painted gables, and a double-pitch roof. If the owners arrived he could swing out of the second-floor window and walk along the roof. Caravaggio looked at architecture with a perception common to thieves who saw cupboards as having weak backs, who knew fences were easier to go through than over.

He stood breathing heavily in the dusk, looking up at the cottage, tired of running, having eaten only bits of chocolate the boy had given him. *Al.* Behind him the landscape was darkening down fast. He was inside the cottage in ten seconds.

He walked around the rooms, excited, his hand trailing off the sofa top, noticed the magazines stacked on the shelf. He turned left into a kitchen and used a knife to saw open a can. Darkness. He wanted no lights on tonight. He dug the knife into the can and gulped down beans, too hungry and tired for a spoon. Then he went upstairs and ripped two blankets off a bed and spread them out in the upstairs hall beside the window which led to the roof.

He hated the hours of sleep. He was a man who thrived and worked in available light. At night his wife would sleep in his embrace but the room around him continued to be alive, his body porous to every noise, his stare painting out darkness. He would sleep as insecurely as a thief does, which is why they are always tired.

*   *   *

He climbs into black water. A temperature of blood. He sees and feels no horizon, no edge to the liquid he is in. The night air is forensic. An animal slips into the water.

This river is not deep, he can walk across it. His boots, laces tied to each other, are hanging around his neck. He doesn't want them wet but he goes deeper and he feels them filling, the extra weight of water in them now. The floor of the river feels secure. Mud. Sticks. A bridge a hundred yards south of him made of concrete and wood. A tug at his boot beside the collarbone.

As Caravaggio sleeps, his head thrown back, witnessing a familiar nightmare, three men enter his prison cell in silence. The men enter and Patrick in the cell opposite on the next level up watches them and all language dries up. As they raise their hands over Caravaggio, Patrick breaks into a square-dance call – *"Allemande left your corners all"* – screaming it absurdly as warning up into the stone darkness. The three men turn to the sudden noise and Caravaggio is on his feet struggling out of his nightmare.

The men twist his grey sheet into a rope and wind it around his eyes and nose. Caravaggio can just breathe, he can just hear their blows as if delayed against the side of his head. They swing him tied up in the sheet until he is caught in the arms of another. Then another blow. Patrick's voice continuing to shout out, the other cells alive now and banging too. *"Birdie fly out and the crow fly in, crow fly out and give birdie a spin."* His father's language emerging from somewhere in his past, now a soundtrack for murder.

The animal from the nightmare bares its teeth. Caravaggio swerves and its mouth rips open the boot to the right of his neck. Water is released. He feels himself becoming lighter. Being swung from side to side, no vision, no odour, he is ten years old and tilting wildly in a tree. A wall or an arm hits him. "Fucking wop! Fucking dago!" *"Honour your partner, dip and dive."* His hands are up squabbling with this water creature – sacrificing the hands to protect the body. The inside of his heart feels bloodless. He swallows dry breath. He needs more than anything to get on his knees and lap up water from a saucer.

Three men who have evolved smug and without race slash out. "Hello wop." And the man's kick into his stomach lets free the singer again as if a Wurlitzer were nudged, fast and flat tones weaving through a two-step as the men begin to beat the blindfolded Caravaggio. What allies with Caravaggio is only the singer, otherwise his mind is still caught underwater. Then they let him go.

He stands there still blindfolded, his hands out. The caller in the cell opposite quietens, knowing Caravaggio needs to listen within the silence for any clue as to where the men are. They are dumb beasts. He could steal the teeth out of their mouths. Everyone watches but him, eyes covered, hands out.

The homemade filed-down razor teeth swing in an arc to his

throat, to the right of the ripped-open boot. He drops back against the limestone wall. The other leather boot releases its cup-like hold on the water as if a lung gives up. A vacuum of silence.

He realizes the men have gone. The witness, the caller from the upper level, begins to talk quietly to him. "They have cut your neck. Do you understand! They have cut your neck. You must staunch it till someone comes." Then Patrick screams into the limestone darkness for help.

Caravaggio finds the bed. He gets to his knees on the mattress – head and elbows propping up his bruised body so nothing touches the pain. The blood flows along his chin into his mouth. He feels as if he has eaten the animal that attacked him and he spits out everything he can, old saliva, blood, spits again and again. Everything is escaping. His left hand touches his neck and it is not there.

*   *   *

The next morning Caravaggio explored the shoreline around the cottage in a canoe. He was out on the lake when a woman in another canoe emerged into the bay and hailed him. Red hair. The clear creamy skin of a witch. She wore a hat tied with a scarf and she waved to him in absolute confidence that if he was in a canoe on this lake he was acceptable and safe, even though every piece of clothing he wore was stolen from the blue bureau in the cottage. The lavender shirt, the white ducks, the tennis shoes. He stopped paddling. Performing intricate strokes, she pulled up alongside him.

– You are staying with the Neals.

— How did you know?

She gestured to the canoe. Here people recognized canoes.

— Are they coming up for August?
— I think so. They were unsure.
— They always are. I'm Anne, a neighbour.

She pointed to the next property. She had on a bathing suit and a light skirt and was barefoot, the paddle resting on her shoulder.

— I'm David.

Drops of water slid along the brown wood and onto her skin. He looked at her stunningly poreless face that now and then revealed itself out from the shadow of her straw hat. He decided to be direct about his tentative status.

— I'm here to get my bearings.
— This is a *good* place for that.

He looked up at her again, differently now, past the white creamy face and bare arms.

— Why did you say it like that?

Her hand up to shield off the sun. A questioning look.

— What you just said . . .
— Just that I love this place. It can heal you if you are here alone. Are you an artist?
— What?
— You have aquamarine on your neck.

He smiled. He had spent so long calling it blue.

— I should go, he said.

She lifted her paddle forward so it was across her knees, nodding to herself, realizing a wall had just been placed between them. Their canoes banged together and she backpaddled. He had never heard anyone speak as generously as she had in that one sentence. *This is a good place.*

– Thank you.

She turned, puzzled.

> – For pointing out the aquamarine.
> – Well . . . enjoy the lake.
> – I will.

She sensed his withdrawal. Alone, not having seen anyone for weeks, she had come too close, spoken too loudly. He watched the frailness of her back as she canoed away from him.

Caravaggio looked over the body of water as if it were human now, a creature on whose back he shifted. He did not think of approaches or exits, suddenly there could be only descent or companionship.

*   *   *

The first time Caravaggio had noticed Patrick Lewis gazing down from the opposite cell, he had simply waved and looked elsewhere. Most of Caravaggio's time in prison was spent in restless sleep. The night light of cells, the constant noise, made him nervous. The prisoner opposite who had tried to burn down the Muskoka Hotel was worse. He always sat up erect on the bed watching the movements below him. When Caravaggio returned from the hospital, his throat sewn up after the attack, Patrick was waiting for him. And when Caravaggio woke in pain suddenly the next afternoon, he turned to find the man's gaze reassuring him. Patrick had sat up there smoking precisely, moving his hand and cigarette fully away from his face when he blew the smoke out.

– Do you have a red dog? he asked Caravaggio a few days later.
– Russet, he whispered back.
– You're the thief, right?
– The best there is; that's why, as you can see, I'm here.
– Someone let you down, I suppose.
– Yes. The red dog.

He had trained as a thief in unlit rooms, dismantling the legs of a kitchen table, unscrewing the backs of radios and the bottoms of toasters. He would draw the curtains to block out any hint of streetlight and empty the kitchen cupboards, then put everything back, having to remember as he worked where all the objects were on the floor. Such pelmanism. While his wife slept he moved the furniture out of her bedroom and brought in the sofa, changed the pictures on the wall, the doilies on the bedside table.

In daylight he moved slowly as if conserving remnants of energy – a bat in post-coital flight. He would step into an upholstery shop to pick up a parcel for his wife and read the furniture, displacing in his mind the chairs through that window, the harvest table through the door at a thirty-degree angle veering right.

As a thief he had a sense of the world which was limited to what existed for twenty feet around him.

During his first robbery Caravaggio injured himself leaping from a second-storey window. He lay on his back with a cracked ankle on the Whitevale lawn, a Jeffreys drawing in his arms. He lay there as the family walked into the house and shrieked when they came upon the chloroformed dog. All the porch lights went on, the shadow of a tree luckily falling across him.

Two hours later he stumbled on a settlement of long barns, not certain what they were till he was gathered in the smell. A mushroom factory. Only the hallways and offices were lit, the long dormitories where the mushrooms were grown were in permanent darkness. He knew what he needed. In the main lobby were the helmets with battery lamps attached to them. Now it was almost dawn. A Sunday. He had a day without being disturbed. Later in the sunlight he cut open his boot and sock. He made a splint and strapped it with electrical tape. Worse than the pain was his hunger. He looked at his stolen drawing in the sunlight, the clean lines, the shaky signature.

Around dusk he hobbled across the road to a vegetable garden, pulled up a few carrots and dropped them into his shirt. He tried to catch a chicken but it sped up its walk and left him behind. He returned to the minimal light in the halls of the mushroom factory. He read the punch cards of the workers. *Salvatorelli, Mascardelli, Daquila, Pereira, De Francesca*. Most of them Italian, some Portuguese. Shifts from eight to four. He felt safer. In the office he looked through the drawers and cabinets.

He knew people who took shits on desks whenever they broke into office buildings but he wasn't one of them. It was, he was told, a formal act. Most amateur thieves could not control themselves. With all their discipline focused on the idea of robbery, there was no governor of the body. The act implied grossness, but the professional thief turned from this gesture to a medicinal clarity in his survey of the room. Detailed receipts memorized, key pages razor-bladed. At the centre of the symmetrical plot was this false act of madness.

When Caravaggio joined the company of thieves he was struck first of all by their courtesy. Even the shitters looked refined and wore half-moon glasses; they would have taken snuff but for the fact it would destroy their sense of smell. The cafés in the west end of Toronto were full of these men who had no work in the afternoons, who woke at noon and, after shaving, lunched with their friends. Caravaggio was welcomed into their midst and lectured with great conservatism on the art of robbery. Some were "displacers," some stole animals, some kidnapped dogs and wives, some would deal only in meat products or paper information. They were protective of their style and area of interest. They tried to persuade the young man that what *they* did was the most significant but at the same time they did not wish to encourage too much competition.

He was young. He was in awe of them, wanted to be all of them in their moments of extreme crisis. He hung around them not so much to learn their craft but to study the way they lived when they stepped back into the world of order. He still had that to learn. He was twenty-two at the Blue Cellar Café and he was fascinated only by character. He was a young man stepping into a mansion and being overcome with the generosity of envy. He slid his hand down the smoothness of a banister and his palm and fingers luxuriated in it. The intricate light switches! The carpets your feet melted into! He did this with their character – he walked away with their mannerisms and their brand names, the rhythm and abstract tone of their musings.

Later he trailed each of them for a week in order to watch their performances. Some of them went into houses and spent three hours and came out with objects so small they fit into a side pocket. Some removed every moveable object on the ground floor in half an hour.

And now, in the midst of his first robbery, Caravaggio read through the finances of the mushroom factory and came across a till of cash. Never steal where you sleep. All this inquiry was out of boredom. He wanted a book, he wanted meat. If he was going to have to hole up for a few days he wanted chicken and literature. Caravaggio switched on the light attached to the foreman's helmet and stepped into one of the mushroom dormitories he had selected earlier as his. Shelves at various levels ran the length of the long room. There were troughs on the shelves which held manure and earth and young growing mushrooms.

Now he was in a dark prison with millions of them. He snuggled into a space beneath the low shelf at the end farthest away from the door, his Jeffreys drawing beside him. He switched off the helmet, breathed in the thick vegetable air. He had not slept for a day and a half, had chloroformed his first dog, jumped out of a window, tried to race down a chicken . . .

Something brushed his face. Without opening his eyes he moved back. Earlier he had awakened with fragments of light above him as figures leaned over the troughs to select mushrooms. The mushrooms were grown at different stages, a few weeks apart, so there would always be a section ready. He had fallen back to sleep among the sounds of overalls rubbing against the shelves. Now the cloth against his face startled him. A woman on his right stood tentatively on one foot. She struggled with a shoe, leaning against the plaster wall in a slip, the upper half of her body naked. Her helmet balanced on the top shelf was facing her so she could see what she was doing as she dressed. Her black shadow moved parallel to her whiteness.

He remained still. Raven hair and an angular face, her body reaching up to pull down a blouse from a hook, more secure now with both shoes on.

— Psst.

She looked sternly out into darkness, picked up the helmet, and diverted light across the room through the shelves.

— Angelica? Is that you? she called out.

She pulled on her skirt with one hand holding the helmet, stopped, put the helmet on, and did up the buttons. She began singing to herself. He had to get her attention without terrifying her. He started humming along with her. Her helmet light came down fast to where he was and she lashed out, kicking his face. After a yell of pain he began to laugh.

— Please, tomorrow bring me something to eat.
— *Perchè?*
— I'm a thief. I've broken my ankle.

She bent down and put her hand out.

— *Tartufi?* What are you stealing? Mushrooms?

Her hands were on his foot, felt the ankle strapped up, and believed everything, knowing already he was gentle by his laugh.

— I broke it a mile or two from here. I'm very hungry. Please bring me some chicken tomorrow.

He could not see her face at all, just the hem of the skirt at her knees where the light bounced as she crouched. Now all he could know of her was a voice, confident, laughing with him.

– *Come si chiama?*
– Giannetta.
– I'm Caravaggio.
– A thief.
– *Sicuro.*
– I'll bring you some chicken tomorrow. And a bible.
– Let me see your face.
– *Basta! Ha visto abbastanza.*

She patted his foot.

– Do you need anything else?
– Ask what I should do about my ankle.

There was darkness again and he yearned for light. The thin beam from her helmet, the delicate ribs as she reached up for the blouse, her shadow overcoming his memory so he had to begin the scene again, a small loop of film, seven or eight seconds, until she reached for the lamp and put herself in darkness. He repeated it again and again and then turned to her voice. Strange how he wanted chicken above all else. It was that useless chase in the yard across the road, itching in his memory.

The next morning she arrived and asked him to turn his head while she changed. She told him how each of the workers chose a room or one corner for changing into and out of their overalls. She unwrapped a large cloth and gave him the food. Chicken and some salad and milk and banana cake. It was the worst banana cake he had eaten up to that point in his life.

– *Devo partire. Ritornerò.*

In the afternoon Giannetta and three other women workers came by to have a look at him. There were the expected jokes, but he enjoyed the company after so much solitude. When they left, noisily, she put her hand out. She touched his mouth gently. Then she brought out bandages and restrapped his ankle.

> — *Cosí va meglio.*
> — When can I get out of here?
> — We've planned something for you.
> — *Bene.* Let me see your face.

Her lamp remained still at his foot. So he reached back for his foreman's helmet and shone it on her. She remained looking down. He realized his right hand was still holding her ankle from when she had removed the electrical tape off him painfully.

> — Thank you for helping me.
> — I am sorry I kicked you so hard.

The next day Giannetta crouched beside him, smiling.

> — We must shave off your moustache. Only women work here.
> — *Mannaggia!*
> — We have to get you out as a woman.

He reached out his hand and put his fingers into her hair, into that darkness.

> — Giannetta.
> — You have to put your arm down.

Her hand rested at his shoulder, holding onto the straight razor. He would not let her go.

Their faces darkened as they leaned forward, her lamp shining past his head. He could smell her skin.

– Here comes the first kiss, she whispered.

She handed him the dress.

– *Non guardare*, please. Don't look.

He realized he was standing exactly where she had been a few days earlier. He switched on his lamp so it beamed onto her, then began to take off his shirt, paused, but she kept looking at him. He saw his own shadow on the wall. She came forward, smiling, calming his balance as he stood on his good foot.

– Here, I'll show you how to put on a dress. Unbutton this first.

She held the cloth bunched over his nakedness.

– Ahh Caravaggio, shall we tell our children how we met?

*   *   *

This time he did not take the canoe. He had already walked the shoreline before dusk, remembering the swamp patches. Now, dressed in dark clothes, he traced his path towards the compound belonging to the woman with the canoe – the main building, outlying cottages, a boathouse, an icehouse. He had no idea what the lake was called. He had passed a sign when he was running that claimed the area was Featherstone Point. That was when he saw the telephone wires which he knew must come from her group of houses.

He came through the last of the trees into the open area and everything was in darkness, as if the owners had packed up and left. He had expected to see rectangles of light. Now he lost all perspective and did not know how fully he would have to turn to be aimed back at his cottage. He needed some context of the human. A dog on a chain, a window, a sound. He turned once more and saw moonlight on the lake. But there was no moon. He realized it had to be light from the boathouse. The landscape, the blueprint of the compound, sprang back into his brain. He walked towards the water knowing where the low shrubs were, the stone hedge, the topiary he could not see. He slipped inside the boathouse and listened for sounds of activity. Nothing. With a pulley-chain used for hoisting up boat engines he swung up onto the first roof which was like a skirt around the upper cabin. He walked up the slope. The woman named Anne was sitting inside at a table.

Light from an oil lamp. She faced the water, her night window, and was writing hunched over the table unaware of anything else in the room. A summer skirt, an old shirt of her husband's, sleeves rolled up. She glanced up from the page and peered into the kerosene of the lamp. The mind behind the gaze did not know where it was. Caravaggio had never witnessed someone writing before. He saw her put down the fountain pen and later pick it up, try it, and realizing the nib was dry, lift the tail of her shirt to wipe the dry ink off the nib, preening the groove, as if the pause were caused not by the hesitation of her mind but by the atrophy of the pen. Now she bent over earnestly, half-smiling, the tongue moving in her mouth.

If she had turned to her right she would have seen his head at one of the small panes of glass, the light from the oil lamp just reaching it. He thought of that possible glance and moved back further. He thought of all those libraries he had stepped into in Toronto homes, the grand vistas of bookcases that reached the ceiling, the books of pigskin and other leathers that fell into his arms as he climbed up the shelves looking for whatever valuables he imagined were there, his boots pushing in the books to get a toe-hold. And then from up there, his head close to the ceiling, looking down on the rectangle of the rooms, hearing his dog's clear warning bark, not moving. And the door opening below him – a man walking in to pick up the telephone and dialling, while Caravaggio hung high up on the bookcases knowing now he should move the second he was seen up there in his dark trousers and singlet, as still as a gargoyle against Trollope and H.G. Wells. He could land on the leather sofa and bounce into the man's body before he even said a word into the phone. Then go through the French doors without opening them, a hunch of his body as he breaks through the glass and thin wood, then a blind leap off the balcony into the garden, where he would curse his dog for the late warning, and take off.

But this boathouse had no grandeur. The woman's bare feet rested one on top of the other on the stained-wood floor. A lamp on the desk, a mattress on the floor. In this light, and with all the small panes of glass around her, she was inside a diamond, mothlike on the edge of burning kerosene, caught in the centre of all the facets. He knew there was such intimacy in what he was seeing that not even a husband could get closer than him, a thief who saw this rich woman trying to discover what she was or what she was capable of making.

He put his hands up to his face and smelled them. Oil and rust. They smelled of the chain. That was always true of thieves, they smelled of what they brushed against. Paint, mushrooms, printing machines, yet they never smelled of the rich. He liked people who smelled of their trade – carpenters cutting into cedar, dog-catchers who carried the odour of wet struggling hounds with them. And what did this woman smell of? In this yellow pine room past midnight she was staring into a bowl of kerosene as if seeing right through the skull of a lover.

He was anonymous, with never a stillness in his life like this woman's. He stood on the roof outside, an outline of a bear in her subconscious, and she quarried past it to another secret, one of her own, articulated wet and black on the page. The houses in Toronto he had helped build or paint or break into were unmarked. He would never leave his name where his skill had been. He was one of those who have a fury or a sadness of only being described by someone else. A tarrer of roads, a house-builder, a painter, a thief – yet he was invisible to all around him.

He leapt through darkness onto the summer grass and then walked up to the main building. Without turning on lights he found the telephone in the kitchen and phoned his wife in Toronto.

    – Well I got out.

    – *Lo so.*

    – How?

    – The police were here. *Scomparso.* Not that you escaped but that you disappeared.

    – When did they come there?

    – Last week. A couple of days after you got away.

    – How's August?

    – He's with me. He misses his night walks.

She began to talk about her brother-in-law's house, which she had moved into. This time through a darkness which was distance.

> – I'll be back when I can, Giannetta.
> – Be careful.

She was standing in the centre of the living room in the darkness as he came away from the phone. His ear had been focused to Giannetta's voice, nothing else. His head imagining her – the alabaster face, the raven head.

> – *Non riuscivo a trovarti.*
> – Speak English.
> – I couldn't find you to ask.
> – You found the cottage, you found the phone, you could have found me.
> – I could have. It's a habit . . . usually I don't ask.
> – I'm going to light a lamp.
> – Yes, that's always safer.

She lifted the glass chimney and held the match to the wick. It lit up the skirt and shirt and her red hair. She moved away from it and leaned against the back of the sofa.

> – Where were you calling?
> – Toronto. My wife.
> – I see.
> – I'll pay for it.

She waved the suggestion away.

> – Is that your husband's shirt?
> – No. My husband's shirts are here, though. You want them?

He shook his head, looking around the room. A fireplace, a straight staircase, bedrooms upstairs.

    – What do you want? You are a thief, right?

    – With cottages all you can steal is the space or the people. I needed to use your phone.

    – I'm going to eat something. Do you want some food?

    – Thank you.

He followed her into the kitchen feeling relaxed with her – as if this was a continuation of his conversation with Giannetta.

    – Tell me . . .

    – David.

    – David, why I am not scared of you?

    – Because you've come back from someplace. . . . You got something there. Or you're still there.

    – What are you talking about?

    – I was on the roof of the boathouse. I did find you.

    – I thought there was a bear around tonight.

She sits across from him laughing at the story of his escape, not fully believing it. A fairy tale. She cups her hand over the glass chimney and blows out the lamp. Two in the morning. As they go into darkness his mind holds on to the image of her slightness, the poreless skin, the bright hair leaning into the light. The startling colours of her strange beauty.

    – I can't stand any more light, she says.

    – Yes, this *is* the night. Allow the darkness in.

    – I had to stay in a dark room once . . . with measles.

Her voice is exact, crystal clear. He has his eyes closed, listening to her.

– I was a kid. My uncle – he's a famous doctor – came to see me. In my room, all the blinds were down, the lights drowned. So I could do nothing. I wasn't allowed to read. He said I've brought you earrings. They are special earrings. He pulled out some cherries. Two, joined by their stalks, and he hung them over one ear and took out another pair and hung them over the other ear. That kept me going for days. I couldn't lie down at night without carefully taking them off and laying them on the night table.

– Do you have any children?

– I have a son. He comes up with my husband in a day or so. I have a brother who doesn't speak. This is his shirt. He hasn't spoken for years.

Caravaggio lies on the carpet. He had, when there was light earlier, been looking up at the tongue and groove, theorizing how one removed such floors. She continues talking.

– In a few days all the husbands come to the lake. A strange custom. I've been so happy these last three weeks. Listen . . . no sound. In the boathouse there is always the noise of the lake. I feel bereaved when the lake is still, mute.

There is now a silence in the room. He stands up.

– I should go.

– You can sleep on the sofa.

– No. I should go.

– You can sleep here. I'm going up to bed.

– I'm a *thief*, Anne, *un ladro*.

– That's right. You broke out of jail.

He sees her clearly on the other side of the unlit lamp, her chin on her clenched fist.

– I have literally fallen in love with the lake. I dread the day I will have to leave it. Tonight I was writing the first love poem I have written in years and the lover was the sound of lakewater.
– I've always had a fear of water creatures.
– But water is benign . . .
– Yes, I know. Goodbye, Anne.

*   *   *

After his marriage to Giannetta, Caravaggio had one pit to fall into before his career as a thief became successful – he was overwhelmed suddenly by a self-consciousness. He broke into houses and became certain there was a plot concocted to snare him. Giannetta could not stand it. She did not wish to live with a well-trained thief who feared going out.

– Get a partner!
– I can never work with someone else, you know that!
– Then get a dog!

He stole a dark-red fox terrier and named it August. A summer robbery. The dog was his salvation. He had a quick bark, like an exclamation – one announcement, take it or leave it – enough warning for his master as far as the dog was concerned.

On a job they behaved like strangers – Caravaggio strolling along one side of the street and August aimless on the other.

When he entered a house the dog sat on the lawn. If the owners returned early the dog would stand up and give one clear bark. Moments later a figure would leap from a window with a carpet or a suitcase in his arms.

*   *   *

Now he pours milk into the tall glass and drinks as he walks through his brother-in-law's house, the coolness of milk filling him on this hot Toronto night. He is seated on the stairs, facing the door. He hears the dog's one clear bark and her laugh as she approaches the front door.

In the dark hall the whiteness of the milk disappears into his body. Her shoulders nestle against his hands. The home of the other. Touching her, a wetness passed from her lip to him, his hands in her dark hair. She moves within the shadow of his shoulder.

She steps into the half-lit kitchen and her bare arms pick up light. He catches the blink of her earrings. Removing one, she drops it to the floor. Her hands go up to the other ear – unscrewing the second pin of gold. Her laughter with her breast in his mouth.

He breaks the necklace and pearls fall around them. He can smell soaps in her hair. Her wrist moves up his arm, riding on the sweat. Her cheek against the warm tile. Her other hand, sweeping out, touches the loose jewel.

Giannetta feels the scar on his throat. Her soft kiss across it. He carries her, still in her, holding up each thigh, her eyes wide open, crockery behind her crashing from shelf to shelf, as she nudges the corner cupboard. Blue plates bounce and come through the lower panes like water and smash on the floor.

With each step her bare foot on a pearl or a fragment of plate. She opens the fridge door. In its light she pulls her foot up to her stomach and examines it, brushing something away. He lies back and she sits over him, swallowing the cold wine. He traces the path down her body at the speed he imagines liquid takes.

Her chin on her knee. Planting her foot on his shoulder she leaves blood when she moves it. When she opens her eyes wide he sees glass and crockery and thin china plates tumbling down from shelf to shelf losing their order, their shades of blue and red merging, her fingers on his scar, her fingers on the thumping vein on his forehead. She's a laugher who laughs while they make love, not earnest like a tightrope-walker.

Her low laugh when they stop, exhausted.

His breath is now almost whisper, almost language. She turns, a pearl embedded in her flesh. A violin with stars walking in this house. Fridge light sink light street light. At the sink she douses her face and shoulders. She lies beside him. The taste of the other. A bazaar of muscles and flavours. She rubs his semen into his wet hair. Her shoulders bang against the blue-stained cupboard. A kitchen being fucked. Sexual portage. Her body forked off him.

She smells him, the animal out of the desert that has stumbled back home, back into oasis. Her black hair spreads like a pool over the tiles. She pins the earring her fingers had strayed upon into his arm muscle, beginning a tattoo of blood.

There are jewels of every colour he has stolen for her in the past in the false drawers of her new bedroom, which he can find by ripping out the backs of the bureaus. Photographs of her relatives in old silver frames. A clock encased in glass which turns its gold stomach from side to side to opposite corners of the room. A wedding ring he can pull off her finger with his teeth.

He removes nothing. Only the chemise she withdraws from as if skin. He carries nothing but the jewellery pinned to his arm, a footstep of blood on his shoulder. The feather of her lip on his mouth.

A last plate tips over to the next shelf. He waits for her eye to open. Here comes the first kiss.

All she can see as she enters the dark hall is the whiteness of the milk, a sacred stone in his hands, disappearing into his body.

He lifts his wife onto his shoulders so her arms ascend into the chandelier.

MARITIME THEATRE

IN 1938, WHEN Patrick Lewis was released from prison, people were crowding together in large dark buildings across North America to see Garbo as Anna Karenina. Everyone tried to play the Hammond Organ. 'Red Squads' intercepted mail, tear-gassed political meetings. By now over 10,000 foreign-born workers had been deported out of the country. Everyone sang "Just One of Those Things." The longest bridge in the world was being built over the lower Zambesi and the great water-works at the east end of Toronto neared completion.

At Kew Park a white horse dove every hour from a great height into Lake Ontario. T.S. Eliot's *Murder in the Cathedral* opened in England and a few weeks later Dr. Carl Weiss – who had always admired the poetry of the expatriate American – shot Huey Long to death in the Louisiana capitol building. Just one of those things.

Released from prison in January, he took the Kingston train to Toronto's Union Station. *Ten Story Gang, Weird Tales, Click, Judge Sheard's Best Jokes,* and *Look* were in the magazine stalls. Patrick sat down on the smooth concrete bench facing the ramp down to the gates. This cathedral-like space was the nexus of his life. He had been twenty-one when he arrived in this city. Here he had watched Clara leave him, walking past that sign to the left of the ramp which said HORIZON. *Look up,* Clara had said when she left him for Ambrose, *you know what that stone is?* He had been lost in their situation, not caring. *It's*

Missouri Zumbro. Remember that. The floors are Tennessee marble. He looked up. Sitting now on this bench Patrick suddenly had no idea what year it was.

He brought Clara's face directly back into memory – as if it were a quizzical smiling face on a poster advertising a hat to strangers. But Alice's face, with its changeability, he could not evoke. A group of redcaps were standing with three large cages full of dogs, all of whom were barking like aristocrats claiming to be wrongly imprisoned. He went up to the cages. They were anxious with noise. He had come from a place where a tin cup against a cell wall was the sole form of protest. He got closer to the cages, looked into the eyes which saw nothing, the way his own face in prison had looked in a metal mirror.

He was still crouched when the redcaps wheeled the cages down the ramp. On his knees in Union Station. He felt like the weight on the end of a plumb-bob hanging from the very centre of the grand rotunda, the absolute focus of the building. Slowly his vision began to swing. He turned his head to the left to the right to the left, discovering the horizon.

He moved tentatively into the city, standing in front of strangers, studying the new fashions. He felt invisible. Outside Union Station the streets were deep in snowdrifts. He walked towards the east end, along Eastern Avenue, till he eventually came to the Geranium Bakery, entering the warm large space where winter sun pierced through the mist of flour in the air. He passed the spotless machines, looking for Nicholas. Buns moved forward along rollers till they were flipped over into the small lake of sizzling shortening. Finally he saw him in his suit covered with white dust at the far end of the bakery, choreographing the movement of food. Nicholas Temelcoff walked forward and embraced him. A bear's grip. The grip of the world.

– Welcome back, my friend.

– Is she here?

Nicholas nodded.

– She has packed her things.

Patrick climbed into the service elevator and pulled the rope beside him which took him up to Nicholas' living quarters on the next floor. He went in and knocked on the door of the small room.

Hana was sitting on the bed wearing a frock, her hands on her lap. Looking down, then up slowly, the way Alice used to glance up, the eyes moving first. So much like Alice it was terrible to him. He turned away and looked at the girl's neat room, at the packed suitcase, the light on beside her bed in the daylight.

She watched him, understanding what kind of love was behind his stare. His cheek was pressed against the door frame, the new jacket collar rough against his neck. Five years earlier, before he had taken the train to the Muskokas, they had come to the Geranium Bakery. And Nicholas had offered to look after her. She was welcome to stay with his family. He had suggested this casually and with no hesitation, sitting in his office under the clock Hana loved, where each hour was represented by a different style of doughnut. *"Each of us is on our own for a while now,"* Patrick had said. *"I know."* She had been eleven years old then.

She rose from the bed. "Hey, Patrick, look how tall I've got!" Stepping forward towards him and embracing him quietly, her arms all the way around him, the top of her head just reaching his chin.

At the Balkan Café they sat down and ordered *sujuk*, the sausages with leeks and pork and garlic that he had not eaten for so long.

– Are you healthy?

– Oh yes. As a horse.

– Good.

– I'll have to get used to things, though.

– That's okay, Patrick . . . and being in jail's okay too. Don't let it go to your head, though.

– No.

He felt comfortable joking with her, gathering her perspective. In prison when he imagined freedom it was as a solitary. Nothing to carry, nothing to fall back into the arms of. This was the image he luxuriated in, awake all night, watching the other prisoners turning like great grey fish in their cells. In prison he had protected himself with silence – as if any sentence would be unsafe territory, as if saying even one word would begin a release of Alice out of his body. Secrecy kept him powerful. By refusing communication he could hold her within himself, in his arms. But on the night Caravaggio was attacked, his father's neutral song slid out as warning. And Patrick turned from himself.

– Did you make any friends in prison? Hana asked.

– I made one friend. He escaped.

– Too bad. What did *he* do?

– He was a thief. Some people tried to cut his throat in jail.

– Then he's lucky he escaped.

– He was most clever.

Ambrose Small, as a millionaire, had always kept the landscapes of his world separate, high walls between them. Lovers, compatriots, businessmen, were anonymous to each other. As far as they knew there were no others, or they assumed the others lived in far countries.

When Clara Dickens joined Ambrose Small after he evaporated from the world of financial power she thought she would see the vista of his nature. But during the years that she lived with Ambrose she would know him only as he wanted to be known by her. There was no other road towards him. She was too close to him now – to his new daily obsessions, his temporary charm. She wanted to climb above him even once and gaze down, see the horizon that held him together.

What she discovered in the end – when he sat on the floor of the emptied room in Marmora, nothing else around him but Clara and the walls and the wood floor and the curtainless windows so he could sleep at night neatly within the coffin of moonlight – was much worse.

In the days before he died, Small's mind slipped free of its compartments as if what had kept all his diverse worlds separate had been pulled out of him like a spine. So as he talked and muttered towards Clara, events fell against each other – a night with a lover, a negotiation at the Grand Opera House. Strangers and corpses of his past arrived in this sparse room with its one lamp lit during the day, so the shadows were like moon-tides around it.

Words fell from his mouth and shocked her in the intricacy of his knowledge of so many women, such deep interiors of the financial sea. She heard his varied portraits of her which had gone unspoken for years, his affections and passions and irritations and reversals, his sweet awe at her sense of colour with certain flowers, the memory of her standing in a hall years earlier and smelling each of her armpits when she thought she was alone.

Clara crouched in front of Ambrose and now he could not see her. He was sitting lotus, bare-chested, his hands moving over his face sensuously rubbing the front of his skull, as he revealed the mirrors of himself, his voice slowing as his fingers discovered his right ear. Then he bent forward as he sat so his head would touch the floor in a long grace-attempted bow, ascetic. A heron stretching his head further underwater, the eyes open within the cold flow, open for the fish that could then be raised into the air and dropped moving in the tunnel of the heron's blue throat.

She sat on the floor, ten feet away from Ambrose, the lamp beside her, attacked by all the discontinuous moments of his past. Who were these women? Where did those destroyed enemies go? Ambrose spoke slowly, the uninterested words came from his dark, half-naked shape as if all this was just the emptying of pails to be free of ballast. The theatres, his wife, his sisters, the women, enemies, Briffa, even Patrick, spilled free.

The only clarity for him now was this bare room where Clara brought him food. He had imploded, had become a Gothic child suddenly full of a language which was aimed nowhere, only out of his body. Bitten flesh and manicures and greyhounds and sex and safe-combinations and knowledge of suicides. She saw his world as if she were tied to a galloping horse, caught glimpses of faces and argument and there was no horizon. After all these years she would not be satisfied, would not know him. She pulled back.

Now his face serene. Now his upper torso bent forward long and athletic and the mouth of the heron touched the blue wood floor and his head submerged under the water and pivoted and saw in the fading human light a lamp that was the moon.

The girl was shaking him from side to side as he slept in the kitchen chair, in the apartment on Albany Street. Fragments of lobster were scattered across the table.

– Patrick! Patrick! You've got to wake up.

– What . . .

– It's urgent. I don't know how I forgot but I forgot. Wake up, Patrick, please. She was going to wait. I don't know how I forgot.

– What is it?

– Someone called Clara Dickens. She's on the phone.

– What is this? Where am I?

– It's important, Patrick.

– I'm sure it is.

– Can you get to the phone?

– Yup. You go to bed.

He put his face under the kitchen tap. Clara Dickens. After a hundred years.

He stood there breathing deeply. He walked into the dark room, his face still wet, and got to his knees. One arm was in a cast and he reached out the other hand feeling for the telephone. "Don't hang up. Don't hang up," he was yelling, hoping she could hear him until he found the telephone.

– This is Patrick.
– I know who it is.

He heard her half-laugh at the other end.

– Who was that who answered the phone?
– A friend. You've never met her.
– That's good.
– She's sixteen, Clara, I'm looking after her.
– I'm in Marmora. Will you come and get me?
Ambrose is dead.

He was silent, lying on his back in a dark room. He knew this room well in the dark. He had been here often.

– You take Highway 7 . . . are you there? I need help, Patrick.

He could see the swirls in the ceiling.

– Have I been to Marmora?
– It's four hours from Toronto. It's supposedly the sled-dog capital of Ontario. I'm calling from a restaurant. I've been here for four hours.
– Four hours! What year is it?
– Don't be cynical, Patrick. Not now, okay?
– Describe where you are, the place you are standing in. I just need to hear you.
– I've been outside, sitting next to one of those artificial negro fishermen you see all over the place nowadays. It was damn cold. I phoned about ten. You were supposed to call back.
– She forgot. She got excited because I brought home a lobster. But now we have goddamn *deus ex*

machina. You're on the phone. Did Ambrose get shot with a silver bullet?

— He died of natural causes.

— Run over by a sled-dog, was he?

At this he couldn't stop laughing and turned from the phone. He could hear her voice, tinny in the distance.

    — I'm sorry, he said.

    — No, that's probably funny. Want to hear more?

    — Yes.

    — I've read the *Marmora Herald* pretty thoroughly.

    — You're not carrying a book?

    — That's right. I forgot you're the man who taught me to always carry a book. . . . What are you doing?

    — I'm lying in the dark. I'll come and get you, Clara.

    — Will you be okay? The girl said you have a broken arm.

    — I'll bring her with me. She'll keep me awake. She's very earnest about things like that.

    — The kind of woman you always wanted.

    — That's right. She saved my life.

    — Are you her father, Patrick?

    — What's the name of the restaurant?

    — "Heart of Marmora."

    — Give us about five hours or so. I need a short rest . . . wait. Are you there?

    — Yes.

    — I am her father.

He rose and went to Hana's room. He felt exhausted.

    — Who is she, Patrick?

— Hana, I need you to come with me, to drive up to Marmora.

— The sled-dog capital of Ontario?

— What? . . . *What!*

She was beaming.

— She told me, Patrick, when I asked her where the call was coming from. We're going all the way there to pick her up?

— Yeah.

She stood by the door, watching him, wanting him to say more.

— How the hell did she end up there . . .

— Was she running away from you?

— I think so . . . with another man anyway. I need a little sleep first. Wake me in about forty minutes.

— Sure. You going to tell me about her on the drive?

— Yes.

— Great!

When Patrick had come out of prison six months earlier many dissident groups were already voicing themselves within the city. The events in Spain, the government's crackdown on unions, made the rich and powerful close ranks. Troops were in evidence everywhere. When the last shift left the water-filtration plant the police and the army moved in to guard it. Military tents bivouacked on the rolling grounds. There were soldiers on the roofs and searchlights dipped now and then along the waves of the lake, protecting against any possible attack from the direction of the lakeshore. While most public buildings were guarded, the waterworks was obsessively watched – partly because of the warnings of Commissioner Harris, who reminded officials that the Goths could have captured Rome by destroying the aqueducts which led into the city. Cutting off the water supply or poisoning it would bring the city to its knees.

Harris saw the new building as a human body. For him there were six locations where it could be seriously crippled – the raw water pumps, the Venturi meters, the entrance to the tanks where ferric chloride was poured, the twenty-four-foot-deep settling basins, and any one of the twenty filter pools where an explosion would cause floods and permanently rust all engines and electrical equipment. There was also the intake-pipe tunnel that ran almost a mile and a half out into the lake. No boats were allowed within a half-mile of the shoreline and no one, not even military personnel, was admitted into the building at night. Only Harris, who now insisted on sleeping there in his office, was allowed in, a pistol kept beside his bed.

In his dressing-gown, at two in the morning, Commissioner Harris was happy in the cocoon of humming machines. He would get up and roam through the palace of water which he had dreamed and desired and built. Every electrical outlet blazed, lighting up disappearing corridors as if Viennese streets, turning the subterranean filter pools into cloudy ballrooms. The building pulsed all night in the east end of the city on the edge of Lake Ontario. It was rumoured that people on the south shore in New York State could see the aura from it.

The filtration plant was one corner of a triangle of light that seemed to chart the city on this Saturday night in the summer of 1938. Another was a river of lights moving north up Yonge Street from the lake. And third was the dazzle from the Yacht Club on Toronto Island – holding its summer costume ball, with water taxis ferrying bizarrely dressed society across the bay on the one-mile trip over rough water.

Such dance floors the rich spent their evenings on! Strutting like colts in a warm barn, out of the rain. And in bed the following morning they would reconstruct the choreography of temptations which had carried them from the crowded periphery of the hall to the sprung dance floor beneath the thirty-foot coconut palms – clusters of which adorned the ballroom that seemed to have no ceiling, only false stars and false moonlight. In each set of trees was a live monkey, never able to reach the diners because of a frail chain. The animals had to dodge the champagne corks aimed at them – if you hit a monkey you were brought a free bottle. Sales of champagne soared and only now and then was there a shriek followed by a cheer.

There was a silk canopy over the band. Along the walls were

dioramas. Sometimes cotton snowballs were distributed and a battle broke out promptly, the guests soaking them in champagne or butter before flinging them around the room. The ballroom was lit indirectly; it seemed they were all in a moment of time that resembled the half-hour before the sun comes up over an oasis.

There is an image of Caravaggio among the rich which Patrick will always remember: meticulous, rude, and confident. A parting in his dark hair like Yonge Street at midnight. Dressed as a pirate, he had leapt off the motor launch on that midsummer night with his dog and Giannetta and Patrick, yelled his greetings to total strangers, and strolled into the false moonlight of the Yacht Club ballroom claiming to be Randolph Frog. Society women accepted his name with a straight face – the rich, being able to change everything but their names and looks, would defend these characteristics with care. In this circle a man with the face of a pit bull was considered distinguished.

They had not been invited. Caravaggio was eating canapés with his left hand and patting women on the ass with his right. When the orchestra's playing brought out the couples, Caravaggio lifted his dog into his arms and waltzed among them kissing August wildly, exclaiming over the beauty of his moles. For the next hour he danced with women who noted to themselves the odour of hound on his neck. Patrick and Giannetta meanwhile hung back on the periphery of the ballroom, refusing to leave it as if they might fall into a snakepit. But Caravaggio was a man who had traipsed through the gardens and furnishings of the wealthy for many years. He nudged men, told jokes, discussed china and crystal with wives and connoisseurs, complaining about getting Louis XIV chairs cleaned, and in the privacy behind his drunkenness cemented away information and addresses.

Finally he found the couple he wanted. In their early forties, drinking hard, a flirtatious wife and a bully of a husband. He danced with his eyes against hers singing "Night and Day."

> *"Vicina o lontana da me*
> *non importa mia cara, dove sei . . ."*

She was impressed by his Italian, which he claimed to have picked up in Tuscany the previous summer. His fingers circled her shoulder blade. She leaned back.

> – Do you see my husband over there near the chandelier propositioning that girl? He's probably suggesting the yacht.
> – A yacht here?
> – Yes, we came in one, across the bay. Did you?
> – No. I never sail.
> – We'll take you.

He laughed, dropping a half-smoked cigarette onto the floor.

> – That's my shy sister over there.

She glanced across the room to the hollow glare of Giannetta, who held on to Patrick's arm.

> – Perhaps she could join us too.

Taking the bus down to the dock earlier that evening, Caravaggio had said, "Let me tell you about the rich – they have a way of laughing." And Patrick thought, Alice had said that. The exact words. "The only thing that holds the rich to the earth is property," Caravaggio continued, "their bureaus, their marble tables, their jewellery. . . ." Patrick had been quiet, not even bothering to laugh.

There was an image he remembered of Caravaggio, waving

goodbye with a blue hand as he hung on the prison roof. And when Patrick had come out of jail he traced the thief down through his Blue Cellar compatriots. "Mr. Wilful Destruction of Property saved my life," Caravaggio had explained to Giannetta. They showed him the city, where everything was five years older, and they became his friends. Late into those spring nights they had talked about each other's lives.

On reconnaissance the week before the Yacht Club dance, Giannetta had watched Patrick get drunk, and during the ride back on the ferry she had held him, his head in her lap. She leaned over him in the darkness, her hand in his hair. He looked up. There was a tenderness in this sky of her warm face he hadn't noticed before. Then everything had leapt from focus as Giannetta and Caravaggio lifted him off the ferry and brought him home to sleep on their living-room floor.

Now they step from the last stages of the costume ball out onto the dock: Caravaggio, his two rich friends, his dog, his 'sister,' and Patrick, who is supposedly her escort for the evening.

> "... *notte e giorno*
> *Questo ... mmm ...*
> *mi segue ovunque io vada*"

Caravaggio sings to the night, a bottle like a pendulum in his fingers, his arm sprawled over the woman's shoulder. He pours out monologues about cut glass and bevelled mirrors and rubs her nipple to the beat of his singing as her husband unlaces the boat from its moorings. Patrick walks behind dressed as a thief in black, a red scarf floating behind him and carrying a bag of tools with SWAG written across it.

Boarding the couple's yacht, *The Annalisa*, Caravaggio flings himself down the stairs laughing, looking for alcohol. He is beyond order. He and the husband uncork several bottles and climb back up on deck. The wife winds up the gramophone, the silk dress with a thousand sequins fluttering upon her. Giannetta leans against the rail receiving the air while the husband unleashes the sails and they break loose out into the bay – from the island towards the city. Bunny Berigan pierces the air with his trumpet whirling up in scales, leaving the orchestras of the Yacht Club behind. They are off. Rich.

Caravaggio claims helplessness with ropes and asks the wife to dance. He is charmed by her flippant sexuality. They fumble against each other with the motion of the waves, Giannetta and Patrick somewhere by the prow. The boat tacks back and forth towards the city a mile away. Caravaggio and the husband and the wife drink fast. The wife winds up the gramophone and "I Can't Get Started" emerges again under the hiss of the needle.

Caravaggio catches Patrick's eye and raises his glass. "Here's to impatience," he toasts, "here's to H.G. Wells," then flings his glass overboard. It is a hot night and he removes his cloak. The woman touches his costume earrings with her fingernails. *Ting.* "Ting," she mouths at him. "Are you hungry?"

Down below she opens the fridge door. He sits and swivels in the chair round and round passing the blur of her salmon-coloured dress, the drink spilling from his glass. He rotates to a halt and she is there by the fridge holding ice against her face for the heat, unhooking the brooch at her shoulder so a part of the dress falls revealing a doorway of skin to one side of her. The smell from the gas lamp beside him fills his head. He puts all his effort into his shoulders and bends forward so he can get up out of the chair and stand. Now he must be still. Music everywhere. He starts laughing. Can a man lose his balance with an erection? Deep thoughts. He turns to face her. Dear

Salmon. She steps forward to hold him. His cheek on the moist skin under her arm, at the rib, about where they pierced Jesus he thinks. He falls drunkenly to his knees. He holds her dress at the thighs as she slips down, slips through the dress so there is a bunched sequin sheath in his hands. The music ceases. A serious pause. They jerk with the swell of waves and he holds her hair from the back. He pulls his handkerchief out of his pocket and in direct light brings it to her face and chloroforms her.

Patrick's hand comes round the large face in the night air and chloroforms the husband.

Caravaggio is on the floor of the hold, the unconscious woman in his arms, the dress around her waist. She dreams of what? he wonders. He lies there comfortable against her, in the silence left by Giannetta's hand lifting the needle off the record. He slides from under her, looks around, puts a blanket on top of her, and goes up on deck.

The husband lies nestled in the ropes. In his tuxedo he looks like a prop, a stolen mannequin. Above him, balanced on the rail of the boat, Patrick stands and pisses into the waves. Caravaggio mans the boat as Giannetta turns out the deck lights. "Is this the prow?" Patrick yells. "Am I pissing off the prow? Or bow?" Giannetta laughs. "I better get you ready." "Yes," he says. He walks to the back of the boat, scoops up the gramophone, and flings it overboard.

Caravaggio aims the yacht towards the east end of the city, towards the lights of Kew Park and the waterworks. Patrick and Giannetta go below deck. He takes some food out of the fridge, steps past the unconscious woman, and sits at the table. He is like a bullet that has been sleeping. That is how he has felt all night, in the slipstream of Caravaggio, fully relaxed, calm among his two friends. They have stopped him from thinking ahead. He wants the heart of the place. He wants to step in and destroy meticulously, efficiently. This is not to be a gesture of an egg hurled against a train window.

*   *   *

Throughout the night the giant intake pipe draws water into the filtration plant at a speed faster than during the day. Patrick knows that. From the plans Caravaggio has stolen for him, he knows its exact length, slightly under two miles, knows its angle and grade, knows the diameter of the pipe and the roughness of the metal inside and the narrower bands where the sections have been riveted together. He knows all the places he should assault once he is in the building.

On deck Giannetta watches Patrick, a small lantern beside them, the only light on the boat. He takes off his shirt and she begins to put grease onto his chest and shoulders. He watches her black hair as she rubs this darkness onto his body. The sweat on her collarbone. Her serious face. She suddenly leans forward and he feels her mouth briefly on his cheek. Then she pulls her head back into mystery and smiles at him, covering his face with the thick oil. When Caravaggio joins them, carrying the heavy SWAG bag, Patrick is ready. Giannetta embraces Caravaggio. With her fingers she plucks a sequin out of the darkness of his hair. Then the men climb down into the rowboat, absolute blackness around them. Only the filtration plant blazes on the shore a half-mile away. They pull free as Giannetta veers the yacht away, back towards the island.

Now the two men sit facing each other, knees touching. They are twenty or thirty yards from the floating structure where the intake pipe begins. "This is a charm," Caravaggio says, putting a metal spile attached to a leather thong around Patrick's neck. Caravaggio begins to dress Patrick with water-resistant dynamite – wrapping the sticks tightly against his chest under the thin black shirt. They both wear dark trousers. Patrick is invisible except by touch, grease covering all unclothed skin, his face, his hands, his bare feet. *Demarcation.* Caravaggio can sense his body, can feel and distinguish the belt straps, the button-locks that secure the fuses. The floating structure has sentries. They see lit cigarettes as they row towards them, Caravaggio leaning forward to touch Patrick's right arm to gesture him right, his left to gesture him left. No words. Only Caravaggio it seems can see into the weak spots of this absolute.

He attaches the tank onto Patrick's shoulders. Just one tank. They have estimated the speed of the water and the length of the tunnel. He could travel its distance in twelve minutes, but there is one risk. At some point in the night, pump generators are switched and for three minutes there is no suction at all. Then the water in the pipe does not move, it lies still. It would be the effect of a moving sidewalk stopping. They both know this could happen, have imagined Patrick no longer caught in the speed of the intake but languid, in a shock of stillness. The tank gives him only fifteen minutes of air. If the suction pump is off, the level of water in the normally full pipe might recede for a while and Patrick could possibly move to the top and breathe the air there. Neither of them is sure about this.

Just below the tank Caravaggio straps on the blasting-box and plunger. Small, brown, the maximum size Patrick can carry in order to get through the iron bars at the mouth of the intake pipe, which is there to stop logs and dead bodies from being drawn in. An animate body can squeeze through. In one of Patrick's nightmares while waiting for this evening he has imagined that in the pipe somewhere is a dead body which has magically slipped in and that he will clutch it during his journey.

At the far end of the tunnel is another barrier of iron bars which he will have to squeeze through. Then he will enter a forty-foot well where just above the water level will be a metal screen to keep out small objects and fish when the water is made to rise. He has the wire-cutters to get through this. Then he will be among the grey machines of the waterworks.

Caravaggio straps the battery lamp onto Patrick's head, then he embraces him. *"Auguri, amico mio."*

Patrick nods, puts the mouthpiece of the breathing apparatus between his lips, and rolls out of the boat. He holds on, treading water. Caravaggio leans over and switches on the lamp. They have choreographed this carefully for they knew there would be men near the entrance to the intake pipe. As the light goes on Patrick drives his head under water and his body follows downwards in an arc.

This is July 7, 1938. A night of no moon, a heat-wave in the city. The lemon-coloured glare from the waterworks delineates the east end. Caravaggio could lean forward and pluck it like some jewel from the neck of a negress. He rows in a straight line towards the waterworks, knowing Patrick is underneath him in the five-foot-diameter pipe racing within the current, his movement under water like a clenching fist, doubling up and releasing to full length, then doubling up, awkward because of the weight he carries.

In all of his imagining Caravaggio sees Patrick move with the light glancing wildly against the sides of the pipe. Whereas Patrick, having crawled through the iron bars, nearly unable to because of the tank, having done that and begun to swim, has discovered the lamp slows him too much so within seconds he has discarded it and it sinks to the foot of the pipe, the light still on, burning out an hour later. Patrick swims in darkness, just the pull of the water to guide him, clenching and releasing like that fist Caravaggio imagines, but banging his legs and hands against the sides of the pipe, doing this so often they are already bleeding from the blows and scrapes. Grease moves from his hair down his cheeks into his mouth. Most of all his body fears no air if the tank runs out, and the danger of silence among the pumps a mile away so he will suddenly move only at human speed. These fears are greater than the fear of no light or the remembered nightmare where he embraces the lost corpse. So his body, moving without thought, listens for silence. If the pumps stop, Caravaggio has told him to dynamite the pipe and climb out, leap from the water and yell. He will be there. But both know there is little chance of climbing out of that gashed metal while the whole lake pours in.

The searchlights from the filtration plant glance over the water. Now Caravaggio has to leave Patrick. He changes direction and rows towards Kew Beach a half-mile further west. The lights of the amusement park are slowly being turned off, past midnight. The outline of the Ferris wheel disappears.

Patrick swallows the first flutter of the dying tank.

He heaves faster along with the current and he takes deeper breaths from the tank. In the middle of the third breath he crashes against bars. He is almost there. Gasping, the mouth-piece dry, empty, torn out of his mouth. He is almost there with an empty tank. Now he needs the light. He slips off the tank, an arm painful from the crash, and dives through the bars and swings up, no air in him, no light, up into the brick of the well, avoiding the suction of the side-screens built into the walls. If these catch his body fully the suction can hold him and never release him. He swims up by feel till he reaches the bar-rier screen. Thinking where should he go, down again? How to get up further? For precious seconds, his chest vacuumed and almost imploded before he realizes he is *in* air. His shoulders and head and forearms are in the delicious air. This is the screen he is supposed to cut himself through. He can breathe if he opens his mouth. He is in the natural air of the waterworks.

He hangs, his fingers hooked through the wires of the screen, everything below his waist in water. The wire-cutters must have fallen in the crash against the bars or when he unstrapped the tank. For a while he doesn't care. He has air now. He knows he can never fight his way back against the current, down to the foot of the well. He is caught.

He hangs from one arm. A very small explosion to dislodge the firmly riveted screen and he will be out. He has five detona-tors. Sacrifice one location. How *small* an explosion can some-one make? He attaches a blasting cap to the screen with a clip fuse, sets it off, and dives down as far as he can go. He does not hear the sound at all, he is just picked up and flung hard against the brick and then sucked upwards in a hunched ball with the water towards the buckled screen so his back and face are lacerated. Then he falls back down. There has been no sound for him, just movement, sideways and up, skin coming off his cheek and his back. There was, he remembers, temporary light. He can taste blood if he puts his tongue outside his mouth. And he can taste blood which comes down his nose through the roof of his mouth.

Patrick climbs out of the well and stands on the floor of the screen room among the grey machines, touching them to see if any are hot, a faint light from the main pumping station coming through a high window. He begins unwrapping the sticks of dynamite from his body and lays them in a row on the floor. Finding some cloth he wipes them dry. He removes from his pockets fuses, crimpers, timers, and detonator caps, which are wrapped in oil cloth. He unwinds the electrical wire and begins to assemble the blasting-box and plunger.

Stripping completely naked he squeezes the water out of his clothes and lays his shirt and pants against the hot machines. He lies down now and tries to rest. Trying to control his breathing, even now he desires to take large gasps in case this will be his last air. *King Solomon's Mines*. He smiles up in the darkness.

Harris, half-asleep on the makeshift bed in his office, has heard the thump, one thump that didn't fit into the pattern of noises made by the row of water pumps. He walks onto the mezzanine of the pumping station. It is brilliantly lit and stark. In his dressing-gown he descends the stairs to the low-level pumping station, walks twenty-five yards into the Venturi tunnels, and then returns slowly, listening again for that false thump. He has seen nothing but the grey-painted machines. On the upper level he looks out of the windows and sees the military patrols. He relaxes and goes back to his room.

Patrick rests without closing his eyes, his gaze on the high window that brings light into this dark screen room. Soon he will go along the corridor where he had searched for her and found her, bathing beside a candle among all those puppets . . . years ago. He cannot touch his own face because of the pain. He has no idea what he has broken.

After twenty minutes he gets up, puts on his clothes, and begins to attach the blasting caps onto the dynamite. He walks into the humidity of the pumping station. As he settles and beds the explosives he can see what will occur. A column of water will shoot up seventy feet into the air and break through the glass windows of the roof. The floor buckles, other pumps overload and burn out in seconds. When the settling basins explode, the military tents on the lawn above them will collapse downwards into twenty-four feet of pure water. He picks up the wheel of wire and lines the electrical fuses through the Venturi tunnels.

> "On the golf course I'm under par
> Metro-Goldwyn has asked me to star . . ."

The machine roar drowns him out as he half mutters half sings, unaware that the song from the boat has attached itself to him like a burr. He wades across the raw water of the filter pools with the wire wheel in his outstretched hand, selecting the key columns on which to lay the dynamite. The water from here will burst through the wired glass into the corridors of rosy marble.

> "I've got a house – a showplace
> Still I can't get no place – with you . . ."

He lays a charge with its electric detonator over the plaque that says Dominion Centrifugal Pump. The last ones he nestles under the ferric chloride tanks, and beside the rose marble tower clock with its code lights. He runs the wires into the blasting-box.

Barefoot, he walks up the staircase trailing the live wires behind him, around the mezzanine gallery and into Harris' office.

Harris sitting at his desk, the gooseneck lamp on, happens to be watching the door when it opens. Even if he had known the man before he would not recognize him now. Black thin cotton trousers and shirt, grease-black face – blood in the scrapes and scratches. The man's knuckles bleeding, one arm hanging loose at his side. He notices the shirt ripped open at the back when the intruder turns to close the door.

He walks towards Harris, the blasting-box carried like a chicken under his right arm.

— Do you know me?

— I worked for you, Mr. Harris. I helped build the tunnel I just swam through.

— Who are you? How dare you try to come in here!

— I'm not trying this, I've done it. Everything is wired. I just press the plunger on this blasting-box.

— What do you want? Who are you?

— I'm Patrick Lewis.

There was silence. Patrick leaned forward and rubbed his cut fingers over the smoothness of Harris' desk.

— Feldspar, he murmured.

Harris watched the eyes darting in the man's dark face. He walked over to the sideboard and returned with a decanter of brandy and glasses. He was thinking. Then he began to speak. He talked about how he hated the officials of the city but how he loved City Hall.

— I was practically *born* in City Hall. My mother was a caretaker. I worked up.

— You forgot us.

– I hired you.

– Your goddamn herringbone tiles in the toilets cost more than half our salaries put together.

– Yes, that's true.

– Aren't you ashamed of that?

– You watch, in fifty years they're going to come here and gape at the herringbone and the copper roofs. We need excess, something to live up to. I fought tooth and nail for that herringbone.

– *You* fought. *You* fought. Think about those who built the intake tunnels. Do you know how many of us died in there?

– There was no record kept.

– Turn off the light.

– What?

– Turn your light off.

Harris pulled the beaded cord on the gooseneck lamp. So the room was dark.

Patrick moved in shadow now, the blasting-box still under his right arm. He needed to stretch, to walk. He had been drowning in Harris' eyes and sleepy hand-movements, felt hypnotized by that calm voice, the solitary focus of the lamp. Without light he felt more awake, discerning shapes, the smell of a bed somewhere in the room. Harris spoke out of the darkness.

– You don't understand power. You don't like power, you don't respect it, you don't want it to exist but you move around it all the time. You're like a messenger. Think about it, Patrick. . . . No answer. I'll keep talking. But turn the light on before you decide to plunge that thing. Allow me that.

— I will. Just keep talking, Harris.

— What you are looking for is a villain.

Harris knew he had to survive until early morning. Then a column of sunlight would fall directly onto his large desk, the pad of grid paper, his fountain pen. His gun was by the bed. He had to survive till the first hint of morning colour came through the oculus above him, eight feet in diameter, made up of eight half-moons of glass. He leaned forward.

— One night, I had a dream. I got off the bus at College – it was when we were moving College Street so it would hook up to Carlton – and I came to this area I had never been to. I saw fountains where there used to be an intersection. What was strange was that I knew my way around. I knew that soon I should turn and see a garden and more fountains. When I woke from the dream the sense of familiarity kept tugging me all day. In my dream the next night I was walking in a mysterious park off Spadina Avenue. The following day I was lunching with the architect John Lyle. I told him of these landscapes and he began to laugh. "These are real," he said. "Where?" I asked. "In Toronto." It turned out I was dreaming about projects for the city that had been rejected over the years. Wonderful things that were said to be too vulgar or expensive, too this, too that. And I was walking through these places, beside the traffic circle at Yonge and Bloor, down the proposed Federal Avenue to Union Station. Lyle was right. These *were* all real places. They could have existed. I mean the Bloor Street Viaduct and this building here are just a hint of what could have been done here.

You must realize you are like these places, Patrick. You're as much of the fabric as the aldermen and the millionaires. But you're among the dwarfs of enterprise who never get accepted or acknowledged. Mongrel company. You're a lost heir. So you stay in the woods. You reject power. And this is how the bland fools – the politicians and press and mayors and their advisers – become the spokesmen for the age. You must realize the trick is to be as serious when you are old as when you are young.

– Did you know a woman named Alice Gull?
– No . . . should I?
– Yes.
– Is she dead?
– Why do you say that?
– You said *did*.
– Yes.

Patrick turned the light on and saw Harris' eyes looking directly into his.

– Have you decided?
– Not yet.

He switched off the light. Again they disappeared from each other.

– Alice Gull, Harris said very slowly, was killed by an anarchist.
– No.
– She was the actress. Is that correct?

In the darkness Patrick heard Harris sip his brandy and return the glass to the table. Patrick sat on the floor, his one good arm resting on the blasting-box.

— I think I saw her once, Harris said.

— She used to perform here. There used to be meetings in your unfinished waterworks. That's where I met her, after many years.

— What meetings? What do you mean?

— Then I lost her. . . . Someone gave her the wrong bag. A simple mistake. Picked up the wrong bag. So she was carrying dynamite with a timing device, a clock bomb. She was walking with it through the crowds along the Danforth, near Broadview, walking towards the centre of the city. Who knows what she thought she was carrying? They knew she was in danger as soon as it was discovered.

Patrick was almost inaudible, whispering. If he were writing this down, Harris thought, his handwriting would be getting smaller and smaller.

— I don't want to talk of this anymore.

— Then it will always be a nightmare.

— It *will* always be a nightmare, Harris. She had a line, an old saying. "In a rich man's house there is nowhere to spit except in his face."

— Diogenes.

— I don't know.

A silence.

— Patrick, talk to me.

— They found me at the tannery, screaming to me about what had happened. And I ran. I ran north along the edge of the valley, no streetcars, all the demonstrations had caused chaos that day. I passed the Geranium Bakery and grabbed her friend Temelcoff to help find her. And the two of us ran all the way up to the Danforth where the crowd was, where she was supposed to be. By the time I got there, I had nothing in me to shout. *Alice!* I couldn't even whisper it. We kept leaping up to look for her over the heads of the crowd. She was carrying the clock bomb, not even knowing what it was, and soon everything she held would rocket out into her. Temelcoff and I jumped up and down, the mob around us, now and then seeing each other's frantic faces. . . . Then I heard the explosion. Not far away, near enough to have found her and picked up that bag and flung it anywhere else on the street. . . .

Then nobody moved, Patrick remembered, the whole crowd locked in stillness. There was already a distance between Alice bent over, holding her ribs, and the jolted people twenty feet away. As he came towards her she recognized him, her eyes indelible, the wound at her side.

He cradled her gently, he could hardly touch her without causing pain. Most of all he was holding her eyes with his, terrified they would close, would shut him out. One eye was flickering up and down, then the other, as if stuttering. Then the bag ten feet away exploded again.

Harmless. And when he looked back her eyes were closed. Her dead hand gripping the side of his jacket.

He got up and ran, her blood on him, along the horrified corridor in the crowd. The groan subconscious, slubbering out of his mouth. He banged into something very tough which brought his eyes back into focus.

He looked into the face of Temelcoff, who held him and wouldn't let go. Not to capture him but to calm him. Patrick struggling from side to side. The former bridge-builder's face held together only by the formality of two clear tears. Two little silver coaches.

Then Nicholas Temelcoff let him go and walked over to the body of Alice.

— Patrick . . .

There was a permanent darkness to the room. A permanent silence. Harris was still, quiet, unable to see. All he knew now was where the voice had been.

On the ceiling high above him was the window with eight half-moons. If he looked up in a while there would be a suggestion of blue. My god, he swam here, Harris suddenly realized. That's how he got in, through the tunnel. What vision, what dream was that? He pressed his repeater watch and it struck five. The sound fell clearly into the room.

The knowledge it would be daybreak soon kept Harris awake. He remained where he was during the next hour and by then the first light was in the room. It nestled in the corners of the ceiling, suggested cupboards, the damn herringbone that seemed to irritate everyone, and then it clarified the alcove where his bed was, where Patrick lay strangely – the lower half of his body crouched, knees drawn up, and the top half sprawled out, head back. There was blood across his neck and shirt. He had cut his throat in the darkness. My god. Harris got up. Then sat down again. No, he was asleep. He was asleep! The cuts old. From the journey here. Harris realized that he was relieved. The blasting-box was on the floor. Earlier Harris had understood why the man had chosen him, knew he was one of the few in power who had something tangible around him. But those with real power had nothing to show for themselves. They had paper. They didn't carry a cent. Harris was an amateur in their midst. He had to sell himself every time.

He stood over Patrick. "He lay down to sleep, until he was woken from out of a dream. He saw the lions around him glorying in life; then he took his axe in his hand, he drew his sword from his belt, and he fell upon them like an arrow from the string."

There was a knock on the door. Six o'clock. He said nothing. A knock again. Harris was concerned that Patrick would wake suddenly. "Come in," he whispered. An officer efficiently stepped in and saluted. Harris put his finger to his lips before the man could bark out information. He pointed to the man on the bed.

 – Take that blasting-box and defuse it. Let him sleep on. Don't talk. Just take it away. Bring a nurse with some medical supplies here, he's hurt himself.

– Patrick?

He woke slowly, Hana's hand on his shoulder.

    – Patrick? We have to go to Marmora.
    – Five more minutes, ten more minutes.
    – No, we *have* to go. I made a thermos of coffee
for us.
    – Thank you.

He felt his clothes wet with the sweat of sleep.

    – I'm awake. Marmora. Okay.

On the balcony in the night air, he peered down into the
landlord's long green garden. The last of the previous day's
heat was still in the atmosphere. Hana locked up and they went
down the two flights of metal stairway and then walked along
Albany Street towards the car. The houses at this hour beautiful and large, stray lights on within them, and he could see the
faint interiors, their privacy and character revealed, each room
a subplot. His good arm was around Hana's shoulder while she
hugged the thermos to her.

    – Tell me about her.

– She was your mother's best friend. I'll tell you the whole story.

The second-floor balconies curved out to the street. Odours from each hedge. Mr. Rivera hosing his garden at three A.M. having just returned from a night shift, private as they passed him. A dog's chain hung off a step railing. They were off to guide Clara back to this street. He found it most beautiful, felt most comfortable at this hour when they often saw racoons pausing on steps, seemingly tamed, as if owning the territory of the porch.

They stopped by the Ford and unlocked the passenger door. He was about to climb over into the driver's seat.

> – Do you want to drive? he asked.
> – Me? I don't know the gears.
> – Go ahead. I'll talk the gears to you till we are out of town.
> – I'll try it for a bit.

Hana sat upright, adapting the rear-view mirror to her height. He climbed in, pretending to luxuriate in the passenger seat, making animal-like noises of satisfaction.

> – Lights, he said.

The Cinnamon Peeler

Selected Poems

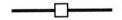

For Barrie Nichol

Contents

There's a trick
with a knife
I'm learning to do

'Deep colour and big, shaggy nose. Rather a jumbly, untidy sort of wine, with fruitiness shooting off one way, firmness another, and body pushing about underneath. It will be as comfortable and comforting as the 1961 Nuits St Georges when it has pulled its ends in and settled down.'

MAGAZINE DESCRIPTION OF A WINE

LIGHT

for Doris Gratiaen

Midnight storm. Trees walking off across the fields in fury
naked in the spark of lightning.
I sit on the white porch on the brown hanging cane chair
coffee in my hand midnight storm midsummer night.
The past, friends and family, drift into the rain shower.
Those relatives in my favourite slides
re-shot from old minute photographs so they now stand
complex ambiguous grainy on my wall.

This is my Uncle who turned up for his marriage
on an elephant. He was a chaplain.
This shy looking man in the light jacket and tie was infamous,
when he went drinking he took the long blonde beautiful hair
of his wife and put one end in the cupboard and locked it
leaving her tethered in an armchair.
He was terrified of her possible adultery
and this way died peaceful happy to the end.
My Grandmother, who went to a dance in a muslin dress
with fireflies captured and embedded in the cloth, shining
and witty. This calm beautiful face
organized wild acts in the tropics.
She hid the milkman in her house
after he had committed murder and at the trial
was thrown out of the court for making jokes at the judge.
Her son became a Q.C.
This is my brother at 6. With his cousin and his sister
and Pam de Voss who fell on a penknife and lost her eye.
My Aunt Christie. She knew Harold Macmillan was a spy
communicating with her through pictures in the newspapers.
Every picture she believed asked her to forgive him,
his hound eyes pleading.

Her husband, Uncle Fitzroy, a doctor in Ceylon,

had a memory sharp as scalpels into his 80's,
though I never bothered to ask him about anything
 – interested then more in the latest recordings of Bobby Darin.

And this is my Mother with her brother Noel in fancy dress.
They are 7 and 8 years old, a hand-coloured photograph,
it is the earliest picture I have. The one I love most.
A picture of my kids at Halloween
has the same contact and laughter.
My Uncle dying at 68, and my Mother a year later dying at 68.
She told me about his death and the day he died
his eyes clearing out of illness as if seeing
right through the room the hospital and she said
he saw something so clear and good his whole body
for a moment became youthful and she remembered
when she sewed badges on his trackshirts.
Her voice joyous in telling me this, her face light and clear.
(My firefly Grandmother also dying at 68).

These are the fragments I have of them, tonight
in this storm, the dogs restless on the porch.
They were all laughing, crazy, and vivid in their prime.
At a party my drunk Father
tried to explain a complex operation on chickens
and managed to kill them all in the process, the guests
having dinner an hour later while my Father slept
and the kids watched the servants clean up the litter
of beaks and feathers on the lawn.

574

These are their fragments, all I remember,
wanting more knowledge of them. In the mirror and in my kids
I see them in my flesh. Wherever we are
they parade in my brain and the expanding stories
connect to the grey grainy pictures on the wall,
as they hold their drinks or 20 years later
hold grandchildren, pose with favourite dogs,
coming through the light, the electricity, which the storm
destroyed an hour ago, a tree going down by the highway
so that now inside the kids play dominoes by candlelight
and out here the thick rain static the spark of my match
                                   to a cigarette
and the trees across the fields leaving me, distinct
lonely in their own knife scars and cow-chewed bark
frozen in the jagged light as if snapped in their run
the branch arms waving to what was a second ago the dark sky
when in truth like me they haven't moved.
Haven't moved an inch from me.

EARLY MORNING, KINGSTON
TO GANANOQUE

The twenty miles to Gananoque
with tangled dust blue grass
burned, and smelling burned
along the highway
is land too harsh for picnics.
Deep in the fields
behind stiff dirt fern
nature breeds the unnatural.

Escaping cows canter white
then black and white
along the median, forming out of mist.
Crows pick at animal accidents,
with swoops lift meals—
blistered groundhogs, stripped snakes
to arch behind a shield of sun.

Somewhere in those fields
they are shaping new kinds of women.

A HOUSE DIVIDED

This midnight breathing
heaves with no sensible rhythm,
is fashioned by no metronome.
Your body, eager
for the extra yard of bed,
reconnoitres and outflanks;
I bend in peculiar angles.

This nightly battle is fought with subtleties:
you get pregnant, I'm sure,
just for extra ground
  – immune from kicks now.

Inside you now's another,
thrashing like a fish,
swinging, fighting
for its inch already.

THE DIVERSE CAUSES

for than all erbys and treys renewyth a man and woman,
and in lyke wyse lovers callyth to their mynde olde
jantylnes and olde servyse, and many kynde dedes that
was forgotyn by necylgence

Three clouds and a tree
reflect themselves on a toaster.
The kitchen window hangs scarred,
shattered by winter hunters.

We are in a cell of civilized magic.
Stravinsky roars at breakfast,
our milk is powdered.

Outside, a May god
moves his paws to alter wind
to scatter shadows of tree and cloud.
The minute birds walk confident
jostling the cold grass.
The world not yet of men.

We clean buckets of their sand
to fetch water in the morning,
reach for winter cobwebs,
sweep up moths who have forgotten to waken.
When the children sleep, angled
behind their bottles, you can hear mice prowl.

I turn a page
careful not to break the rhythms
of your sleeping head on my hip,
watch the moving under your eyelid
that turns like fire,
and we have love and the god outside
until ice starts to limp
in brown hidden waterfalls,
or my daughter burns the lake
by reflecting her red shoes in it.

SIGNATURE

The car carried him
racing the obvious moon
beating in the trees like a white bird.

Difficult to make words sing
around your appendix.
The obvious upsets me,
everyone has scars which crawl
into the mystery of swimming trunks.

I was the first appendix in my family.
My brother who was given the stigma
of a rare blood type
proved to have ulcers instead.

The rain fell like applause as I approached the hospital.

It takes seven seconds she said,
strapped my feet,
entered my arm.
I stretched all senses
on *five*
the room closed on me like an eyelid.

At night the harmonica plays,
a whistler joins in respect.
I am a sweating marble saint
full of demerol and sleeping pills.
A man in the armour of shining plaster
walks to my door, then past.
Imagine the rain
falling like white bees on the sidewalk
imagine Snyder
high on poetry and mountains

Three floors down
my appendix
swims in a jar.

O world, I shall be buried all over Ontario

HENRI ROUSSEAU AND FRIENDS

for Bill Muysson

In his clean vegetation
the parrot, judicious,
poses on a branch.
The narrator of the scene,
aware of the perfect fruits,
the white and blue flowers,
the snake with an ear for music;
he presides.

The apes
hold their oranges like skulls,
like chalices.
They are below the parrot
above the oranges—
a jungle serfdom which
with this order
reposes.

They are the ideals of dreams.
Among the exactness,
the symmetrical petals,
the efficiently flying angels,
there is complete liberation.
The parrot is interchangeable;
tomorrow in its place
a waltzing man and tiger,
brash legs of a bird.

Greatness achieved
they loll among textbook flowers
and in this pose hang
scattered like pearls
in just as intense a society.
On Miss Adelaide Milton de Groot's walls,
with Lillie P. Bliss in New York.

And there too
in spangled wrists and elbows
and grand façades of cocktails
are vulgarly beautiful parrots, appalled lions,
the beautiful and the forceful locked in suns,
and the slight, careful stepping birds.

APPLICATION FOR A DRIVING LICENCE

Two birds loved
in a flurry of red feathers
like a burst cottonball,
continuing while I drove over them.

I am a good driver, nothing shocks me.

THE TIME AROUND SCARS

A girl whom I've not spoken to
or shared coffee with for several years
writes of an old scar.
On her wrist it sleeps, smooth and white,
the size of a leech.
I gave it to her
brandishing a new Italian penknife.
Look, I said turning,
and blood spat onto her shirt.

My wife has scars like spread raindrops
on knees and ankles,
she talks of broken greenhouse panes
and yet, apart from imagining red feet,
(a nymph out of Chagall)
I bring little to that scene.
We remember the time around scars,
they freeze irrelevant emotions
and divide us from present friends.
I remember this girl's face,
the widening rise of surprise.

And would she
moving with lover or husband
conceal or flaunt it,
or keep it at her wrist
a mysterious watch.
And this scar I then remember
is medallion of no emotion.

I would meet you now
and I would wish this scar
to have been given with
all the love
that never occurred between us.

FOR JOHN, FALLING

Men stopped in the heel of sun,
hum of engines evaporated;
the machine displayed itself bellied with mud
and balanced – immense.

No one ran to where
his tensed muscles curled unusually,
where jaws collected blood,
the hole in his chest the size of fists,
hands clutched to eyes like a blindness.

Arched there he made
ridiculous requests for air.
And twelve construction workers
what should they do but surround
or examine the path of falling.

And the press in bright shirts,
a doctor, the foreman scuffing a mound,
men removing helmets,
the machine above him
shielding out the sun
while he drowned
in the dark orgasm of his mouth.

THE GOODNIGHT

With the bleak heron Paris
imagine Philoctetes
the powerful fat-thighed man,
the bandaged smelling foot
with rivers of bloodshot veins
scattering like trails into his thighs:
a man who roared on an island for ten years,
whose body grew banal
while he stayed humane
behind the black teeth and withering hair.

Imagine in his hands – black
from the dried blood of animals,
a bow of torn silver
that noised arrows loose like a wild heart;

in front of him – Paris
darting and turning, the perfumed stag,
and beyond him the sun
netted in the hills, throwing back his shape,
until the running spider of shadow
gaped on the bandaged foot of the standing man
who let shafts of eagles into the ribs
that were moving to mountains.

PHILOCTETES ON THE ISLAND

Sun moves broken in the trees
drops like a paw
turns sea to red leopard

I trap sharks and drown them
stuffing gills with sand
cut them with coral till
the blurred grey runs
red designs.

And kill to fool myself alive
to leave all pity on the staggering body
in order not to shoot an arrow up
and let it hurl
down through my petalling skull
or neck vein, and lie
heaving round the wood in my lung.
That the end of thinking.
Shoot either eye of bird instead
and run and catch it in your hand.

One day a bird went mad
flew blind along the beach
smashed into a dropping wave
out again and plummeted.
Later knocked along the shore.

To slow an animal
you break its foot with a stone
so two run wounded
reel in the bush, flap
bodies at each other
till free of forest
it gallops broken in the sand,
then use a bow
and pin the tongue back down its throat.

With wind the rain wheels like a circus hoof,
aims at my eyes, rakes up the smell of animals
of stone moss, cleans me.
Branches fall like nightmares in the dark
till sun breaks up
and spreads wound fire at my feet

then they smell me,
the beautiful animals

ELIZABETH

Catch, my Uncle Jack said
and oh I caught this huge apple
red as Mrs Kelly's bum.
It's red as Mrs Kelly's bum, I said
and Daddy roared
and swung me on his stomach with a heave.
Then I hid the apple in my room
till it shrunk like a face
growing eyes and teeth ribs.

Then Daddy took me to the zoo
he knew the man there
they put a snake around my neck
and it crawled down the front of my dress.
I felt its flicking tongue
dripping onto me like a shower.
Daddy laughed and said Smart Snake
and Mrs Kelly with us scowled.

In the pond where they kept the goldfish
Philip and I broke the ice with spades
and tried to spear the fishes;
we killed one and Philip ate it,
then he kissed me
with raw saltless fish in his mouth.

My sister Mary's got bad teeth
and said I was lucky, then she said
I had big teeth, but Philip said I was pretty.
He had big hands that smelled.

I would speak of Tom, soft laughing,
who danced in the mornings round the sundial
teaching me the steps from France, turning
with the rhythm of the sun on the warped branches,
who'd hold my breast and watch it move like a snail
leaving his quick urgent love in my palm.
And I kept his love in my palm till it blistered.

When they axed his shoulders and neck
the blood moved like a branch into the crowd.
And he staggered with his hanging shoulder
cursing their thrilled cry, wheeling,
waltzing in the French style to his knees
holding his head with the ground,
blood settling on his clothes like a blush;
this way
when they aimed the thud into his back.

And I find cool entertainment now
with white young Essex, and my nimble rhymes.

She said, 'What about Handy? Think I should send it to him?'

'He's supposed to call in a little while. I'll ask him.'

'He retired, didn't he?'

'Yes.'

She waited and then said, 'Say something, Parker. God to get you to gossip, it's like pulling teeth.'

'Handy retired.' Parker said.

'I know he retired! Tell me about it. Tell me why he retired, tell me where he is, how's he doing. Talk to me, Parker, goddamit.'

RICHARD STARK, *The Sour Lemon Score*

DATES

It becomes apparent that I miss great occasions.
My birth was heralded by nothing
but the anniversary of Winston Churchill's marriage.
No monuments bled, no instruments
agreed on a specific weather.
It was a seasonal insignificance.

I console myself with my mother's eighth month.
While she sweated out her pregnancy in Ceylon
a servant ambling over the lawn
with a tray of iced drinks,
a few friends visiting her
to placate her shape, and I
drinking the life lines,
Wallace Stevens sat down in Connecticut
a glass of orange juice at his table
so hot he wore only shorts
and on the back of a letter
began to write 'The Well Dressed Man with a Beard'.

That night while my mother slept
her significant belly cooled
by the bedroom fan
Stevens put words together
that grew to sentences
and shaved them clean and
shaped them, the page suddenly
becoming thought where nothing had been,
his head making his hand
move where he wanted
and he saw his hand was saying
the mind is never finished, no, never
and I in my mother's stomach was growing
as were the flowers outside the Connecticut windows.

595

BILLBOARDS

'Even his jokes were exceedingly drastic.'

My wife's problems with husbands, houses,
her children that I meet
at stations in Kingston, in Toronto, in London Ontario
– they come down the grey steps
bright as actors after their drugged four hour ride
of spilled orange juice and comics.
Reunions for Easter egg hunts.
Kite flying. Christmases.
All this, I was about to say,
invades my virgin past.

When she was beginning
this anthology of kids
I moved – blind but for senses
jutting *faux pas*, terrible humour,
shifted with a sea of persons,
breaking when necessary
into smaller self sufficient bits of mercury.
My mind a carefully empty diary
till I hit the barrier reef
that was my wife—
                              there
the right bright fish
among the coral.

With her came the locusts of history—
innuendoes she had missed
varied attempts at seduction
dogs who had been bred
and killed by taxis or brain disease.
Here was I trying to live
with a neutrality so great
I'd have nothing to think about.
Nowadays I get the feeling
I'm in a complex situation,
one of several billboard posters
blending in the rain.

I am writing this with a pen my wife has used
to write a letter to her first husband.
On it is the smell of her hair.
She must have placed it down between sentences
and thought, and driven her fingers round her skull
gathered the slightest smell of her head
and brought it back to the pen.

LETTERS & OTHER WORLDS

'for there was no more darkness for him and, no doubt like Adam before the fall, he could see in the dark'

My father's body was a globe of fear
His body was a town we never knew
He hid that he had been where we were going
His letters were a room he seldom lived in
In them the logic of his love could grow

My father's body was a town of fear
He was the only witness to its fear dance
He hid where he had been that we might lose him
His letters were a room his body scared

He came to death with his mind drowning.
On the last day he enclosed himself
in a room with two bottles of gin, later
fell the length of his body
so that brain blood moved
to new compartments
that never knew the wash of fluid
and he died in minutes of a new equilibrium.

His early life was a terrifying comedy
and my mother divorced him again and again.
He would rush into tunnels magnetized
by the white eye of trains
and once, gaining instant fame,
managed to stop a Perahara in Ceylon
 – the whole procession of elephants dancers
local dignitaries – by falling
dead drunk onto the street.

As a semi-official, and semi-white at that,
the act was seen as a crucial
turning point in the Home Rule Movement
and led to Ceylon's independence in 1948.

(My mother had done her share too—
her driving so bad
she was stoned by villagers
whenever her car was recognized)

For 14 years of marriage
each of them claimed he or she
was the injured party.
Once on the Colombo docks
saying goodbye to a recently married couple
my father, jealous
at my mother's articulate emotion,
dove into the waters of the harbour
and swam after the ship waving farewell.
My mother pretending no affiliation
mingled with the crowd back to the hotel.

Once again he made the papers
though this time my mother
with a note to the editor
corrected the report – saying he was drunk
rather than broken hearted at the parting of friends.
The married couple received both editions
of *The Ceylon Times* when their ship reached Aden.

And then in his last years
he was the silent drinker,
the man who once a week
disappeared into his room with bottles
and stayed there until he was drunk
and until he was sober.

There speeches, head dreams, apologies,

the gentle letters, were composed.
With the clarity of architects
he would write of the row of blue flowers
his new wife had planted,
the plans for electricity in the house,
how my half-sister fell near a snake
and it had awakened and not touched her.
Letters in a clear hand of the most complete empathy
his heart widening and widening and widening
to all manner of change in his children and friends
while he himself edged
into the terrible acute hatred
of his own privacy
till he balanced and fell
the length of his body
the blood entering
the empty reservoir of bones
the blood searching in his head without metaphor.

GRIFFIN OF THE NIGHT

I'm holding my son in my arms
sweating after nightmares
small me
fingers in his mouth
his other fist clenched in my hair
small me
sweating after nightmares.

BIRTH OF SOUND

At night the most private of a dog's long body groan.
It comes with his last stretch
in the dark corridor outside our room.
The children turn.
A window tries to split with cold
the other dog hoofing the carpet for lice.
We're all alone.

WE'RE AT THE GRAVEYARD

Stuart Sally Kim and I
watching still stars
or now and then sliding stars
like hawk spit to the trees.
Up there the clear charts,
the systems' intricate branches
which change with hours and solstices,
the bone geometry of moving from there, to there.

And down here – friends
whose minds and bodies
shift like acrobats to each other.
When we leave, they move
to an altitude of silence.

So our minds shape
and lock the transient,
parallel these bats
who organize the air
with thick blinks of travel.
Sally is like grey snow in the grass.
Sally of the beautiful bones
pregnant below stars.

NEAR ELGINBURG

3 a.m. on the floor mattress.
In my pyjamas a moth beats frantic
my heart is breaking loose.

I have been dreaming of a man
who places honey on his forehead before sleep
so insects come tempted by liquid
to sip past it into the brain.
In the morning his head contains wings
and the soft skeletons of wasp.

Our suicide into nature.
That man's seduction
so he can beat the itch
against the floor and give in
move among the sad remnants
of those we have destroyed,
the torn code these animals ride to death on.
Grey fly on windowsill
white fish by the dock
heaved like a slimy bottle into the deep,
to end up as snake
heckled by children and cameras
as he crosses lawns of civilization.

We lie on the floor mattress
lost moths walk on us
waterhole of flesh, want
this humiliation under the moon.
Till in the morning we are surrounded
by dark virtuous ships
sent by the kingdom of the loon.

LOOP

My last dog poem.
I leave behind all social animals
including my dog who takes
30 seconds dismounting from a chair.
Turn to the one
who appears again on roads
one eye torn out and chasing.

He is only a space filled
and blurred with passing,
transient as shit – will fade
to reappear somewhere else.

He survives the porcupine, cars, poison,
fences with their spasms of electricity.
Vomits up bones, bathes at night
in Holiday Inn swimming pools.

And magic in his act of loss.
The missing eye travels up
in a bird's mouth, and into the sky.
Departing family. It is loss only of flesh
no more than his hot spurt across a tree.

He is the one you see at Drive-Ins
tearing silent into garbage
while societies unfold in his sky.
The bird lopes into the rectangle nest of images

and parts of him move on.

HERON REX

Mad kings
blood lines introverted, strained pure
so the brain runs in the wrong direction

they are proud of their heritage of suicides
– not just the ones who went mad
balancing on that goddamn leg, but those

whose eyes turned off
the sun and imagined it
those who looked north, those who
forced their feathers to grow in
those who couldn't find the muscles in their arms
who drilled their beaks into the skin
those who could speak
and lost themselves in the foul connections
who crashed against black bars in a dream of escape
those who moved round the dials of imaginary clocks
those who fell asleep and never woke
who never slept and so dropped dead
those who attacked the casual eyes of children and were led away
and those who faced corners for ever
those who exposed themselves and were led away
those who pretended broken limbs, epilepsy,
who managed to electrocute themselves on wire
those who felt their skin was on fire and screamed
                              and were led away

There are ways of going
physically mad, physically
mad when you perfect the mind
where you sacrifice yourself for the race
when you are the representative when you allow
yourself to be paraded in the cages
celebrity a razor in the body

These small birds so precise
frail as morning neon
they are royalty melted down
they are the glass core at the heart of kings
yet 15-year-old boys could enter the cage
and break them in minutes
as easily as a long fingernail

RAT JELLY

See the rat in the jelly
steaming dirty hair
frozen, bring it out on a glass tray
split the pie four ways and eat
I took great care cooking this treat for you
and tho it looks good
and tho it smells of the Westinghouse still
and tastes of exotic fish or
maybe the expensive arse of a cow
I want you to know it's rat
steaming dirty hair and still alive

(caught him last Sunday
thinking of the fridge, thinking of you.)

KING KONG MEETS WALLACE STEVENS

Take two photographs—
Wallace Stevens and King Kong
(Is it significant that I eat bananas as I write this?)

Stevens is portly, benign, a white brush cut
striped tie. Businessman but
for the dark thick hands, the naked brain
the thought in him.

Kong is staggering
lost in New York streets again
a spawn of annoyed cars at his toes.
The mind is nowhere.
Fingers are plastic, electric under the skin.
He's at the call of Metro-Goldwyn-Mayer.

Meanwhile W. S. in his suit
is thinking chaos is thinking fences.
In his head – the seeds of fresh pain
his exorcising,
the bellow of locked blood.

The hands drain from his jacket,
pose in the murderer's shadow.

'THE GATE IN HIS HEAD'

for Victor Coleman

Victor, the shy mind
revealing the faint scars
coloured strata of the brain,
not clarity but the sense of shift

a few lines, the tracks of thought

Landscape of busted trees
the melted tires in the sun
Stan's fishbowl
with a book inside
turning its pages
like some sea animal
camouflaging itself
the typeface clarity
going slow blonde in the sun full water

My mind is pouring chaos
in nets onto the page.
A blind lover, dont know
what I love till I write it out.
And then from Gibson's your letter
with a blurred photograph of a gull.
Caught vision. The stunning white bird
an unclear stir.

And that is all this writing should be then.
The beautiful formed things caught at the wrong moment
so they are shapeless, awkward
moving to the clear.

TAKING

It is the formal need
to suck blossoms out of the flesh
in those we admire
planting them private in the brain
and cause fruit in lonely gardens.

To learn to pour the exact arc
of steel still soft and crazy
before it hits the page.
I have stroked the mood and tone
of hundred year dead men and women
Emily Dickinson's large dog, Conrad's beard
and, for myself,
removed them from historical traffic.
Having tasted their brain. Or heard
the wet sound of a death cough.
Their idea of the immaculate moment is now.

The rumours pass on
the rumours pass on
are planted
till they become a spine.

BURNING HILLS

for Kris and Fred

So he came to write again
in the burnt hill region
north of Kingston. A cabin
with mildew spreading down walls.
Bullfrogs on either side of him.

Hanging his lantern of Shell Vapona Strip
on a hook in the centre of the room
he waited a long time. Opened
the Hilroy writing pad, yellow Bic pen.
Every summer he believed would be his last.
This schizophrenic season change, June to September,
when he deviously thought out plots
across the character of his friends.
Sometimes barren as fear going nowhere
or in habit meaningless as tapwater.
One year maybe he would come and sit
for four months and not write a word down
would sit and investigate colours, the
insects in the room with him.

What he brought: a typewriter
tins of ginger ale, cigarettes. A copy of *Strangelove*,
of *The Intervals*, a postcard of Rousseau's *The Dream*.
His friends' words were strict as lightning
unclothing the bark of a tree, a shaved hook.
The postcard was a test pattern by the window
through which he saw growing scenery.

Eventually the room was a time machine for him.
He closed the rotting door, sat down
thought pieces of history. The first girl
who in a park near his school
put a warm hand into his trousers
unbuttoning and finally catching the spill
across her wrist, he in the maze of her skirt.
She later played the piano
when he had tea with the parents.
He remembered that surprised—
he had forgotten for so long.
Under raincoats in the park on hot days.

The summers were layers of civilization in his memory
they were old photographs he didn't look at anymore
for girls in them were chubby not as perfect as in his mind
and his ungovernable hair was shaved to the edge of skin.
His friends leaned on bicycles
were 16 and tried to look 21
the cigarettes too big for their faces.
He could read those characters easily
undisguised as wedding pictures.
He could hardly remember their names
though they had talked all day, exchanged styles
and like dogs on a lawn hung around the houses of girls.

Sex a game of targets, of throwing firecrackers
at a couple in a field locked in hand-made orgasms,
singing dramatically in someone's ear along with the record
'*How do you think I feel / you know our love's not real*
The one you're made about / Is just a gad-about
How do you think I feel'.
He saw all that complex tension the way his children would.

There is one picture that fuses the five summers.
Eight of them are leaning against a wall
arms around each other
looking into the camera and the sun
trying to smile at the unseen adult photographer
trying against the glare to look 21 and confident.
The summer and friendship will last forever.
Except one who was eating an apple. That was him
oblivious to the significance of the moment.
Now he hungers to have that arm around the next shoulder.
The wretched apple is fresh and white.

Since he began burning hills
the Shell strip has taken effect.
A wasp is crawling on the floor
tumbling over, its motor fanatic.
He has smoked 5 cigarettes.
He has written slowly and carefully
with great love and great coldness.
When he finishes he will go back
hunting for the lies that are obvious.

CHARLES DARWIN PAYS A VISIT,
DECEMBER 1971

View of the coast of Brazil.
A man stood up to shout
at the image of a sailing ship
which was a vast white bird from over the sea
now ripping its claws into the ocean.
Faded hills of March
painted during the cold morning.
On board ship Charles Darwin sketched clouds.

One of these days the Prime Mover will
paint the Prime Mover out of his sky.
I want a . . . centuries being displaced
. . . *faith*

> 23rd of June, 1832.
> He caught sixty-eight species
> of a particularly minute beetle.

The blue thick leaves who greeted him
animals unconscious of celebration
moved slowly into law.
Adam with a watch.
Look past and future, (*I want a* . . .),
ease our way out of the structures
this smell of the cogs
and diamonds we live in.

I am waiting for a new ship, so new
we will think the lush machine
an animal of God.
Weary from travelling over the air and the water
it will sink to its feet at our door.

THE VAULT

Having to put forward candidates for God
I nominate Henri Rousseau and Dr Bucke,
tired of the lizard paradise
whose image banks renew off the flesh of others
 – those stories that hate, which are remnants and insults.
Refresh where plants breed to the edge of dream.

I have woken to find myself covered in white sheets
walls and doors, food.
There was no food in the world I left
where I ate the rich air. The bodies of small birds
who died while flying fell into my mouth.
Fruit dripped through our thirst to the earth.

All night the traffic of apes floats across the sky
a worm walks through the gaze of a lion
some birds live all their evenings on one branch.

They are held by the celebration of God's wife.
In Rousseau's *The Dream* she is the naked lady
who has been animal and tree
her breast a suckled orange.
The fibres and fluids of their moral nature
have seeped within her frame.

The hand is outstretched
her fingers move out in
mutual transfusion to the place.
Our low speaking last night
was barely audible among the grunt
of mongrel meditation.

She looks to the left
for that is the direction we leave in
when we fall from her room of flowers.

WHITE DWARFS

This is for people who disappear
for those who descend into the code
and make their room a fridge for Superman
— who exhaust costume and bones that could perform flight,
who shave their moral so raw
they can tear themselves through the eye of a needle
this is for those people
that hover and hover
and die in the ether peripheries

There is my fear
of no words   of
falling without words
over and over   of
mouthing the silence
Why do I love most
among my heroes those
who sail to that perfect edge
where there is no social fuel
Release of sandbags
to understand their altitude—

       that silence of the third cross
       3rd man hung so high and lonely
       we don't hear him say
       say his pain, say his unbrotherhood
       What has he to do with the smell of ladies,
       can they eat off his skeleton of pain?

The Gurkhas in Malaya
cut the tongues of mules
so they were silent beasts of burden
in enemy territories
after such cruelty what could they speak of anyway
And Dashiell Hammett in success

suffered conversation and moved
to the perfect white between the words

This white that can grow
is fridge, bed,
is an egg – most beautiful
when unbroken, where
what we cannot see is growing
in all the colours we cannot see

there are those burned out stars
who implode into silence
after parading in the sky
after such choreography what would they wish to speak of   anyway

'Newly arrived and totally ignorant of the Levantine languages, Marco Polo could express himself only with gestures, leaps, cries of wonder and of horror, animal barkings or hootings, or with objects he took from his knapsacks – ostrich plumes, pea-shooters, quartzes – which he arranged in front of him . . . '

ITALO CALVINO

THE AGATHA CHRISTIE BOOKS
BY THE WINDOW

In the long open Vancouver Island room
sitting by the indoor avocados
where indoor spring light
falls on the half covered bulbs

and down the long room light falling
onto the dwarf orange tree
vines from south america
the agatha christie books by the window

Nameless morning
solution of grain and colour

There is this light,
colourless, which falls on the warm
stretching brain of the bulb
that is dreaming avocado

COUNTRY NIGHT

The bathroom light burns over the mirror

In the blackness of the house
beds groan from the day's exhaustion
hold the tired shoulders bruised
and cut legs the unexpected
3 a.m. erections. Someone's dream
involves a saw someone's
dream involves a woman.
We have all dreamed of finding the lost dog.

The last light on upstairs
throws a circular pattern
through the decorated iron vent
to become a living room's moon.

The sofa calls the dog, the cat
in perfect blackness walks over the stove.
In the room of permanent light
cockroaches march on enamel.
The spider with jewel coloured thighs the brown moth
with corporal stripes
                              ascend pipes
and look into mirrors.

All night the truth happens.

MOVING FRED'S OUTHOUSE/
GERIATRICS OF PINE

All afternoon (while the empty drive-in
screen in the distance promises)
we are moving the two-seater
100 yards across his garden

We turn it over on its top
and over, and as it slowly
falls on its side
the children cheer

60 years old and a change in career—
from these pale yellow flowers emerging
out of damp wood in the roof
to become a room thorough with flight, noise,
and pregnant with the morning's eggs,
a perch for chickens.

Two of us. The sweat.
Our hands under the bottom
then the top as it goes
over, through twin holes the
flowers, running to move the roller, shove,
and everybody screaming to keep the dog away.
Fred the pragmatist – dragging the ancient comic
out of retirement and into a television series
among the charging democracy of rhode island reds

Head over heels across the back lawn
old wood collapsing in our hands

All afternoon the silent space is turned

BUCK LAKE STORE AUCTION

Scrub lawn.
                    A chained
dog tense and smelling.
50 cents for a mattress. 50 cents
for doors that allowed privacy.

                        A rain
swollen copy of Jack London
a magazine drawing of a rabbit
bordered with finishing nails.
6 chickens, bird cage (empty),
sauerkraut cutting board

down to the rock
                    trees

not bothering to look
into the old woman's eyes
as we go in, get a number
have the power to bid
on everything that is exposed.
After an hour in this sun
I expected her to unscrew
her left arm and donate it
to the auctioneer's excitement.
In certain rituals we desire
only what we cannot have.
While for her, Mrs Germain,
this is the needle's eye
where maniacs of earth select.
Look, I wanted to say,
$10 for the dog
with faded denim eyes

FARRE OFF

There are the poems of Campion I never saw till now
and Wyatt who loved with the best
and suddenly I want 16th-century women
round me devious politic aware
of step ladders to the king

Tonight I am alone with dogs and lightning
aroused by Wyatt's talk of women who step
naked into his bedchamber

Moonlight and barnlight constant
lightning every second minute
I have on my thin blue parka
and walk behind the asses of the dogs
who slide under the gate
and sense cattle
deep in the fields

I look out into the dark pasture
past where even the moonlight stops

my eyes are against the ink of Campion

WALKING TO BELLROCK

Two figures in deep water.

Their frames truncated at the stomach
glide along the surface. Depot Creek.
One hundred years ago lumber being driven down this river
tore and shovelled and widened the banks into Bellrock
down past bridges to the mill.

The two figures are walking
as if half sunk in a grey road
their feet tentative, stumbling on stone bottom.
Landscapes underwater. What do the feet miss?
Turtle, watersnake, clam. What do the feet ignore
and the brain not look at, as two figures slide
past George Grant's green immaculate fields
past the splashed blood of cardinal flower on the bank.

Rivers are a place for philosophy but all thought
is about the mechanics of this river is about
stones that twist your ankles
the hidden rocks you walk your knee into—
feet in slow motion and brain and balanced arms
imagining the blind path of foot, underwater sun
suddenly catching the almond coloured legs
the torn old Adidas tennis shoes we wear
to walk the river into Bellrock.

What is the conversation about for three hours
on this winding twisted evasive river to town?
What was the conversation about all summer.
Stan and I laughing joking going summer crazy
as we lived against each other.
To keep warm we submerge. Sometimes
just our heads decapitated
glide on the dark glass.

There is no metaphor here.
We are aware of the heat of the water, coldness of the rain,
smell of mud in certain sections that farts
when you step on it, mud never walked on
so you can't breathe, my god you can't breathe this air
and you swim fast your feet off the silt of history
that was there when the logs went
leaping down for the Rathburn Timber Company
when those who stole logs had to leap
right out of the country if caught.

But there is no history or philosophy or metaphor with us.
The problem is the toughness of the Adidas shoe
its three stripes gleaming like fish decoration.
The story is Russell's arm waving out of the green of a field.

The plot of the afternoon is to get to Bellrock
through rapids, falls, stink water
and reach the island where beer and a towel wait for us.
That night there is not even pain in our newly used muscles
not even the puckering of flesh
and little to tell except you won't
believe how that river winds and when you
don't see the feet you concentrate on the feet.
And all the next day trying to think
what we didn't talk about.
Where was the criminal conversation
broken sentences lost in the splash in wind.

Stan, my crazy summer friend,
why are we both going crazy?
Going down to Bellrock
recognizing home by the colour of barns
which tell us north, south, west,
and otherwise lost in miles and miles of rain
in the middle of this century
following the easy fucking stupid plot to town.

PIG GLASS

Bonjour.   This is pig glass
a piece of cloudy sea

nosed out of the earth by swine
and smoothed into pebble
run it across your cheek
it will not cut you

and this is my hand a language
which was buried for years   touch it
against your stomach

                        The pig glass
I thought
was the buried eye of Portland Township
slow faded history
waiting to be grunted up
There is no past until you breathe
on such green glass
                        rub it
over your stomach and cheek

The Meeks family used this section
years ago to bury tin
crockery forks dog tags
and each morning
pigs ease up that ocean
redeeming it again
into the possibilities of rust
one morning I found a whole axle
another day a hand crank
but this is pig glass
tested with narrow teeth
and let lie. The morning's green present.
Portland Township jewellery.

There is the band from the ankle of a pigeon
a weathered bill from the Bellrock Cheese Factory
letters in 1925 to a dead mother I
disturbed in the room above the tractor shed.
Journals of family love
servitude to farm weather
a work glove in a cardboard box
creased flat and hard like a flower.

A bottle thrown
by loggers out of a wagon
past midnight
explodes against rock.
This green fragment has behind it
the *booomm* when glass
tears free of its smoothness

now once more smooth as knuckle
a tooth on my tongue.
Comfort that bites through skin
hides in the dark afternoon of my pocket.
Snake shade.
Determined histories of glass.

THE HOUR OF COWDUST

It is the hour we move small
in the last possibilities of light

now the sky opens its blue vault

I thought this hour belonged to my children
bringing cows home
bored by duty swinging a stick,
but this focus of dusk out of dust
is everywhere – here by the Nile
the boats wheeling
like massive half-drowned birds
and I gaze at water that dreams
dust off my tongue,
in this country your mouth
feels the way your shoes look

Everything is reducing itself to shape

Lack of light cools your shirt
men step from barbershops
their skin alive to the air.
All day
dust covered granite hills
and now
suddenly the Nile is flesh
an arm on a bed

In Indian miniatures
I cannot quite remember
what this hour means
– people were small,
animals represented
simply by dust
they stamped into the air.
All I recall of commentaries
are abrupt lovely sentences where
the colour of a bowl
a left foot stepping on a lotus
symbolized separation.
Or stories of gods
creating such beautiful women
they themselves burned in passion
and were reduced to ash.
Women confided to pet parrots
solitary men dreamed into the conch.
So many
graciously humiliated
by the distance of rivers

The boat turns languid
under the hunched passenger
sails
ready for the moon
fill like a lung

there is no longer
depth of perception
it is now possible
for the outline of two boats
to collide silently

THE PALACE

7 a.m.   The hour of red daylight

I walk through palace grounds
waking the sentries
                    scarves
around their neck and mouths
leak breath mist
The gibbons stroll
twenty feet high
through turret arches
and on the edge
of brown parapet
I am alone
            leaning
            into flying air

Ancient howls of a king
who released his aviary
like a wave to the city below
celebrating the day of his birth
and they when fed
would return to his hand
like the payment of grain

All over Rajasthan
palaces die young
                    at this height
                    a red wind
my shirt and sweater cold

From the white city below
a beautiful wail
of a woman's voice rises
300 street transistors
simultaneously playing
the one radio station of Udaipur

USWETAKEIYAWA

Uswetakeiyawa. The night mile

through the village of tall
thorn leaf fences
sudden odours
which pour through windows of the jeep.

We see nothing, just
the grey silver of the Dutch canal
where bright coloured boats
lap like masks in the night
their alphabets lost in the dark.

No sight but the imagination's
story behind each smell
or now and then a white sarong
pumping its legs on a bicycle
like a moth in the headlights

        and the dogs
who lean out of night
strolling the road
with eyes of sapphire
and hideous body
            so mongrelled
they seem to have woken
to find themselves tricked
into outrageous transformations,
one with the spine of a snake
one with a creature in its mouth
(car lights rouse them
from the purity of darkness).

This is the dream journey
we travel most nights
returning from Colombo.

The road hugs the canal
the canal every mile
puts an arm into the sea.

In daylight women bathe
waist deep beside the road
utterly still as I drive past
their diya reddha cloth
tied under their arms.
Brief sentences of women
lean men with soapy buttocks
their arms stretching up
to pour water over themselves,
or the ancient man in spectacles
crossing the canal
only his head visible
pulling something we cannot see
in the water behind him.
The women surface
bodies the colour of shadow
wet bright cloth
the skin of a mermaid.

In the silence of the night drive
you hear ocean you swallow odours
which change each minute – dried fish
swamp toddy a variety of curries
and something we have never been able to recognize.
There is just this thick air
and the aura of dogs
in trickster skin.

Once in the night we saw
something slip into the canal.
There was then the odour we did not recognize.
The smell of a dog losing its shape.

THE WARS

Dusk in Colombo

the Bo tree   dark all day
gathers the last of our light

and in its green rooms which yawn
over Pettah stores
is its own shadow
– hundreds of unseen bats
tuning up the auditorium
in archaic Tamil

Trincomalee
                    they whisper
is my brother
source of my exile
long slow miles to the scrub north
whose blossoms are dirty birds
so bright they are extracts of the sea

Swim
        into the north's blue eye
over the milk floor of ocean
that darkens only with depth

The Ray
flies in silence
muttering bubbles to himself
Tread over his avenue

The ancient warrior
whose brother
stole his operatic tongue

                    plunges

in pure muscle
towards his neighbours
bloodless   full
of noon moonlight

only his twin
knows how to charm
the waters against him

SWEET LIKE A CROW

for Hetti Corea, 8 years old

*'The Sinhalese are beyond a doubt one of the least musical
people in the world. It would be quite impossible to have
less sense of pitch, line or rhythm'* PAUL BOWLES

Your voice sounds like a scorpion being pushed
through a glass tube
like someone has just trod on a peacock
like wind howling in a coconut
like a rusty bible, like someone pulling barbed wire
across a stone courtyard, like a pig drowning,
a vattacka being fried
a bone shaking hands
a frog singing at Carnegie Hall.

Like a crow swimming in milk,
like a nose being hit by a mango
like the crowd at the Royal-Thomian match,
a womb full of twins, a pariah dog
with a magpie in its mouth
like the midnight jet from Casablanca
like Air Pakistan curry,
a typewriter on fire, like a hundred
pappadans being crunched, like someone
trying to light matches in a dark room,
the clicking sound of a reef when you put your head into the sea,
a dolphin reciting epic poetry to a sleepy audience,
the sound of a fan when someone throws brinjals at it,
like pineapples being sliced in the Pettah market
like betel juice hitting a butterfly in mid-air
like a whole village running naked onto the street
and tearing their sarongs, like an angry family
pushing a jeep out of the mud, like dirt on the needle,
like 8 sharks being carried on the back of a bicycle
like 3 old ladies locked in the lavatory
like the sound I heard when having an afternoon sleep
and someone walked through my room in ankle bracelets.

LATE MOVIES WITH SKYLER

All week since he's been home
he has watched late movies alone
terrible one star films and then staggering
through the dark house to his bed
waking at noon to work on the broken car
he has come home to fix.

21 years old and restless
back from logging on Vancouver Island
with men who get rid of crabs with Raid
2 minutes bending over in agony
and then into the showers!

Last night I joined him for *The Prisoner of Zenda*
a film I saw three times in my youth
and which no doubt influenced me morally.
Hot coffee bananas and cheese
we are ready at 11.30 for adventure.

At each commercial Sky
breaks into midnight guitar practice
head down playing loud and intensely
till the movie comes on and the music suddenly stops.
Skyler's favourite hours when he's usually alone
cooking huge meals of anything in the frying pan
thumbing through *Advanced Guitar* like a bible.
We talk during the film
and break into privacy during commercials
or get more coffee or push
the screen door open and urinate under the trees.

Laughing at the dilemmas of 1920 heroes
suggestive lines, cutaways to court officials
who raise their eyebrows at least 4 inches
when the lovers kiss . . .
only the anarchy of the evil Rupert of Hentzau
is appreciated.
                And still somehow
by 1.30 we are moved
as Stewart Granger girl-less and countryless
rides into the sunset with his morals and his horse.
The perfect world is over. Banana peels
orange peels ashtrays guitar books.
2 a.m. We stagger through
into the slow black rooms of the house.

I lie in bed fully awake. The darkness
breathes to the pace of a dog's snoring.
The film is replayed to sounds
of an intricate blues guitar.
Skyler is Rupert then the hero.
He will leave in a couple of days
for Montreal or the Maritimes.
In the movies of my childhood the heroes
after skilled swordplay and moral victories
leave with absolutely nothing
to do for the rest of their lives

SALLIE CHISUM/LAST WORDS
ON BILLY THE KID 4 A.M.

for Nancy Beatty

The moon hard and yellow where Billy's head is.
I have been moving in my room
these last 5 minutes. Looking for a cigarette.
That is a sin he taught me.
Showed me how to hold it and how to want it.

I had been looking and stepped forward
to feel along the windowsill
and there was the tanned moon head.
His body the shadow of the only tree on the property.

I am at the table.
Billy's mouth is trying
to remove a splinter out of my foot.
Tough skin on the bottom of me.
Still. I can feel his teeth
bite precise. And then moving his face back
holding something in his grin, says he's got it.

Where have you been I ask
Where have you been he replies

I have been into every room about 300 times
since you were here
I have walked about 60 miles in this house
Where have you been I ask

Billy was a fool
he was like those reversible mirrors
you can pivot round and see youself again
but there is something showing on the other side always.
Sunlight. The shade beside the cupboard.

He fired two bullets into the dummy
on which I built dresses
where the nipples should have been.
That wasn't too funny, but we laughed a lot.

One morning he was still sleeping
I pushed the door and watched him from the hall
he looked like he was having a serious dream.
Concentrating. Angry. As if wallpaper
had been ripped off a wall.

Billy's mouth at my foot
removing the splinter.
Did I say that?

It was just before lunch one day.

I have been alive
37 years since I knew him. He was a fool.
He was like those mirrors I told you about.

I am leaning against the bed rail
I have finished my cigarette
now I cannnot find the ashtray.
I put it out, squash it
against the window
where the moon is.
In his stupid eyes.

PURE MEMORY/CHRIS DEWDNEY

*'Listen, it was so savage and brutal and powerful
that even though it happened out of the blue I
knew there was nothing arbitrary about it'*

CHRISTOPHER DEWDNEY

I

On a B.C. radio show the man asked me, coffee half way up to
his mouth, what are the books you've liked recently? Christopher
Dewdney's *A Palaeozoic Geology of London Ontario*. Only I didn't say
that, I started stumbling on the word Palaeozoic . . . Paleo . . .
Polio . . . and then it happened on Geology too until it seemed a
disease. I sounded like an idiot. Meanwhile I was watching the
man's silent gulps. The professional silent gulping of coffee an
inch or two away from the microphone. Unconcerned with my
sinking 'live' all over the province.

2

I can't remember where I first met him. Somewhere I became
aware of this giggle. Tan hair, tan face, tan shirt and a giggle-
snort as his head staggered back. His arms somewhere.

3

The baby. He shows me the revolving globe in the 4-month-old
kid's crib. Only it has been unscrewed and the globe turned
upside down and rescrewed in that way so Africa and Asia all
swivel upside down. This way he says she'll have to come to
terms with the shapes all over again when she grows up.

642

4

He comes to dinner, steps out of the car and transforms the
10-year-old suburban garden into ancient history. Is on his knees
pointing out the age and race and character of rocks and earth.
He loves the Norfolk Pine. I give him a piece of wood 120 million
years old from the tar sands and he smokes a bit of it.

5

When he was a kid and his parents had guests and he was
eventually told to get to bed he liked to embarrass them by
running under a table and screaming out Don't hit me
Don't hit me.

6

His most embarrassing moment. A poetry reading in Toronto.
He was sitting in the front row and he realized that he hated the
poetry. He looked around discreetly for the exit but it was a long
way away. Then to the right, quite near him, he saw another door.
As a poem ended he got up and officially walked to the door
quickly opened it went out and closed it behind him. He found
himself in a dark cupboard about 2 feet by 3 feet. It contained
nothing. He waited there for a while, then he started to laugh and
giggle. He giggled for 5 minutes and he thinks the audience could
probably hear him. When he had collected himself he opened the
door, came out, walked to his seat and sat down again.

7

Coach House Press, December 1974. I haven't seen him for a
long time. His face is tough. Something has left his face. It is
not that he is thinner but the face has lost something distinct
and it seems like flesh. But he is not thinner. He is busy
working on his new book *Fovea Centralis* and I watch him as he

sits in the empty back room upstairs all alone with a computer
typesetting terminal. I can't get over his face. It is 'tight', as
if a stocking were over it and he about to perform a robbery.
He plucks at the keys and talks down into the machine. I am
relieved when he starts giggling at something. I tell him I'm
coming down to London in a week and he says he will show
me his butterflies, he has bought two mounted butterflies for a
very good price. If I don't tell anyone he will let me know where
I could get one. A Chinaman in London Ontario sells them. I
start to laugh. He doesn't. This is serious information,
important rare information like the history of rocks – these frail
wings of almost powder have their genealogies too.

8

His favourite movie is *Earthquake*. He stands in the middle of
his apartment very excited telling me all the details. He shows
me his beautiful fossils, a small poster of James Dean hitting
his brother in *East of Eden*, and the two very impressive
mounted butterflies.

9

On the bus going back to Toronto I have a drawing of him by
Robert Fones. Wrapped in brown paper it lies above me on the
luggage rack. When the bus swerves I put my arm out into the
dark aisle ready to catch him if it falls. A strange drawing of him
in his cane chair with a plant to the side of him, reading Frank
O'Hara with very oriental eyes. It was done in 1973, before the
flesh left his face.

10

His wife's brain haemorrhage. I could not cope with that.
He is 23 years old. He does. Africa Asia Australia upside down.
Earthquake.

BEARHUG

Griffin calls to come and kiss him goodnight
I yell ok. Finish something I'm doing,
then something else, walk slowly round
the corner to my son's room.
He is standing arms outstretched
waiting for a bearhug. Grinning.

Why do I give my emotion an animal's name,
give it that dark squeeze of death?
This is the hug which collects
all his small bones and his warm neck against me.
The thin tough body under the pyjamas
locks to me like a magnet of blood.

How long was he standing there
like that, before I came?

Elimination Dance
(an intermission)

'Nothing I'd read prepared me for a body this unfair'

JOHN NEWLOVE

'Till we be roten, kan we not be rypen'

GEOFFREY CHAUCER

Those who are allergic to the sea

Those who have resisted depravity

Men who shave off beards in stages, pausing to take photographs

American rock stars who wear Toronto Maple Leaf hockey sweaters

Those who (while visiting a foreign country) have lost the end of a Q tip in their ear and have been unable to explain their problem

Gentlemen who have placed a microphone beside a naked woman's stomach after lunch and later, after slowing down the sound considerably, have sold these noises on the open market as whale songs

All actors and poets who spit into the first row while they
perform

Men who fear to use an electric lawn-mower feeling they could
drowse off and be dragged by it into a swimming pool

Any dinner guest who has consumed the host's missing contact
lens along with the dessert

Any person who has had the following dream. You are in a
subway station of a major city. At the far end you see a coffee
machine. You put in two coins. The Holy Grail drops down.
Then blood pours into the chalice

Any person who has lost a urine sample in the mail

All those belle-lettrists who feel that should have been
'*an* urine sample'

Anyone who has had to step into an elevator with all of the Irish Rovers

Those who have filled in a bilingual and confidential pig survey from Statistics Canada. (Une enquête sur les porcs, strictement confidentielle)

Those who have written to the age old brotherhood of Rosicrucians for a free copy of their book 'The Mastery of Life' in order to release the inner consciousness and to experience (in the privacy of the home) momentary flights of the soul

Those who have accidently stapled themselves

Anyone who has been penetrated by a mountie

Any university professor who has danced with a life-sized cardboard cut-out of Jean Genet

Those who have unintentionally locked themselves within a
sleeping bag at a camping goods store

Any woman whose i.u.d. has set off an alarm system
at the airport

Those who, after a swim, find the sensation of water dribbling
out of their ears erotic

Men who have never touched a whippet

Women who gave up the accordion because of pinched breasts

Those who have pissed out of the back of moving trucks

Those who have woken to find the wet footprints of a peacock across their kitchen floor

Anyone whose knees have been ruined as a result of performing sexual acts in elevators

Those who have so much as contemplated the possibility of creeping up to one's enemy with two Bic lighters, pressing simultaneously the butane switches – one into each nostril – and so gassing him to death

Literary critics who have swum the Hellespont

Anyone who has been hired as a 'professional beater' and frightened grouse in the direction of the Queen Mother

Any lover who has gone into a flower shop on Valentine's Day and asked for clitoris when he meant clematis

Those who have come across their own telephone numbers underneath terse insults or compliments in the washroom of the Bay Street Bus Terminal

Those who have used the following techniques of seduction:
  -small talk at a falconry convention
  -entering a spa town disguised as Ford Madox Ford
  -making erotic rotations of the pelvis, backstage, during the storm scene of *King Lear*
  -underlining suggestive phrases in the prefaces of Joseph Conrad

Anyone who has testified as a character witness for a dog in a court of law

Any writer who has been photographed for the jacket of a book in one of the following poses: sitting in the back of a 1956 Dodge with two roosters; in a tuxedo with the Sydney Opera House in the distance; studying the vanishing point on a jar of Dutch Cleanser; against a gravestone with dramatic back lighting; with a false nose on; in the vicinity of Macchu Pichu; or sitting in a study and looking intensely at one's own book

The person who borrowed my Martin Beck thriller, read it in
a sauna which melted the glue off the spine so the pages drifted
to the floor, stapled them together and returned the book,
thinking I wouldn't notice

Any person who has burst into tears at the Liquor Control
Board

Anyone with pain

Secular Love

'You're an actor, aren't you?'

The man nodded silently and averted his eyes.

'I've seen you in films. You always seem embarrassed at the thought of what you have to say next.'

The man laughed and again averted his eyes.

'Your trouble, I believe, is that you always hold back something of yourself. You're not shameless enough for an actor. In my opinion you should learn how to run properly and scream properly, with your mouth wide open. I've noticed that even when you yawn you're afraid to open your mouth all the way. In your next film make a sign to show that you've understood me. You haven't even been discovered yet. I'm looking forward to seeing you grow older from film to film.'

PETER HANDKE The left-handed woman

Claude Glass

*A somewhat convex dark or coloured hand-mirror, used to
concentrate the features of the landscape in subdued tones.*
    *'Grey walked about everywhere with that pretty toy, the claude glass,
in his hand, making the beautiful forms of the landscape compose in its
luscious chiaroscuro.' Gosse* (1882)

He is told about
the previous evening's behaviour.

Starting with a punchbowl
on the volleyball court.
Dancing and falling across coffee tables,
asking his son Are *you* the bastard
who keeps telling me I'm drunk?
kissing the limbs of women
suspicious of his friends serenading
five pigs by the barn
heaving a wine glass towards garden
and continually going through gates
into the dark fields
and collapsing.
His wife half carrying him home
rescuing him from departing cars,
complains this morning
of a sore shoulder.
                              And even later
his thirteen-year-old daughter's struggle
to lift him into the back kitchen
after he has passed out, resting his head on rocks,
wondering what he was looking for in dark fields.

For he has always loved that ancient darkness
where the flat rocks glide like Japanese tables
where he can remove clothes
and lie with moonlight on the day's heat
hardened in stone, drowning
in this star blanket this sky
like a giant trout

conscious how the heaven
careens over him
as he moves in back fields
kissing the limbs of trees
or placing ear on stone which rocks him
and then stands to watch the house
in its oasis of light.
And he knows something is happening there to him
solitary while he spreads his arms
and holds everything that is slipping away together.

He is suddenly in the heat of the party
slouching towards women, revolving
round one unhappy shadow.
That friend who said he would find
the darkest place, and then wave.
He is not a lost drunk
like his father or his friend, can,
he says, stop on a dime, and he can
he could because even now, now in
this brilliant darkness where
grass has lost its colour and it's all
fucking Yeats and moonlight, he knows
this colourless grass is making his bare feet green
for it is the hour of magic
which no matter what sadness
leaves him grinning.
At certain hours of the night
ducks are nothing but landscape
just voices breaking as they nightmare.
The weasel wears their blood
home like a scarf,
cows drain over the horizon
                              and the dark
vegetables hum onward underground

but the mouth
        wants plum.

Moves from room to room
where brown beer glass
smashed lounges at his feet
opens the long rust stained gate
and steps towards invisible fields
that he knows from years of daylight.
He snorts in the breeze
which carries a smell
of cattle on its back.

What this place does not have
is the white paint of bathing cabins
the leak of eucalyptus.
During a full moon
outcrops of rock shine
skunks spray abstract into the air
cows burp as if practising
the name of Francis Ponge.
His drunk state wants the mesh of place.
Ludwig of Bavaria's Roof Garden—
glass plants, iron parrots
Venus Grottos, tarpaulins of Himalaya.
By the kitchen sink he tells someone
from now on I will drink only landscapes
– here, pour me a cup of Spain.

Opens the gate and stumbles
blood like a cassette through the body
away from the lights, unbuttoning,
this desire to be riverman.

Tentatively
            he recalls
his drunk invitation to the river.
He has steered the awesome car
past sugarbush to the blue night water

and steps out
speaking to branches
and the gulp of toads.
Subtle applause of animals.
A snake leaves a path
like temporary fossil.
                    He falls
back onto the intricacies
of gearshift and steering wheel
alive as his left arm
which now departs out of the window
trying to tug passing sumac
pine   bush   tamarack
into the car
              to the party.
Drunkenness opens his arms like a gate
and over the car invisible insects
ascend out of the beams like meteorite
crushed dust of the moon
 . . . he waits for the magic star called Lorca.

On the front lawn a sheet
tacked across a horizontal branch.
A projector starts a parade
of journeys, landscapes, relatives,
friends leaping out within pebbles of water
caught by the machine as if creating rain.

Later when wind frees the sheet
and it collapses like powder in the grass
pictures fly without target
and howl their colours over Southern Ontario
clothing burdock
rhubarb a floating duck.
Landscapes and stories
flung into branches
and the dog walks under the hover of the swing
beam of the projection bursting in his left eye.

The falling sheet the star of Lorca swoops
someone gets up and heaves his glass
into the vegetable patch
towards the slow stupid career of beans.

This is the hour
when dead men sit
and write each other.
            'Concerning the words we never said
            during morning hours of the party
            there was glass under my bare feet
            laws of the kitchen were broken
            and each word moved
            in my mouth like muscle . . . '

This is the hour for sudden journeying.
            Cervantes accepts
a 17th Century invitation
from the Chinese Emperor.
Schools of Chinese-Spanish Linguistics!
Rivers of the world meet!
And here
ducks dressed in Asia
pivot on foreign waters.

At 4 a.m. he wakes in the sheet
that earlier held tropics in its whiteness.
The invited river flows through the house
into the kitchen up
stairs, he awakens and moves within it.
In the dim light
he sees the turkish carpet under water,
low stools, glint
of piano pedals, even a sleeping dog
whose dreams may be of rain.

It is a river he has walked elsewhere
now visiting moving with him at the hip
to kitchen where a friend sleeps in a chair
head on the table his grip
still round a glass, legs underwater.

He wants to relax
and give in to the night
fall horizontal and swim
to the back kitchen where his daughter sleeps.
He wishes to swim
to each of his family and gaze
at their underwater dreaming
this magic chain of bubbles.
Wife, son, household guests, all
comfortable in clean river water.

He is aware that for hours
there has been no conversation,
tongues have slid to stupidity on alcohol
sleeping mouths are photographs of yells.

He stands waiting, the sentinel,
shambling back and forth, his anger
and desire against the dark
which, if he closes his eyes,
will lose them all.

                The oven light
shines up through water at him
a bathysphere   a ghost ship
and in the half drowned room

the crickets like small pins
begin to tack down
the black canvas of this night,
begin to talk their hesitant
gnarled epigrams to each other
across the room.
                    Creak and echo.
Creak and echo. With absolute clarity
he knows where he is.

Tin Roof

She hesitated. 'Are you being romantic now?'
'I'm trying to tell you how I feel without
exposing myself. You know what I mean?'

ELMORE LEONARD

*

You stand still for three days
for a piece of wisdom
and everything falls to the right place

or wrong place

          You speak
       don't know whether
seraph or bitch
flutters at your heart

and look through windows
for cue cards
blazing in the sky.
            The solution.
This last year I was sure
I was going to die

*

The geography of this room   I know so well
tonight   I could rise in the dark
sit at the table   and write without light.
I am here in the country of warm rains.
A small cabin – a glass, wood,
tin bucket on the Pacific Rim.

        Geckoes climb
the window to peer in,
and all day the tirade pale blue waves
touch the black shore of volcanic rock

and fall to pieces here

*

How to arrive at this
drowning
on the edge of sea

       (How to drive
the Hana Road, he said—
one hand on the beer
one hand on your thigh
and one eye for the road)

Waves leap to this cliff all day
and in the evening lose
their pale blue

he rises from the bed
as wind from three directions
falls, takes his place
on the peninsula of sheets
which also loses colour

stands in the loose green kimono
by a large window and gazes

through gecko
past the deadfall
into sea,

      the unknown magic he loves
throws himself into

           the blue heart

*

Tell me
all you know
about bamboo

growing wild, green
growing up into soft arches
in the temple ground

the traditions

driven through hands
through the heart
during torture

and most of all

                    this

small bamboo pipe
not quite horizontal
that drips
every ten seconds
to a shallow bowl

I love this
being here
not a word
just the faint
fall of liquid
the boom of an iron buddhist bell
in the heart rapid
as ceremonial bamboo

*

A man buying wine
Rainier beer at the store
would he be satisfied with this?
Cold showers, electric skillet,
Red River on tv
Oh he could be

(Do you want
                to be happy and write?)

He happens to love the stark
luxury of this place
– no armchairs, a fridge of beer and mangoes

        Precipitation.

To avoid a story   The refusal to move

All our narratives of sleep
a mild rumble to those inland

            Illicit pockets of
            the kimono

Heart like a sleeve

*

The cabin
        its tin roof
a wind run radio
catches the noise of the world.
He focuses on the gecko
almost transparent body
how he feels now
everything passing through him like light.
In certain mirrors
he cannot see himself at all.
He is joyous and breaking down.
The tug over the cliff.
What protects him
is the warmth in the sleeve

that is all, really

*

We go to the stark places of the earth
and find moral questions everywhere

Will John Wayne and Montgomery Clift
take their cattle to Missouri or Kansas?

Tonight I lean over the Pacific
and its blue wild silk
ringed by creatures
who
    tchick tchick tchick
my sudden movement
who say nothing else.

There are those who are in
and there are those who look in

Tiny leather toes
hug the glass

*

On the porch
thin ceramic
chimes

      ride wind
off the Pacific

bells of the sea

      I do not know
the name of large orange flowers
which thrive on salt air
lean half drunk
against the steps

Untidy banana trees
thick moss on the cliff
and then the plunge
to black volcanic shore

It is impossible to enter the sea here
except in a violent way

      How we have moved
from thin ceramic

to such destruction

*

All night
            the touch

of wave on volcano.

There was the woman
who clutched my hair
like a shaken child.
The radio whistles
round a lost wave length.

All night slack-key music
and the bird whistling *duino*
duino, words and music
entangled in pebble
ocean static.
The wild sea and her civilization
the League of the Divine Wind
and traditions of death.

            Remember
those women in movies
who wept into the hair
of their dead men?

*

Going up stairs
I hang my shirt
on the stiff
ear of an antelope

Above the bed
        memory
restless green bamboo
        the distant army
assembles wooden spears

her feet braced
on the ceiling
sea in the eye

Reading the article
an 1825 report *Physiologie du Gout*
on the artificial growing of truffles
speaks
        of 'vain efforts
and deceitful promises,'
commandments of culinary art

Good
morning to your body
hello nipple
and appendix scar like a letter
of too much passion
from a mad Mexican doctor

All this noise at your neck!

heart clapping
like green bamboo

       this earring
   which
has flipped over
   and falls
      into the pool of your ear

The waves against black stone
that was a thousand year old
burning red river
could not reach us

*

Cabin

'hana'

       this *flower* of wood
in which we rose
out of the blue sheets
you thin as horizon
reaching for lamp or book
my shirt

       hungry
for everything about the other

here we steal places to stay
as we steal time
       never too proud to beg,
even if we never
see the other's grin and star again

there is nothing resigned
in this briefness
we swallow complete

I will know everything here

       this cup
         balanced on my chest
       my eye witnessing the petal
       drop away from its order,
       your arm

for ever

precarious in all our fury

Every place has its own wisdom. Come.
Time we talked about the sea,
the long waves
                    'trapped around islands'

*

There are maps now whose portraits
have nothing to do with surface

Remember the angels, floating compasses
– Portolan atlases so complex
we looked down and never knew
which was earth which was sea?
The way birds the colour of prairie
confused by the sky
flew into the earth
(Remember those women
who claimed dead miners
the colour of the coal they drowned in)

The bathymetric maps startle.
Visions of the ocean floor
troughs, naked blue deserts,
Ganges Cone, the Mascarene Basin

so one is able now
in ideal situations
to plot a stroll
to new continents
'doing the Berryman walk'

And beneath the sea
there are
these giant scratches
of pain
the markings of
some perfect animal
who has descended
burying itself
under the glossy
ballroom

or they have to do with ascending,
what we were, the earth creatures
longing for horizon.
I know one thing
our sure non-sliding
civilized feet
our small leather shoes
did not make them

(Ah you should be happy and write)

I want the passion
which puts your feet on the ceiling
this fist
to smash forward

take this silk
          somehow *Ah*
out of the rooms of poetry

(Listen, solitude, X wrote,
is not an absolute,
it is just a resting place)

listen   in the end
the pivot from angel to witch
depends on small things
this animal, the question
are you happy?

No I am not happy

lucky though

*

Rainy Night Talk

Here's to
the overlooked
nipples of Spain
　　　brown Madrid aureoles
kneecaps of Ohio girls
kneeling in the palms of men
waiting to be thrown high
into the clouds
of a football stadium

Here's to
the long legged
woman from Kansas
whispering good morning at 5,
　　　dazed
in balcony moonlight

All that drizzle the night before
walking walking through the rain
slam her car door
and wrote my hunger out, the balcony
like an entrance
to a city of suicides.

Here's to the long legs
driving home
in more and more rain
weaving like a one-sided
lonely conversation
over the mountains

And what were you
carrying? in your head
that night Miss
Souri? Miss Kansas?

while I put my hands
sweating
on the cold
window
on the edge
of the trough of this city?

*

Breaking down after logical rules
couldn't be the hit and run driver
I wanted Frank Sinatra
I was thinking blue pyjamas
I was brought up on movies and song!

I could write my suite of poems
for Bogart   drunk
six months after the departure at Casablanca.
I see him lying under the fan
at the Slavyansky Bazar Hotel
and soon he will see the truth
the stupidity of his gesture
he'll see it in the space
between the whirling metal

          Stupid fucker
he says to himself, stupid fucker
and knocks the bottle
leaning against his bare stomach
onto the sheet. Gin stems
out like a four leaf clover.
I used to be lucky he says
I had white suits black friends
who played the piano . . .
                    and that
was a movie I saw just once.

What about Burt Lancaster
limping away at the end of *Trapeze*?
Born in 1943. And I saw that six times.
(I grew up knowing I could never fly)

That's me. You. Educated
at the *Bijou*. And don't ask me
about my interpretation of 'Madame George.'
That's a nine minute song
a two hour story

So how do we discuss
the education of our children?
Teach them to be romantics
to veer towards the sentimental?
Toss them into the air like Tony Curtis
and make 'em do the triple somersault
through all these complexities
and commandments?

*

Oh, Rilke, I want to sit down calm like you
or pace the castle, avoiding the path of the cook, Carlo,
who believes down to his turnip soup
that you speak in the voice of the devil.
I want the long lines my friend spoke of
that bamboo which sways muttering
like wooden teeth in the slim volume I have
with its childlike drawing of Duino Castle.
I have circled your book for years
like a wave combing
the green hair of the sea
kept it with me, your name
a password in the alley.
I always wanted poetry to be that
but this solitude brings no wisdom
just two day old food in the fridge,
certain habits you would not approve of.
If I said all of your name now
it would be the movement
of the tide you soared over
so your private angel
could become part of a map.

I am too often busy with things
I wish to get away from, and I want
the line to move slowly now, slow
-ly like a careful drunk across the street
no cars in the vicinity
but in his fearful imagination.
How can I link your flowing name
to geckoes or a slice of octopus?
Though there are Rainier beer cans,
magically, on the windowsill.

And still your lovely letters
January 1912 near Trieste.
The car you were driven in
'at a snail's pace'
through Provence. Wanting
'to go into chrysalis . . .
to live by the heart and nothing else.'
Or your guilt—
              'I howl at the moon
              with all my heart
              and put the blame
              on the dogs'

I can see you sitting down
the suspicious cook asleep
so it is just you
and the machinery of the night
that foul beast that sucks and drains
leaping over us sweeping our determination
away with its tail. Us and the coffee,
all the small charms we invade it with.

As at midnight we remember the colour
of the dogwood flower growing
like a woman's sex outside the window.
I wanted poetry to be walnuts
in their green cases
but now it is the sea
and we let it drown us,
and we fly to it released
by giant catapults
of pain loneliness deceit and vanity

Rock Bottom

O lady hear me. I have no

other
voice left.

ROBERT CREELEY

*

2 a.m.   The moonlight
in the kitchen

Will this be
testamentum porcelli?
Unblemished art and truth
whole hog   the pig's testament
what I know of passion
having written of it
seen my dog shiver
with love and disappear
crazy into trees

                    I want

the woman whose face
I could not believe in the moonlight
her mouth forever as horizon

                    and both of us
grim with situation

now
suddenly
we reside
near the delicate
heart
of Billie Holiday

*

You said, this
doesn't happen so quick
I must remind you of someone

        No,
though I am seduced
by this light, and
frantic arguments
on the porch,
I ain't subtle
you run rings
round me

       but this quietness
white dress   long legs
arguing your body
away from me

and I with all the hunger
I didn't know I had

* *(Inner Tube)*

On the warm July river
head back

upside down river
for a roof

slowly paddling
towards an estuary between trees

there's a dog
learning to swim near me
friends on shore

my head
dips
back to the eyebrow
I'm the prow
on an ancient vessel,
this afternoon
I'm going down to Peru
soul between my teeth

a blue heron
with its awkward
broken backed flap
upside down

one of us is wrong

he
in his blue grey thud
thinking he knows
the blue way
out of here

or me

Summer night came out of the water
climbed into my car and drove home
got out of the car still wet towel round me
opened the gate and walked to the house

Disintegration of the spirit
no stars
leaf being eaten by moonlight

The small creatures who are blind
who travel with the aid
of petite white horns
take over the world

Sound of a moth

The screen door in its suspicion
allows nothing in, as I allow nothing in.
The raspberries my son gave me
wild, cold out of the fridge, a few I put
in my mouth, some in my shirt pocket
and forgot

I sit here
in a half dark kitchen
the stain at my heart
caused by this gift

(Saturday)

The three trunks
of the walnut

the ceremonial ducks
who limbo under the fence
and creep up the lawn

Apple tree   Blue and white house
I know this is beautiful

I wished to write today
about small things
that might persuade me
out of my want

The lines I read
about 'cowardice' and 'loyalty'
I don't know
if this is drowning
or coming up for air

              At night
I give you my hand
like a corpse
out of the water

* *(Insomnia)*

Night and its forces
step through the picket gate
from the blue bush
to the kitchen

Everywhere it moves
and we cannot sleep we cannot sleep
we damn the missionaries
their morals thin as stars
we find ourselves
within the black
circus of the fly
all night long
his sandpaper
tabasco leg

The dog sleepwalks
into the cupboard
into the garden and heart attacks
hello
I've had a dog dream
wake up and cannot find
my long ears

Nicotine   caffeine
hungry bodies
could put us to sleep
but nothing puts us to sleep

*

How many windows have I broken?
And doors and lamps, and last month
a tumbler I smashed into a desk

then stood over the sink
digging out splinters
with an awkward left hand
I have beaten my head with stones
pieces of fence
tried to tear out my eyes
these are not exaggerations
they were acts when words failed
the way surgeons
hammer hearts gone still

now this
small parallel pain
in my finger
the invisible thing inside
circling
          glass
          on its voyage out
          to the heart

* *(After Che-King, 11th Century* BC)

If you love me and think only of me
lift your robe and ford the river Chen

catch
      'the floating world'
8.52 from Chicago

lift your skirt
through customs,

kiss me in the parking lot

('La Belle Romance')

Another deep night
with the National Enquirer

silence

like the unseen
arms of a bat

the book
falls open
to sadness
– dead flowers, dead
horses who carried
lovers to a meeting

On my last walk
through the kitchen
I see it

      I lift
huge arms of a cobweb
out of the air
and carry its Y
slowly to the porch
as if alive

as if it was a wounded bird
or some terrible camouflaged insect
that could damage children

*

The distance between us
and then this small map
of stars
          a concentrated
ocean of the night

when lovers worship heavens
they are worshipping
a lack of distance

my brother the moon
the lofty mattress
of nebula,
rash and spray of love

          It is all
as close as my palm
on your body

                    so you
among pillows and moonlight
look up, search
for the jewellery
bathing in darkness

satellite hunger, remote control,
'the royal we'

               and find
your own dark hand

*

What were the names of the towns
we drove into and through

    stunned lost

having drunk our way
up vineyards
and then Hot Springs
boiling out the drunkenness

What were the names
I slept through
   my head
on your thigh
hundreds of miles
of blackness entering the car

    All this
    darkness and stars
but now
under the Napa Valley night
a star arch of dashboard
the ripe grape moon
we are together
and I love this muscle

I love this muscle
that tenses

    and joins
the accelerator
to my cheek

And sometimes
I think
women in novels are too
controlled by the adverb.
As they depart
a perfume of description

'She rose from the table
and left her shoe
behind, *casually*'

'Let's keep our minds
clear, she said drunkenly,'
the print hardly dry
on words like that

My problem tonight
is this landscape.
Like the sanskrit lover
who sees breasts in the high clouds,
testicles on the riverbed
('The soldiers left their balls
behind, crossing into Bangalore
she said, mournfully')

Every leaf bends
I can put my hand
into various hollows, the dogs
lick their way up the ditch
swallow the scent
of whatever they eat

Always wanted to own
a movie theatre
called 'The Moonlight'

What's playing at *The Moonlight*
she asked
leafily

Men never trail away.
They sweat adjective.
'She fell into
his unexpected arms.'
He mixes a 'devious' drink.
He spills his maddened seed
onto the lettuce—

(Real life)

In real life
men talk about art
women judge men

In the Queen Street tavern
3 p.m. the only one busy
is the waitress
who reads a book a day

Hour of the afternoon soaps

Accusations
which hide the trap
door of tomorrow's guilt.
Men bursting into bedrooms
out of restaurants.
Everyone talks on phones
to the lover's brother
or the husband's mistress

My second beer
my fifth cigarette
the only thing more
confusing venomous
than real life
is this hour of the soaps
where nobody smokes
and nobody talks about art

I've woken in thick
households
all my life
but can nightmare myself
into this future—
last spring I sat here
Sunday Morning
as bachelor drunks
came in, eyes
in prayer to the Billy Graham Show

The pastel bar
grey colours of the tv
this is where people come
after the second failure of redemption

Ramon Fernandez,
                        tell me
what port you
bought that tattoo

Midnight dinner at the *Vesta Lunch*

Here there is nothing
I have taken from you
so I begin with memory
as old songs do

                in this café
against the night

in this villa refrain
where we collect the fragment
no longer near us
to make ourselves whole

             your bright eyes
in a greek bar, the way
you wear your hat

*

I have always
been afflicted
by angular
small breasted
women
from the mid-west,

knew this was true
the minute I met you

*

Repetition of midnight
Every creature doth sleep
But us

and the fanatics

      I want
the roulette of the lightning bolt
to decide all

On this suburban street
the skate-boarder rolls
surrounded by the seeming
hiss of electricity
               unlit
I see him through the trees
up Ptarmigan
         a thick sweater
for the late September night

I am unable to make anything of this
who are these words for

Even the dog
curls away
into himself
the only one to know your name

*

I write about you
as if I own you
which I do not.
As you can say of nothing
this is mine.

When we rise
the last hug
no longer belongs,
is your fiction
or my story.
Mulch for the future.

Whether we pass
through each other
like pure arrows
or fade into rumour
I write down now
a fiction of your arm

or of that afternoon
in Union Station
when we both were lost
pain falling free
the speed of tears
under the Grand Rotunda
as we disappeared
rose from each other

you and your arrow
taking just
what you fled through

*   (*'I want to be lifted up by some great*
    white bird unknown to the police . . . ')

I will never let a chicken
into my life
but I have let you
though you squeezed in
through a screen door
the way some chickens do

I would never let chickens
influence my character
but like them good sense
scatters at your entrance
– 'poetic skill,' 'duty,'
under the fence

Your lean shoulders
studied with greyhounds.
Such ball and socket joints
I've seen only in diagrams
on the cover of *Scientific American.*
I've let greyhounds
into my vicinity
– noses, paws, ribcages
against my arm, I admit
a weakness
for reluctant modesty.
I could spend days lying on the ground
seeing the world with the perspective of snails
stumbling the small territory of obsessions
this leaf and grain of you,
could attempt the epic
journey over your shoulder.

When you were a hotel gypsy
delirious by windows
waving your arms
and singing over the parking lots
I learned from the foolish oyster
and stepped out.
So here I am
saying see this
look what I found
when I opened myself up
before death before the world,
look at this blue eye
this socket in her waving arm
these wonders.

In the night busy as snails
in wet chlorophyll apartments
we enter each other's shells
the way humans at such times
wish to enter mouths of lovers,

sleeping like the rumour of pearl
in the embrace of oyster.

I have never let spectacles into my life
and now I am walking past
where I could see.
Here,
        where the horizon was

* *(The desire under the Elms Motel)*

how I attempted seduction
with a select and
careful playing of
The McGarrigle Sisters

how you seduced me
stereophonically   the laugh

the nose   ankle   nature

     repartee   the knee

your sad determination   letters

the earring

          that falls

          'hey love—

          you forgot your glove'

*

Speaking to you
this hour
these days when
I have lost the feather of poetry
and the rains
of separation
surround us tock
tock like *Go* tablets

Everyone has learned
to move carefully

'Dancing' 'laughing' 'bad taste'
is a memory
a tableau behind trees of law

In the midst of love for you
my wife's suffering
anger in every direction
and the children wise
as tough shrubs
but they are not tough
– so I fear
how anything can grow from this

all the wise blood
poured from little cuts
down into the sink

this hour it is not
your body I want
but your quiet company

*

Dentists disguise their own bad teeth
barbers go bald, foolish birds
travel to one particular tree.
They pride themselves
on focus.
Poets cannot spell.
Everyone claims abstinence.

Reading Neruda to a class
reading his lovely old
curiosity about all things
I am told this is the first time
in months I seem happy.
Jealous of his slide
through complexity.
All afternoon I keep
stepping into his pocket

                whispering
instruct and delight me

* (These back alleys)

for Daphne

In '64 you moved
and where was I?
– somewhere and married.
(In '64 everybody got married)

Whatever we are now we were then.
Some days those maps collide
falling into future land.
It seems for hours
we have sat in your car,
almost valentine's day,
I've got a plane to meet and I
hold your rose for you.
This talking
like a slow dance,
the sharing of earphones.

Since I got separated
I cannot hold
my brain in my arms anymore.
Sitting in the back alley
this new mapping, hello
to the terra nova.
Now we watch each other
in our slow walks towards
and out of everything
we wanted to know in '64

*

And for George moonlight
became her. Curious. After years of wit
he saw it enter her and believed,
singing love songs in the back seat.

Three of us drive downtown
in our confusions

goodbye to the hills of the 30's

Sinned, torn apart, how do each of us
share our hearts

and George still 'hearty,' bad jokes
scattering to the group,
does not converse, but he sings the heartbreakers
badly and precisely in the back seat

so we moon, we tough

*

Kissing the stomach
kissing your scarred
skin boat. History
is what you've travelled on
and take with you

We've each had our stomachs
kissed by strangers
to the other

and as for me
I bless everyone
who kissed you here

(Ends of the Earth)

For you I have slept
like an arrow in the hall
pointing towards your wakefulness
in other time zones

And wary
piece by piece
we put each other together
your past
that of one who has walked
through fifteen strange houses
in order to be here

the charm of Wichita
gunmen in your bones
the 19th century
strolling like a storm
through your long body

that history I read in comic books
and on the flickering screen
when I was thirteen

Now we are cats-cradled
in the Pacific
how does one avoid this?
Go to the ends of the earth?
The loose moon follows

Wet moonlight
recalls childhood

the long legged daughter
            the stars
of Wichita in the distance

midnight and hugging
against her small chest
the favourite book,
Goodnight Moon

under the covers she
reads its courtly order
its list of farewells
to everything

                We grow less complex
We reduce ourselves   The way lovers
have their small cheap charms
silver lizard,
a stone

Ancient customs
that grow from dust
                swirled out
from prairie into tropic

Strange how the odours meet

How, however briefly, bedraggled
history
        focuses

Skin Boat

'A sheet of water near your breasts
where I can sink
like a stone'

PAUL ELUARD

HER HOUSE

Because she has lived alone, her house is the product of nothing but herself and necessity. The necessity of growing older and raising children. Others drifted into her life, in and out and they have changed her, added things, but I have never been into a home that is a revelation of character and time as much as hers. It contains those she knows and has known and she has distilled all of her journey. When I first met her I saw nothing but her, and now, as she becomes familiar, I recognize the small customs.

The problem for her is leaving. She says, 'Last night I was listening to everything I know so well, and I imagined what if I woke up in a year's time and there were different trees.' Streets, the weight of sea air, certain birds who recognize your shrubbery, that too holds you, allows a freedom of habit, is a house.

Everything here is alien to me but you. And your room like a grey well, your coat hangers above the laundry machine where you hang the semi-damp clothes so you do not have to iron them, the green grey walls of wood, the secret drawer which you opened after you knew me two years to show me the ancient Japanese pens. All this I love. Though I carry my own landscape in me and my three bags. But this has become your skin, and as you leave you recognize this.

On certain evenings, when I have not bothered to put on lights, I hit my knees on low bookcases where they should not be. But you shift your hip easily, habitually, around them as you pass by carrying laundry or books. When you can move through a house blindfolded it belongs to you. You are moving like blood calmly within your own body. It is only recently that I am able to wake beside you and without looking, almost in a dream, put out my hand and know exactly where your shoulder or your heart will be – you in your specific posture in this bed of yours that we share. And at times this has seemed to be knowledge. As if you were a blueprint of your house.

THE CINNAMON PEELER

If I were a cinnamon peeler
I would ride your bed
and leave the yellow bark dust
on your pillow.

Your breasts and shoulders would reek
you could never walk through markets
without the profession of my fingers
floating over you. The blind would
stumble certain of whom they approached
though you might bathe
under rain gutters, monsoon.

Here on the upper thigh
at this smooth pasture
neighbour to your hair
or the crease
that cuts your back. This ankle.
You will be known among strangers
as the cinnamon peeler's wife.

I could hardly glance at you
before marriage
never touch you
– your keen nosed mother, your rough brothers.
I buried my hands
in saffron, disguised them
over smoking tar,
helped the honey gatherers . . .

When we swam once
I touched you in water
and our bodies remained free,
you could hold me and be blind of smell.
You climbed the bank and said

                    this is how you touch other women
the grass cutter's wife, the lime burner's daughter.
And you searched your arms
for the missing perfume

                    and knew

                    what good is it
to be the lime burner's daughter
left with no trace
as if not spoken to in the act of love
as if wounded without the pleasure of a scar.

You touched
your belly to my hands
in the dry air and said
I am the cinnamon
peeler's wife. Smell me.

WOMEN LIKE YOU

the communal poem – Sigiri Graffiti, 5th century

They do not stir
these ladies of the mountain
do not give us
the twitch of eyelids

         The king is dead

They answer no one
take the hard
rock as lover.
Women like you
make men pour out their hearts

             'Seeing you I want
             no other life'

             'The golden skins have
             caught my mind'

who came here
out of the bleached land
climbed this fortress
to adore the rock
and with the solitude of the air
behind them
         carved an alphabet
whose motive was perfect desire

wanting these portraits of women
to speak
and caress

Hundreds of small verses
by different hands
became one
habit of the unrequited

Seeing you
I want no other life
and turn around
to the sky
and everywhere below
jungle, waves of heat
secular love

Holding the new flowers
a circle of
first finger and thumb
which is a window

to your breast

pleasure of the skin
earring   earring
curl
of the belly
                and then
stone mermaid
stone heart
dry as a flower
on rock
you long eyed women

the golden
drunk swan breasts
lips
the long long eyes

we stand against the sky

I bring you

a flute
from the throat
of a loon

so talk to me
of the used heart

THE RIVER NEIGHBOUR

All these rumours. You lodge in the mountains
of Hang-chou, a cabin in Portland township,
or in Yüeh-chou for sure

the dust from my marriage
wasted our clear autumn

This month the cactus
under the rains

while you lounge with my children
by the creek snakes, the field asparagus

Across the universe
each room I lit
was a dark garden, I held
nothing but the lamp

this letter paints me
transparent as I am

One dead bird in the hall
conversation of the water-closets
company of the leaf on the stairs

I pass her often

Moon   leaf   memory of asparagus
I find her earrings
at the foot of curtainless windows
In the kitchen
salt fills the body
of an RCA Victor dog

Let us nose our way
next year with the spring waters
and search for each other
somewhere in the east

TO A SAD DAUGHTER

All night long the hockey pictures
gaze down at you
sleeping in your tracksuit.
Belligerent goalies are your ideal.
Threats of being traded
cuts and wounds
– all this pleases you.
O my god! you say at breakfast
reading the sports page over the Alpen
as another player breaks his ankle
or assaults the coach.

When I thought of daughters
I wasn't expecting this
but I like this more.
I like all your faults
even your purple moods
when you retreat from everyone
to sit in bed under a quilt.
And when I say 'like'
I mean of course 'love'
but that embarrasses you.
You who feel superior to black and white movies
(coaxed for hours to see *Casablanca*)
though you were moved
by *Creature from the Black Lagoon*.

One day I'll come swimming
beside your ship or someone will
and if you hear the siren
listen to it. For if you close your ears
only nothing happens. You will never change.

I don't care if you risk
your life to angry goalies
creatures with webbed feet.
You can enter their caves and castles
their glass laboratories. Just
don't be fooled by anyone but yourself.

This is the first lecture I've given you.
You're 'sweet sixteen' you said.
I'd rather be your closest friend
than your father. I'm not good at advice
you know that, but ride
the ceremonies
until they grow dark.

Sometimes you are so busy
discovering your friends
I ache with a loss
– but that is greed.
And sometimes I've gone
into *my* purple world
and lost you.

One afternoon I stepped
into your room. You were sitting
at the desk where I now write this.
Forsythia outside the window
and sun spilled over you
like a thick yellow miracle
as if another planet
was coaxing you out of the house
– all those possible worlds! –
and you, meanwhile, busy with mathematics.

I cannot look at forsythia now
without loss, or joy for you.
You step delicately
into the wild world
and your real prize will be
the frantic search.
Want everything. If you break
break going out not in.
How you live your life I don't care
but I'll sell my arms for you,
hold your secrets for ever.

If I speak of death
which you fear now, greatly,
it is without answers,
except that each
one we know is
in our blood.
Don't recall graves.
Memory is permanent.
Remember the afternoon's
yellow suburban annunciation.
Your goalie
in his frightening mask
dreams perhaps
of gentleness.

ALL ALONG THE MAZINAW

Later the osprey

falling towards
only what he sees

the messenger heron
warning of our progress
up Mud Lake

a paddle is
stranger
to what it heaves out of the way

Wherever you go
within a silence
is witnessed,
                touches.
Everything aware
of alteration but you.
Creatures who veer. The torn leaf
descending into marsh gas
into an ancient breath.

In bony rapids
rock gazed up
with the bright paint
of previous canoes.

But now, you, *c'est là*,
with the clear river water heart
the rock who floats
on her own deep reflection.
Female rock. Limb. Holes of hunger
we climb into and disappear.

One hour in the arms of the Mazinaw.

Those things we don't know we love
we love harder.
                    Tanned face
stern rock   the rock lolling
memorized by the Algonquin
Mohawk lovers. Mineral eye.

O yes I saw your dear sisters too
before this afternoon's passion
those depot creek nights when they
unpacked their breasts
serious and full of the fever of loon
for whoever stumbled
young onto the august
country waters.

PACIFIC LETTER

to Stan of Depot Creek, old friend, pal o'mine

Now I remember that you rebuilt my chicken coop
north of the farmhouse along the pasture fence
with fresh pine from Verona.
In autumn you hid a secret message under floorboards
knowing we would find it in spring.
A fanciful message. Carved with care.
As you carved you imagined the laughing.
We both know the pleasures art and making bring.

And in summer we lounged for month on month
letting slide the publishers and English Departments
who sent concerned letters that slept in the red mailbox.
Men and women came drifting in
from the sea and from the west border
and with them there was nothing at cross purpose.
They made nothing of mountain crossing
to share that fellowship.
The girls danced because
their long sleeves would not keep still
and I, drunk, went to sleep among field rocks.
We spoke out desires without regret.
Then you returned to the west of the province
and I to the south.

After separation had come to its worst
we met and travelled the Mazinaw with my sons
through all the thirty-six folds of that creature river
into the valley of bright lichen,
green rice beds, marble rock, and at night
slept under croaking pine.
The spirit so high it was all over the heavens!

And at Depot Creek we walked
for a last time down river
to a neighbour's southern boundary
past the tent where you composed verses
past the land where I once lived
the water about it clear in my memory as blue jade.
Then you and your wife sang back and forth
in the mosquito filled cabin under the naphtha.
The muskrat, listening at the edge,
heard our sound – guitars and lone violin
whose weavings seduced us with a sadness.

The canoe brushed over open lake
hearing the lighted homes
whose laughter eliminated the paddle
and the loon stumbled
up sudden into the air beside the boat
shocked us awake and disappeared
leaving a ripple that slid the moon away.
And before the last days in August
we scattered like stars and rain.

And I think now that this
is what we are to each other,
friends busy with their own distance
who reappear now and then alongside.
As once you could not believe
I had visited the town of your youth
where you sat in your room
perfecting *Heartbreak Hotel*
that new place to 'dwell' – that
gentle word in the midst of angry song.

All this comes to an end.
During summer evenings
I miss your company.
Things we clung to

stay on the horizon
and we become the loon
on his journey
a lone tropical taxi
to confused depth and privacy.

At such times – no talking
no conclusion in the heart.

I buy postage
                seal this

and send it a thousand miles, thinking.

A DOG IN SAN FRANCISCO

Sitting in an empty house
with a dog from the Mexican Circus!
O Daisy, embrace is my only pleasure.
Holding and hugging my friends. Education.
A wave of eucalyptus. Warm granite.
These are the things I have in my heart.
Heart and skills, there's nothing else.

I usually don't like small dogs but you
like midwestern women take over the air.
You leap into the air and pivot
a diver going up! You are known
to open the fridge and eat when you wish
you can roll down car windows and step out
you know when to get off the elevator.

I always wanted to be a dog
but I hesitated
for I thought they lacked certain skills.
Now I want to be a dog.

TRANSLATIONS OF MY POSTCARDS

the peacock means order
the fighting kangaroos mean madness
the oasis means I have struck water

positioning of the stamp – the despot's head
horizontal, or 'mounted policemen',
mean political danger

the false date means I
am not where I should be

when I speak of the weather
I mean business

a blank postcard says
I am in the wilderness

7 OR 8 THINGS I KNOW ABOUT HER–
A STOLEN BIOGRAPHY

The Father's Guns

After her father died they found nine guns in the house. Two
in his clothing drawers, one under the bed, one in the glove
compartment of the car, etc. Her brother took their mother out
onto the prairie with a revolver and taught her to shoot.

The Bird

For a while in Topeka parrots were very popular. Her father
was given one in lieu of a payment and kept it with him at
all times because it was the fashion. It swung above him in the
law office and drove back with him in the car at night. At
parties friends would bring their parrots and make them
perform what they had been taught: the first line from *Twelfth
Night*, a bit of Italian opera, cowboy songs, or a surprisingly
good rendition of Russ Colombo singing 'Prisoner of Love'. Her
father's parrot could only imitate the office typewriter, along
with the *ching* at the end of each line. Later it broke its neck
crashing into a bookcase.

The Bread

Four miles out of Topeka on the highway – the largest electrical
billboard in the State of Kansas. The envy of all Missouri. It
advertised bread and the electrical image of a knife cut slice
after slice. These curled off endlessly. 'Meet you at the bread,'
'See you at the loaf,' were common phrases. Aroused couples
would park there under the stars on the open night prairie.
Virtue was lost, 'kissed all over by every boy in Wichita'. Poets,
the inevitable visiting writers, were taken to see it, and it
hummed over the seductions in cars, over the nightmares of
girls in bed. Slice after slice fell towards the earth. A feeding
of the multitude in this parched land on the way to Dorrance,
Kansas.

First Criticism

She is two weeks old, her mother takes her for a drive. At the
gas station the mechanic is cleaning the windshield and
watches them through the glass. Wiping his hands he puts his
head in the side window and says, 'Excuse me for saying this
but I know what I'm talking about – that child has a heart
condition.'

Listening In

Overhear her in the bathroom, talking to a bug: 'I don't want
you on me, honey.' 8 a.m.

Self-Criticism

'For a while there was something about me that had a dubious
quality. Dogs would not take meat out of my hand. The town
bully kept handcuffing me to trees.'

Fantasies

Always one fantasy. To be travelling down the street and a
man in a clean white suit (the detail of 'clean' impresses me)
leaps into her path holding flowers and sings to her while an
invisible orchestra accompanies his solo. All her life she has
waited for this and it never happens.

Reprise

In 1956 the electric billboard in Kansas caught fire and smoke plumed into a wild sunset. Bread on fire, broken glass. Birds flew towards it above the cars that circled round to watch. And last night, past midnight, her excited phone call. Her home town is having a marathon to benefit the symphony. She pays $4 to participate. A tuxedoed gentleman begins the race with a clash of cymbals and she takes off. Along the route at frequent intervals are quartets who play for her. When they stop for water a violinist performs a solo. So here she comes. And there I go, stepping forward in my white suit, with a song in my heart.

BESSIE SMITH AT ROY THOMSON HALL

At first she refused to sing.

She had applied for the one concert – that she was allowed
each sabbatical – to take place in Havana. Palms! Oh Pink
Walls! Cuba! she would hum to herself, dazzling within the
clouds.

But here she was. Given the choice of nine Honest Ed
restaurants and then hurried to Roy Thomson Hall which
certainly should never have been called that.

> A long brown dress, with fringes.
> Fred Longshaw at the piano.

She opened the first set with 'Kitchen Man'. Five people left.
Al Neil had flown in from Vancouver on a tip. For the next
ten minutes, after people realized it really *was* Bessie Smith, the
hall was filled with shouted requests. 'Any Woman's Blues',
'Down in the Dumps' . . . until she said I want to sing what I
never was allowed to, because I died. And she brought the
rest of the twentieth century under her wing.

She wore wings. They raised themselves with her arms each
time she coaxed a phrase. Her wings would float up and fall slow
like a hand held out of a car coming down against the wind,
the feathers black as the Steinway. You should have been
there.

During the intermission the stunned audience just sat in their
seats. 'She's looking good' was one of the common remarks.

When she returned she brought out the band. They were glad
to have arrived on earth, but they too had hoped for Havana.
Abraham Wheat on soprano sax was there. Joe Smith on cornet
was there. By midnight her voice was even better. She talked
more between songs.

At 2 a.m. the band levitated. She used no microphone. Above us banners waved and danced like a multitude. She took on and caressed the songs of Jerome Kern. She asked what happened to her friend Charlie Green. And then, to her surprise, to apologize for Toronto, Charlie Green was allowed to join her. He had been found frozen in a Harlem tenement but now stepped forward shyly with his trombone. And now he and Joe Smith and Bessie Smith were alone on stage the audience quiet and the banners still and the air conditioning holding its breath. They wheeled away the Steinway. They brought out an old upright decorated with bullet holes. Al Neil was asked to sit in. She sang, 'It won't be You'.

The encore was made up of two songs. 'Weeping Willow Blues' and 'Far Away Blues'. We stood like sudden wheat. But she could not hear us. She could not see us. Then she died again.

THE CONCESSIONS

i.

Wawanosh.
          In the corn of night
surrounded by the dusty dark green
hot insects and moon
                    a star coat.

We are new and ancient here
talking through midnight's
tired arms,
letting go the newness.
I am home.
Old farmhouse, a defunct red truck
under the trees
conversation all evening
and I have nothing more to say
but this is a magic night.
Our bodies betray us, long for sleep.
Still – talk about the bear, the cause
of theatre, the first time we all met.

A yellow light falls onto the sink
and our arms lean forward
towards Elmira coffee cake.
Hello again, after Pacific months,
and I brought you a seed I never gave you
and I brought you stories and a peace I want
to give, but it is both of you
who bring comfort and friendship.

All night we are at this table.
        Tableau of faint light,
fragment of Ontario.
We would be plotting revolution in the 1830's.
And outside the same heat, old coat of stars,
the released lung of the country, and
great Ontario night beans growing
towards Goderich.
        Lone houses
betrayed by poplar
reached only by long arms
of Wawanosh concessions,
the crow of night.

        Tomorrow
will be all highway
till I get home.
Go to bed, exhausted and alone.
Go to bed with each others' minds.
I do not know what to say
about this kind of love
but I refuse to lose it.

ii.

By the outhouse and red truck
I look up towards a lit window
which seeps a yellow road into trees.
To end in the warm
glove of a maple!
A bear.
Welcome Shakespeare, Sarah Bernhardt,
someone is starting a new story.
Someone is dancing new on this
terrific ancient earth, claiming this
for mute ancestors
and their language of hands.
                    The entertainers
who allow themselves long evenings
while others sleep.
The suspicious work of the community.

The town of Molesworth
which once housed a dancing cow
articulated us. As did the director
from Atwood, the fiddler from Listowel,
and the actress from Fergus, the writer from Wingham,
the mystic from Millbank.
These country hearts, a county conspiracy.
Their determined self-portraits
where alone one picks
up the pencil, begins with nothing
but these blank pages.
Let me tell you, I love them more and more
– all their night silences, their ignored dream.

In daylight the car hums. Bluevale   Seaforth
Newry   Holmesville.
The deer and flamingos, another mythology,
grace every tenth house.
This is not your home
but you are home.
                    Geraniums
in a tractor tire, horse weathervanes.
Moon over the Maitland River . . .

And so that yellow light
man or woman working inside
aware of the cricket night
cricket cricket . . . cicada? he writes, she says
to no one but the page
black hallways behind him
and ahead the windowscreen and then
the yard of yellow highway into maple
which his mind can walk out on
and dream a story
for his friends, the community

as someone once imagined
a dancing cow, a giant cheese.
The dream made name.
The gestures of the barroom
made dictionary.

iii.

When the four piece band sat stony in the Blyth Hotel
and played *Maple Sugar*, the bar got up to dance.
My shoulder banging against the women's room
to avoid flying drunk feet in their boots
that brought the cowshit in. And the bullshit
came too, through the beer and smoke.

This lady on the electric piano, the two fiddlers
and guitarist, the actors from across the street
stepping up to sing, receive stormy ovations.
The tv green and orange above us
recording grade B Hollywood, flamingo art.
And something is happening here.
Town and actors exchanging clothes.
The mechanic holds his harmonica
professionally against the mike
piercing out 'Have you ever been lonely
have you ever been blue,'
and, as the man from Lobo says,
Fuck the Renaissance
– just get me a beer.

iv.

So this midnight choir.

At 2 a.m. everyone is thrown out
and spreads onto the empty streets.
Unseen, as we step into cars,
are the bear and hawk,
who generate us.
And from the unseen sky
the crow watches
traffic light up Highway 4
then turn into unpaved
yellow concession roads.

The car bounces on a grass path
between tall corn and stops.

Light from the open car
reveals the yard.
And, as if painted onto the night,
is the yellow window
where someone, holding a mirror
is drawing a picture of herself.

RED ACCORDION–
AN IMMIGRANT SONG

How you and I talked!
Casually, and side by side,
not even cold at 4 a.m.
New Year's morning

in a double outhouse in Blyth.

Creak of trees and scrub snow.
Was it dream or true memory
this casualness, this ease of talk
after the long night of the previous year.

Nothing important said
just as now the poem
draws together such frail times.
Art steps forward as accident
like a warm breeze from Brazil.

        This whispering
as if not to awaken
what hibernates in firewood
as if not to disturb the blue night
the last memory of the year.

        So we sit
within loose walls of the poem
you and I, our friends indoors
drunk on the home-made wine.
All of us searching to discern ourselves,
the 'gift' we can give each other.
Tell this landscape.
Or the one we came from.

Polkas in a smoky midnight light.

I stepped into this new year
dancing with a small child.
Rachel, so graceful,
we bowed when the dance was over.
If I could paint this I would

                    and if writing
showed colour and incident
removed from time
                    we could be clear.

The bleak view past the door
is where we are, not what we
have made here, or become, or brought
like wolves bringing food to a lair
from another world. And this
is magic.
                    Ray Bird's seven-year-old wine
– transformed! Finally made good.
I drank an early version years ago
and passed out.
                    Time collapses.
The years, the intricate
knowledge now of each other
makes love.

A yard in its scrub snow, stacked wood
brindle in the moonlight, the red truck,
a bare tree at the foot of the driveway
waving to heaven.

                    A full moon the
                    colour of night kitchen.

Ten yards away a high bonfire
(remembered from summer) lifts
its redness above the farmhouse
and the lean figures of children circle
to throw in sticks and arms off a christmas tree
as the woman in long black hair
her left foot on a stump
plays the red accordion.

And the others dance.
                    Embracing or flinging
themselves away from each other.
They bow and they look up
to full moon and white cold sky
and they *move*, even in this stilled painting.
They talk a white breath at each other.
Some appear more than once
with different partners.
We are immune to wind.
Our boots pound down the frozen earth
our children leap from and into our arms.
All of us poised and inspired by music
friendship self-made heat and the knowledge
each has chosen to come here driven for hours
over iced highways, to be here bouncing and leaping

to a reel that carried itself generations ago
north of the border, through lost towns,
settled among the strange names,
and became eventually our own

all the way from Virginia.

IN A YELLOW ROOM

There was another reason for Fats Waller to record, on May 8th, 1935, 'I'm gonna sit right down and write myself a letter.' It is for this moment, driving from Goderich towards and past Blyth, avoiding Blyth by taking the gravel concessions, four adults and a child, who have just swum in a very cold Lake Huron. His piano drips from the cassette player and we all recognize the piece but are mute. We cannot sing before he does, before he eases himself into the lyrics as if into a chair, this large man who is to die in 1943 sitting in a train in Kansas City, finally still.

He was always moving, grand on the street or the midnight taxi rides with Andy Razaf during which it is rumoured he wrote most of his songs. I have always loved him but I love him most in the company of friends. Because his body was a crowd and we desire to imitate such community. His voice staggers or is gentle behind a whimsical piano, the melody ornamental and cool as vichyssoise in that hot studio in this hot car on a late June Ontario summer day. What else of importance happened on May 8th, 1935?

The only creature I've ever met who disliked him was a nervous foxhound I had for three years. As soon as I put on Mr Waller the dog would dart from the room and hide under a bed. The dog recognized the anarchy, the unfolding of musical order, the growls and muttering, the fact that Fats Waller was talking to someone over your shoulder as well as to you. What my dog did not notice was the serenity he should have learned from. The notes as fresh as creek washed clothes.

The windows are open as we drive under dark maples that sniff up a rumour of Lake Huron. The piano energizes the hay bound into wheels, a white field of turkeys, various tributaries of the Maitland River. Does he, drunk, and carrying his tin of tomatoes – 'it feeds the body and cuts the hangover' – does he, in the midnight taxi with Razaf, imagine where the music disappears?

Where it will recur? Music and lyrics they wrote then sold to false composers for ready cash and only later admitting they had written 'Sunny side of the street' and 'I can't give you anything but love' and so many of the best songs of their time. The hidden authors on their two hour taxi ride out of Harlem to Brooklyn and back again to Harlem, the night heat and smells yells overheard from the streets they passed through which they incorporated into what they were making every texture entering this large man, a classical organist in his youth, who strode into most experiences, hid from his ex-wife Edith Hatchett, visiting two kinds of women, 'ladies who had pianos and ladies who did not,' and died of bronchial pneumonia on the Acheson-Topeka and Santa Fe, a song he did not write.

He and the orchestra of his voice have now entered the car with us. This is his first visit to the country, though he saw it from a train window the day before he died. Saw the heartland where the music could disappear, the diaspora of notes, a rewinding, a backward movement of the formation of the world, the invention of his waltz.

754

WHEN YOU DRIVE THE
QUEENSBOROUGH ROADS AT MIDNIGHT

do not look at a star
or full moon. Look out for frogs.
And not the venerable ones who recline
on gravel parallel to the highway
but the foolhardy, bored on a country night
dazzled by the adventure of passing beams.

We know their type of course, local heroes
who take off their bandanas and leap naked,
night green, seduced
by the whispers of michelin.

To them we are distinct death.
I am fond of these foolish things
more than the moon.
They welcome me after absence.
One of them is my youth
still jumping into rivers
take care and beware of him.

Knowing you love this landscape
there are few rules.
Do not gaze at moons.
Nuzzle the heat in granite.
Swim toward pictographs.
Touch only reflections.

PROUST IN THE WATERS

for Scott and Krystyne

Swimming along the bar of moon
the yellow scattered sleeping
arm of the moon
                    on Balsam Lake

releasing the air
                    out of your mouth
the moon under your arm
tick of the brain
submerged. Tick
of the loon's heart
in the wet night thunder
                              below us
knowing its shore is the air

We love things which disappear
and are found
creatures who plummet
and become
an arrow.
To know the syllables
in a loon sentence
                    intricate
shift of preposition
that signals meridian
                    west   south west.
The mother tongue
a bubble caught in my beak
releasing the air
                    of a language

756

Seeing no human in this moon storm
being naked in black water
you approach the corridor
such jewellery! Queen Anne's Lace!
and slide to fathoms.
The mouth swallows river morse
throws a sound
through the loom of liquid
against sky.

Where are you?

On the edge
of the moon bar

ESCARPMENT

He lies in bed, awake, holding her left forearm. It is 4 a.m. He turns, his eyes rough against the night. Through the window he can hear the creek – which has no name. Yesterday at noon he walked along its shallow body overhung with cedar, beside rushes, moss and watercress. A green and grey body whose intricate bones he is learning among which he stumbles and walks through in an old pair of Converse running shoes. She was further upriver investigating for herself and he exploring on his own now crawling under a tree that has uprooted and spilled. Its huge length across a section of the creek. With his left hand he holds onto the massive stump roots and slides beneath it within the white water heaving against him. Shirt wet, he follows the muscle in the water and travels fast under the tree. His dreaming earlier must have involved all this.

In the river he was looking for a wooden bridge which they had crossed the previous day. He walks confidently now, the white shoes stepping casually off logs into deep water, through gravel, and watercress which they eat later in a cheese sandwich. She chews much of it walking back to the cabin. He turns and she freezes, laughing, with watercress in her mouth. There are not many more ways he can tell her he loves her. He shows mock outrage and yells but she cannot hear him over the sound of the stumbling creek.

He loves too, as she knows, the body of rivers. Provide him with a river or a creek and he will walk along it. Will step off and sink to his waist, the sound of water and rock encasing him in solitude. The noise around them insists on silence if they are more than five feet apart. It is only later when they sit in a pool legs against each other that they can talk, their conversation roaming to include relatives, books, best friends, the history of Lewis and Clark, fragments of the past which they piece together. But otherwise this river's noise encases them and now he walks alone with its spirits, the clack and splash, the twig break, hearing only an individual noise if it occurs less than an arm's length away. He is looking, now, for a name.

It is not a name for a map – he knows the arguments of imperialism. It is a name for them, something temporary for their vocabulary. A code. He slips under the fallen tree holding the cedar root the way he holds her forearm. He hangs a moment, his body being pulled by water going down river. He holds it the same way and for the same reasons. Heart Creek? Arm River? he writes, he mutters to her in the darkness. The body moves from side to side and he hangs with one arm, deliriously out of control, still holding on. Then he plunges down, touches gravel and flakes of wood with his back the water closing over his head like a clap of gloved hands. His eyes are open as the river itself pushes him to his feet and he is already three yards down stream and walking out of the shock and cold stepping into the sun. Sun lays its crossword, litters itself, along the whole turning length of this river so he can step into heat or shadow.

He thinks of where she is, what she is naming. Near her, in the grasses, are Bladder Campion, Devil's Paintbrush, some unknown blue flowers. He stands very still and cold in the shadow of long trees. He has gone far enough to look for a bridge and has not found it. Turns upriver. He holds onto the cedar root the way he holds her forearm.

759

BIRCH BARK

for George Whalley

An hour after the storm on Birch Lake
the island bristles. Rock. Leaves still falling.
At this time, in the hour after lightning
we release the canoes.
Silence of water
purer than the silence of rock.
A paddle touches itself. We move
over blind mercury, feel the muscle
within the river, the blade
weave in dark water.

Now each casual word is precisely chosen
passed from bow to stern, as if
leaning back to pass a canteen.
There are echoes, repercussions of water.
We are in absolute landscape,
among names that fold in onto themselves.

To circle the island means witnessing
the blue grey dust of a heron
released out of the trees.
So the dialogue slides
nothing more than friendship
an old song we break into
not needing all the words.

We are past naming the country.
The reflections are never there
without us, without the exhaustion
of water and trees after storm.

BREEZE

for BP *Nichol*

Nowadays I listen only to duets.
Johnny Hodges and The Bean, a thin slip
of piano behind them
on this page on this stage
craft a breeze in a horn.

One friend sits back and listens
to the other. Nowadays
I want only the wild and tender
phrasing of "NightHawk,"
its air groaned out
like the breath of a lover.
Rashomon by Saxophone.

So brother and sister woke, miles apart,
in those 19th century novels you loved,
with the same wound or desire.

We sit down to clean and sharpen
the other's most personal lines
—a proposal of more, a waving dismissal
of whole stanzas—in Lethbridge in Edmonton
you stood with the breeze
in an uncomfortable Chinese restaurant
in Camrose, getting a second cup
at The Second Cup near Spadina.

I almost called you this morning
for a phone number.
Records I haven't yet returned.
Tapes you were supposed to make for me.

And across the country
tears about your death.
I always thought, someone says,
he was very good for you.
Though I still like, Barrie,
the friends who are not good for me.

Along the highway
only the duets and wind fill up my car.
I saw the scar of the jet that Sunday
trying to get you out of the sky.
Ben Webster, Coleman Hawkins.
An A and an H, a bean and a breeze.

All these twin truths

There is bright sumac, once more,
this September, along the Bayview Extension

From now on
no more solos

I tie you to me

A note on the poems

The Cinnamon Peeler contains poems that cover a twenty-five year period. They are poems that were written alongside and between other longer works such as *The Collected Works of Billy the Kid, Coming Through Slaughter, Running in the Family,* and *In the Skin of a Lion.* They cover the period from 1963, when I first started to write, to 1990.

Elimination Dance, which turns up here as an intermission, is a sort of rogue-troubadour poem that seems continually to change—a few lines get dropped and a few get added every year. It is based on those horrendous dances where a caller decides, seemingly randomly, who should not be allowed to continue dancing. So the piece (I still hesitate to call it a poem) is in the voice of a mad, and totally beyond-the-pale, announcer.

Two poems in *Secular Love,* 'The River Neighbour' and 'Pacific Letter', are based on the Rihaku-Tu Fu-Ezra Pound poems. They are not so much translations as re-locations into my landscape, with a few lines by the earlier poets making their appearance in my poem.

Most of these poems were written in Canada. A few were written in Sri Lanka. Tin Roof was written in Hawaii.

Trick with a Knife was dedicated to Kim and Quintin and Griffin. And *Secular Love* was dedicated to Linda.

MICHAEL ONDAATJE

MICHAEL ONDAATJE, born in Ceylon in 1943, is a novelist and poet who now lives in Toronto, Canada. He is the author of *The English Patient*, *In the Skin of a Lion*, *Coming Through Slaughter*, and *The Collected Works of Billy the Kid*; three collections of poems, *The Cinnamon Peeler*, *Secular Love*, and *There's a Trick with a Knife I'm Learning to Do*; and a memoir, *Running in the Family*. He received the Booker Prize for *The English Patient*.